FABULOUS EMPIRE

Colonel Zack Miller's Story

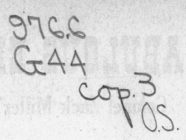

The Riverside Press
CAMBRIDGE · MASSACHUSETTS
PRINTED IN THE U.S.A.

FABULOUS EMPIRE

Colonel Zack Miller's Story

by

FRED GIPSON

With an Introduction by

DONALD DAY

19 46

Houghton Mifflin Company Boston

The Riverside Press Cambridge

CONTENTS

INTRODUCTION

On a spring day in 1944 I stood on First Street in Ponca City, Oklahoma, and stared at a crudely lettered sign: 101 Ranch Indian Traders. As I looked at the sign I remembered as a boy seeing the 101 Ranch wild west show, the greatest show of all times, with its cowboys, Indians, beautiful women, and famous riders. At the blast of a trumpet two men had ridden into the huge tent, on high, prancing horses whose saddles glistened with jewels. They had been Colonel Joe and Colonel Zack Miller. Now, behind this shambling screen door, I was to see Colonel Zack again, last remnant of a fabulous empire.

Junk of every description cluttered the room. Two or three Indians loitered about. Out of this confusion emerged a pair of steady blue eyes under a big white Stetson. A bulky body ended in a pair of worn cowboy boots. Colonel Zack looked at me belligerently, as if I were another impatient creditor. I explained my presence. I wanted to check the facts in an article to be published by the *Southwest Review*. He was still belligerent. But when I told him of that long ago day under the big top, he mellowed. When I read him the article, he sat as in a trance. And then the words came. For nine hours I sat and listened. Here was one of the world's greatest stories.

Could it be preserved? Would he tell it? Yes, if he knew that it would be written as it was and not as a spiritless whitewash. We made a verbal agreement that as soon as I could find the person to take his story down and put it into proper form, and could also find a suitable place away from confusion and distractions, he would tell it.

Back in Dallas I found on my desk a coon-hunt story, 'My Kind of Man,' [1] by a writer I had never heard of. I read it — and let out a Comanche yell. Here was the man to write Colonel Zack's story. A few days later I was on my way to Mason, Texas, where its author, Fred Gipson, lived. We went on a get-acquainted fishing trip, then talked about Colonel Zack. Fred, encouraged by his wife, Tommie, agreed to do the book.

The next step was to arrange Zack's and Fred's affairs so that the necessary time could be given to getting the story on paper. This proved easier than finding a suitable place in which to work. Out of the blue again came an almost unbelievable opportunity. Mrs. Ethel M. Raigorodsky offered us the facilities of her beautiful Texas ranch.

Here, after many unavoidable delays, in November, 1944, the participants in the great adventure assembled: Colonel Zack, Tommie and Fred Gipson, Mrs. Raigorodsky and myself — when I could get away from my duties in Dallas.

Relaxation and nostalgic remembrance were enhanced by wood-burning fireplaces, by the clear-water creek which ran below the bluff on which the ranchhouse was built, by

---

[1] Published in the fall, 1944, issue of the *Southwest Review* and condensed in the November 1944 issue of *Reader's Digest*.

the friendly mountains, by warm hospitality.   In the middle of one of Mrs. Raigorodsky's wonderful meals Zack
would come out with one of his best stories.   Someone
would have to jump up and take it down.   At the end of a
month Tommie and Fred departed for Mason with over a
thousand typewritten pages of Zack's fascinating experi-
ences.   From this material Fred has written this book.   It
is an exciting book and it will keep alive a vivid chapter of
American history.

Here, then, is Colonel Zack's story of a *Fabulous Empire*.
Enjoy it!

DONALD DAY

FORT WORTH, TEXAS, *November,* 1945

FABULOUS EMPIRE

Colonel Zack Miller's Story

1

PRAIRIE SCHOOLING

THE DAY he was born, his father put up a barrel of black-berry wine and said to his mother: 'Molly, we'll open this barrel the day young Zachary here is twenty-one. We'll open it again the day he marries and a third time when his first son is born. That ought to kill off the bulk of it. The balance, his friends can finish at his wake!'

Well, they opened the barrel when Zachary Taylor Miller was twenty-one. They tapped it again when he married in 1904. But the fire that destroyed the 101 Ranch house in 1909 burned it up before Zachary, Jr., was born; and now, when the boys gather to hold a wake at Zack's death, they'll have to bring their own drinking.

It was in Newtonia, Missouri, that the cowman George Washington Miller put up that barrel of wine. That was in 1878, the same year he picked up his 101 Ranch brand that later, along with the new son Zack, got to be known just about any place a cow ever left a track.

Gid Guthrie was Miller's trail boss that year. They'd made their buy in South Texas, and on the way north, they laid over at San Antonio one night to let the hands romp and stomp and paw up a little sand before taking the long trail into Kansas. The hands didn't need any urging; they made up as tough a trail crew as ever looked a cow brute in the rump. They'd located a honkytonk downtown called 'The Hundred and One,' which made a brag of having the wildest women, the rawest whiskey, and the worst gamblers in that old Mexican town. The boys wanted to investigate; this outfit might be bluffing.

They sampled the whiskey. They tried out the women. They matched wits with the gamblers and then fist-whipped them for cheats and swindlers. Before daylight, they were prizing up hell and propping it with a chunk. Some were down and the rest were staggering. It took four trips and half the town police for Miller to get the crew out of the wrecked place and back out to where the cattle were bedded down.

Miller knew trail hands; he knew they had to whoop it up fast while they were at it and squeeze a lot of town-going into a mighty short time. For months to come, day and night, all they'd know would be bawling steers, pitching horses, stampedes, hot suns, and shivery nights. So he said nothing.

But the next year when they started trimming up another South Texas trail herd and Gid Guthrie wanted to know what sort of road brand to put on the steers, G. W. Miller was ready.

'We'll forget the Lee Kokernut brand we've been using,' he told Guthrie. 'I've bought out that iron. We'll brand 101 this time. Before I'm done, I aim to make this tough crew so sick of the sight of them figures they'll ride a ten-mile circle around town to keep from reading that honky-tonk signboard. Too many of 'em got burnt last year; it hinders their work.'

John Hiatt, G. W.'s nephew of Hunnewell, Kansas, laid claim to building the brand fire that burnt the first 101 on a cow. G. W. had had some irons made to horn-brand and some to hide-brand on the left hip. He bobbed the tails of his steers and dewlapped every head, cutting the dewlap from the top down so that when it dried, it stuck straight out. Time he was done, a man couldn't mistake a Miller steer as far as he could see it. And time the hands grazed those steers into Kansas, there wasn't a one of them who ever mentioned the San Antonio honkytonk as a good place for a little general hell-raising.

Miller had that tough bunch of hands broke from sucking eggs. He also had him a cow brand that in years to come his newborn son Zack was to help make world-famous.

This was all history, of course, by the time young Zack got big enough to take notice. He was a short, chunky, towheaded kid with blue eyes and more energy than a mule colt on a frosty morning. Town life in Winfield, Kansas, where the Miller family now lived, didn't suit him at all. And from the time he could fork his bare toes around a pony's front leg and pull up by the animal's mane, he was pestering his father to let him stay with the hands out on the ranch.

He didn't have much luck at first, of course. A cow camp out on the big open ranges was no place for a kid barely out of diapers. There was nobody to see after him. So Zack had to stay around home and play with the neighbor kids, longing for the day when he could ride with old Milton Van Hook, the 101 cowhand who could spin a kid exciting, long-winded range yarns by the hour.

That hope was never fulfilled, though. Old Milton died before Zack ever got big enough to ride with him. Typhoid got the old cowhand in an upstairs room of the Hale Hotel in Hunnewell.

Zack couldn't believe it when they told him Milton was dead. Milton was his favorite cowboy; he couldn't die. Nobody as lean and tall and fierce-looking as kind old Milton Van Hook could die.

Zack went with his father the day they put Milt away. He followed the sober cowhands up to Milton's room where the men went inside to get the old cowboy's body ready for shipment. They couldn't let Zack in; he had to stand around outside and wait till they finally came staggering through the door under the load of a big pine plank box. There was water leaking through the cracks in the box and spattering on the floor.

When Zack saw that, he knew they'd made a terrible mistake. 'He's not dead!' he screamed. 'I tell you, he's not dead! He just wants to pee!'

But nobody paid any attention to him. And they wouldn't stop and open the box to let old Milton pee. They just carried him on outside and loaded him into a rig and set off for Winfield with him.

And it was years before Zack found out that Milton really had been dead, and that the water dripping through those cracks had been melting ice they'd packed the cowboy in to keep him from spoiling before they could get him underground.

As soon as he was big enough, Zack took to dogging his father's heels. G. W. was a big man with a big voice, and he liked to do things in a big way. There were men who claimed they could hear G. W. Miller a mile off when he was talking nice. There was only one man Zack ever knew who was bigger and had a louder voice. That was old Shanghai Pierce, a Texas cowman who used to come up to Winfield sometimes to make cow deals with G. W. Let the two of them get together over a bottle of whiskey and it sounded to Zack like two old longhorn range bulls pawing the dust and talking up a fight. Zack's mother vowed and declared that when their arguments got the hottest, their bawling rattled her dishes out in the kitchen.

Once the two men had come to an agreement, however, they'd shake hands on a fifty-thousand-dollar deal, and that handshake was just as binding as the best contract two jackleg lawyers and a cigar-eating judge could draw up. A man's word was his bond in those days and he took pride in backing it up.

Eventually, the time came when Zack was allowed to be shorn of his Little Lord Fauntleroy curls and stay out at the ranch with his father and the cowhands.

The ranch lay just south of the Kansas line in northern Oklahoma. It lay in the Cherokee Strip, a six-million-acre tract of land granted by the United States Government to the Cherokees as an outlet from their larger reservation farther east to their summer hunting grounds in the Rockies.

The Strip was a cowman's paradise. Fifty-eight miles wide, a hundred and eighty long, it was one of the richest grasslands on the North American continent. It was a land of high, rolling prairies, wide valleys, and sweet living water. Timber grew along the water-courses, wild grape hung in the trees; there were tall pecans, elms, and thickets of wild plum. There were deer and turkey in the bottom-lands where the blue-stem grass grew tall as a horse. Out in the open were prairie chickens, and antelope grazed by the thousands upon buffalo grass so thick a man could pitch his hat out in any direction and it'd never touch the ground.

Right in the middle of the best grassland on the Strip, G. W. held the grazing rights to something like sixty thousand acres. He'd started leasing that land from the Cherokee Agency at two cents an acre after he'd learned that he could make money hand over fist by buying cheap longhorn cattle out of Texas, fattening them on the Strip, then shipping them to northern markets.

His lease was cut into two separate pastures. One was on Deer Creek, some twenty-five miles south of Hunnewell. Headquarters for it was a dugout built into the side of a hill. The other pasture, the Salt Fork Ranch, was located down on the Salt Fork of the Arkansas River south of Deer Creek and west of the Ponca Indian Reservation. It was near the present site of Lamont, Oklahoma. G. W. made the Salt Fork Ranch his main headquarters. There he'd built a three-room cabin, horse corrals, and a feed barn. All his branding was done here.

There on the Strip, G. W. Miller set out to build himself a cattle empire. And it was there on the Strip that his son Zack got his education.

Zack's booklearning, he got from the Limerick girls, whom G. W. had hired to tutor him, his older sister Alma, and his younger brother George. Joe, his older brother, was already too old for apron-string teaching by this time. A little more of Zack's booklearning came from a stretch at Marmaduke Military Academy in Sweet Springs, Missouri, and another at Spaulding's Business College in Kansas City. But his real education came from off the Cherokee Strip where the 101 Ranch had its beginnings. He got it from his father, the cowboys, and the Indians — from the rolling prairies, stretching out to the skylines.

Old Comes-From-War was one of Zack's first teachers. 'Comesy,' as the 101 cowhands called him, was a tall, proud old Ponca warrior who stayed Indian to the last, in spite of government aid and interference. He lived about half a mile from the Salt Fork headquarters. The Government had built him a house there in a big grove of trees and supplied him with horses, harness, and plows — in case he wanted to farm.

Comesy didn't. Farming wasn't Comesy's way of life. He'd known the wild free ways of the prairies when the buffalo roamed in thousands and a young buck could heap glory upon himself in battle. Work was for squaws; Comesy wasn't grubbing in the soil. So he kept his horses, his harness, and his plows inside the house while he lived in a canvas-covered teepee out in the yard.

Comesy didn't like the canvas covering his teepee. He would have preferred buffalo skins. But the buffalo were all gone from the Salt Fork range; the bone-pickers were scouring the prairies, hauling off the last sun-bleached traces of the animal that had been red man's meat since the beginning of time. So now old Comesy spent the bulk of his time sitting cross-legged under a teepee covered with white-man canvas, dreaming of days when he could leap from the back of a fast-running pony onto a lumbering buffalo, where he could hang to the coarse back hair till he'd brought down his kill with a stabbing knife.

But when hunger drove him to it, he came down to the 101 camp to fill out his belly wrinkles. He knew he'd be welcome there; just a few years before, G. W. Miller had helped his people to find a home on the Salt Fork after governmental bungling had robbed the Poncas of their

ancestral homelands on the Niobrara River up in Nebraska.
The way Comesy figured it, a man who would do a thing
like that would never begrudge the feeding of a friend when
hunger prowled around the edges of his teepee.

It was Comesy who taught Zack to shoot his first rifle.
That was an old brass-bound, muzzle-loading gun with a
hammer that, when cocked, looked like a squirrel sitting on
a high limb. Its workings were as tricky as those of a shotgun and its barrel about as thin. But Comesy taught Zack
how to measure powder for it, how to fit the cap into place,
and how to suck in and hold a breath while squeezing off
the trigger. Comesy had had plenty of experience with
muzzle-loading guns back in the days when the knowledge
meant the difference between taking a scalp or losing one.

Comesy was an artist when it came to stalking game.
He showed Zack how to use a horse for cover when slipping
up on an open pond of ducks or geese. He'd start 'way out
from the pond, walking on the off side of his horse, and
circling closer and closer till he was within shooting range.

From Comesy, Zack learned never to draw a gun or cock
the hammer till he was ready to shoot. He learned that the
hard way, and he's never forgotten.

They were after wild geese on the Salt Fork. Comesy
was in the lead, quiet-padding through tall grass to the
edge of a dirt bank overlooking the water. He crouched
on the brink, parted the grasses, then signed for Zack to
get ready.

Zack was shaking all over with the buck ague that at-
tacks the best of experienced hunters at times. In his excitement, he cocked the old gun, then moved forward.

Comesy called over his shoulder in a whisper: 'Wait,
geese too far!'

But Zack couldn't wait. He'd already hung his toe in the grass and was falling flat on his face.

The gun went off with a roar. The load knocked a hole in the ground about a foot behind old Comesy, a hole that the old Indian could have buried his head in.

The frightened geese whipped themselves off the water with heavy wing blows and raucous honkings. But their scare was nothing compared to Comesy's. That old Ponca was worse surprised than a dog with his first porcupine.

Fighting mad, Comesy wheeled and snatched up a heavy sunflower stalk. He swarmed all over Zack with it. Before he was done, he had the seat of Zack's pants smoking.

Once over his excitement and scare, Comesy was sorry about that whipping. The geese were gone; so to make friends again and show that he had no hard feelings, he led Zack down to his teepee and showed him his war trophies. Comesy had Cheyenne scalps, Sioux scalps, and scalps of Arapahoes. Mostly, he had Sioux, long-standing enemies of the Poncas. He was proud of these scalps; he spent the rest of the day giving Zack all the bloody details of how he'd acquired them.

Among his collection was one white woman's scalp. The hair was long, wavy, fine as silk, the most beautiful blond hair Zack had ever seen. The boy picked out that scalp the first thing and started asking questions about it. But the old warrior shoved it quickly aside and kept right on talking of the others as if he hadn't heard.

Afterward, Zack tried time and again to get old Comesy to tell him the story of that beautiful blond scalp. But Comesy ignored the questions when he could; other times, he'd stare straight at the boy with a blank look that gave Zack a strange, uneasy feeling. It was as if old Comesy had deliberately shut a door in his face.

Sometimes, though, Zack would catch the old warrior furtively fingering the long wavy hairs of that scalp and there'd be a queer, soft light in his eyes that Zack couldn't understand.

Zack always hoped that before old Comesy died, he'd tell him the story of the blond-haired woman's scalp. But Comesy carried that secret to his grave, along with his many others.

Zack visited every dance and ceremony the Ponca tribes held. The Sun Dance, pulled off in August, was a thing to watch and remember. That was when the young bucks proved their strength and their endurance by a trial of blood and pain. The medicine man cut slits in the skins of the young bucks, high up on their shoulders. Through these slits he tied one end of a thirty-foot rawhide thong, tying the other end back to the ceremonial pole, set up in the center of the grounds. In the middle of the thong was a buffalo skull to weight it down. The idea was for the young ones to run against this weighted thong till the skin-holds in his shoulders were torn out.

The ceremonial pole was thirty feet high, and decorating the top of it was a buffalo skull, with a cross of willow branches tied to that.

The older bucks, who had already proved their strength, performed a ceremonial dance. As long as the sun shone, the dancers were to keep looking at it through a willow hoop they carried in their hands and to keep step with the drums at the same time. They danced in a long line and blew whistles made of the wing bones of a wild turkey gobbler. Off at a distance, the whistles sounded like sleigh-bells ringing.

Zack, whom the Poncas called 'Spotted Buffalo,' was allowed to set up his soda-pop stand at these ceremonials. No Indian taking part in the ceremonies could take on food or water for the three days and nights of its duration; but to the others, Zack sold groceries, beef, canned goods, sugar, coffee, and mainly, soda pop. His soda pop was the almost forgotten type, bottled so that the drinker hit the bottle cap with the ball of his hand and knocked the rubber seal back into the bottle. If the stuff was a little warm, half of it flew out into the Indian's face. Zack hauled his drink by wagon from Arkansas City, thirty-eight miles away.

Zack always hated to watch those young bucks going without food and water for the three days and nights it required to change them from boys to men. They'd run against those thongs, flopping the buffalo skulls around, trying to tear out their skin and free themselves. They'd do it hour after hour, sweating and bleeding till their strength finally ran out, so that all they could do was stagger around like walking dead men. It was hard to see them suffer like that.

And it was also hard for Zack to think of all the pop he could have been selling those boys if it weren't for that law concerning food and water. Then one day, Zack got an idea. He held a pow-wow with the head medicine man. *Gatuchy*, soda pop, he argued, was neither food nor water. Therefore, the bucks could drink it without inviting the wrath of the Great Spirit!

The medicine man studied on that one a long time. It was true what Spotted Buffalo had told him. Anybody tasting *gatuchy* could tell it was not water. Nor was there the least morsel of food in it. Still, this kind of medicine-making was toying with the laws of the red man's gods and could be dangerous.

It took some fast thinking and faster talking to convince the medicine man, but Zack finally did it. The Indian agreed that pop was neither food nor water, and that the young bucks would not be inviting disaster to drink it. After that, the suffering of the young bucks was relieved a little — and Zack's soda-pop business boomed.

In those days, while Zack was just a shirt-tail kid, the hands at the Salt Fork Ranch used to send him down to the White Eagle Agency for mail. Pretty often, 'Spotted Face' John Maxwell rode with him. Spotted Face was a white boy; he came by his Indian-sounding name through a birthmark that disfigured the whole right side of his face. He was about Zack's age, and together they had lots of fun swimming their horses across the Salt Fork River on their way to the agency. Their horses could swim the river, all right, with the boys sitting up in their saddles. But most of the time, the boys shucked out of their clothes, hung them on their saddles, and clung to the tails of the swimming horses. That was the way grown cowboys made it easier for their horses when a river was flooded and dangerous to cross. And Zack and Spot liked to do it the most desperate-looking way.

On almost every trip to the agency, they'd run into old Sits-On-The-Hill. Sits-On-The-Hill was a Ponca medicine man and a rain-maker. He'd been born bald-headed and for this reason had once been an outcast from his tribe. The Poncas thought his bald head was the mark of a bad spirit. Loneliness, and an effort to escape the tribe's disapproval, drove him in his younger days to a habit of going off by himself and sitting on some hill for hours at a time, looking out over the prairies. That's how he'd come by his name.

Whenever Zack and Spot met old Sits-On-The-Hill riding along with his bald head hidden under a greasy red bandana, they'd size up the pony he rode. If the animal didn't look like much, they'd pester the old medicine man. They'd ride up close and rub their hair and shout 'Ningay! Ningay!' meaning 'not any!'

That never failed to rile old Sits-On-The-Hill and he'd start drumming his pony's ribs with his heels and take out after them, cracking the long cow whip he usually packed. And he'd give the boys a good burning taste of the rawhide popper on that old whip, too, if he caught them.

But this was mighty seldom. Zack and Spot were young, but they were pretty good judges of horseflesh. If Sits-On-The-Hill was riding a pony that looked as if he could catch their mounts, they'd nod and say their howdy's to the medicine man, as polite as if he'd sported a mane of hair that'd rake the saddle behind him.

Sits-On-The-Hill was about twenty when he turned medicine man. One April, while the Ghost Dance was going on, Sits-On-The-Hill rode into the circle of cele-brating Indians. The circle widened, then broke. Nobody wanted to be caught near this man marked by evil spirits.

Sits-On-The-Hill looked them over scornfully. He sat straight and haughty on his pony and spoke.

'You draw away from me because I have no hair,' he said. 'But last night, I had a vision. I learned that the mark was put upon me by the Great Spirit as a blessing. I was to be a medicine man!'

This was pretty strong for the rest of the bunch to swallow, especially the medicine men. They had some doubts. 'If you're so blessed by the Great Spirit,' one jeered, 'maybe you can prophesy a thing to come. Something that will happen during the Sun Dance!'

Sits-On-The-Hill was ready for them. 'On the first night of the Sun Dance,' he predicted solemnly, 'I shall put a ring around the moon. And when the sun goes down for the second night, I shall call up a mighty storm from the west to blow down every teepee in the Ponca camp except mine.'

They sneered; he couldn't do it.

But in August, on the first night of the Sun Dance, there the ring was, a big one, circling the moon.

Some of the braves were frightened. Nobody had much to say. But they all did a lot of thinking.

Next day they watched Sits-On-The-Hill move his teepee right out in the center of the Sun Dance grounds and park himself on his hunkers in the doorway. They grew nervous and scanned the sky for cloud signs.

Along in the middle of the afternoon, the signs appeared. A big black cloud moved in from the northwest. The storm hit just at sundown, a howling, twisting blow with plenty of rain thrown in. It knocked teepees right and left. It picked some up and carried them so far away that their owners never recovered them.

When the blow was over, there was one teepee standing.

And in its doorway sat Sits-On-The-Hill, smoking his clay pipe; from that day on, he was the big medicine man of the Poncas.

Zack once saw old Sits-On-The-Hill whip a case of typhoid fever that a government agency doctor had thrown up for lost. It was at a Ponca Sun Dance given east of Ponca Station. Zack was there with his soda-pop stand. Two of his Indian friends, George and Tom Premeaux, were there with the tribe. But Tom was down with typhoid fever, had been for a couple of weeks.

One day the government doctor attending Tom came by Zack's stand for a chunk of ice to help ease the fever on Tom. He told Zack he'd already given up the case. He said Tom would never live till daylight.

Zack told George Premeaux what the doctor had said about Tom. George left out immediately and returned a little later with Sits-On-The-Hill. They went into Tom's teepee and didn't come out. Next morning, George came down to Zack's stand for a bottle of pop. Zack inquired about the Indian's brother.

'He feel fine today,' George said. 'Not hot like yesterday. I think Sits-On-The-Hill fix him good.'

He said Sits-On-The-Hill had cut slits in Tom's head at each temple, sucked out a lot of blood, then spent the night going through a mysterious ceremony.

Four days later, Tom himself came down to the stand for a bottle of pop. He's alive today, and carries the scars of the slits old Sits-On-The-Hill cut in his temples.

G. W. Miller didn't claim to believe in the medicine of old Sits-On-The-Hill; but during his lifetime, Zack saw his father pay the Indian many a beef to make it rain. Sits-On-

The-Hill would start his rain-making rituals, and if the beeves held out, he never failed.

A bad drought hit the 101 range along in the early nineties. It started in May and ran on into July. The water-holes dried up. The water in the Salt Fork became so salty that no cow could drink it. Big steers trapped themselves and sank in the mire of the dried-up water-holes, while others stood upon them, sucking up the wet mud from the green-scum puddles.

G. W. bought seven windmills and set a drill crew to work. Along the creeks the well-drillers could get sheet water at about twenty feet, but the wells produced only about three or four buckets of this seep water a day. One cow could drink it up faster than a man could draw it. The crew drilled deeper. They drilled twenty wells, going down about three hundred feet. Every well produced water salty enough to cure meat.

By the first of August, the situation was desperate. The Millers had five thousand head of steers gathered and ready to move up into the Osage country. There was no grass there, but there was water.

Then Sits-On-The-Hill came to the rescue, riding up on a spotted pony to where the hands were making a steer-gather.

'Gimme wohaw,' he said to G. W. 'I make rain.'

G. W. gave him a crippled beef and Sits-On-The-Hill rode off to make medicine with the Great Spirit. It was good medicine, plenty strong. That night a regular Noah's flood came, overflowing every pond and drowning half the cattle strung out along the Salt Fork.

Zack's boyhood companions there on the ranch were mostly Indian kids. Jack No-Ear, Harry King, Louis DeLodge, George and Tom Premeaux, and Fred and Mike Roy. Zack learned to play their games. He could beat them at one of their favorites, pitching pecans into the knot-hole of a hollow log. He hunted skunks with them, 'possums, and coyote wolves. By the time he was ten years old, he was riding twenty to twenty-five miles from the ranch with this group of young savages, going after antelope.

They hunted antelope a great deal. They usually headed for the Big Flats between Pond Creek and the Salt Fork, where the antelope numbered in thousands. All they'd take for a three- or four-day trip would be Zack's gun, bows and arrows, parched corn, coffee, and dried wild currants.

Out there on the flats, they'd put up a flag on a high pole, then lie in ambush, screened by a blind of weeds. The antelope would see the flag waving in the breeze, become curious, and start snorting and stamping their forefeet, always moving closer and closer. If the boys were downwind from the antelope, the animals would come within shooting range finally and the grand slaughter would commence.

Zack would hold his fire till the Indians could reach the game with their arrows. They'd jump up and shoot. What antelope didn't fall would bunch together and then Zack would open up and empty his gun into them. That would stampede the herd.

The boys would chase the antelope then. When they saw one stagger, they knew he had an arrow in him and they'd keep after him till they'd brought him down. Finally, they'd pack the meat back to camp, cut it in chunks and hang it to dry over a smoke which kept away the flies. After a day or so of drying, they would load it on their horses and pack it back into headquarters.

Zack always got the tenderloin. It was his by the same unwritten law that made him chief of these parties. He had the only gun!

Bert Freshmeat rode for the 101 awhile. That was the year the Government made it mandatory that cowmen leasing land on the reservation hire Indians for at least a quarter of their crews.

Bert was a big Ponca Indian, built high above his corns, the way the 101 cowhands described him. He liked to draw cowhand pay, but no cowman ever considered him a close companion to work. Riding herd of a night, Bert didn't mind taking it easy if the cattle lay quiet. He had a habit of riding off from the herd a piece and bedding down in the grass for a little shut-eye. He'd tie his horse on a forty-foot picket rope and tie the loose end around his ankle.

One night the 101 crew was holding a loose herd in the bend of the Salt Fork River near the railroad bridge. These were Mexico cattle and wild as corncrib rats. The grass and water had been good, though, and the cattle had given no trouble so far.

Zack, being just a kid, drew the bobtail guard, the first shift of the night watch, with Bert Freshmeat as his partner. They rode out and started circling the herd, riding slow and singing to let the cattle know who they were and what they were doing. It was a still night; there was a quarter moon with one horn hooked over the skyline. The steers were bedded on a slight knoll, belching and blowing off, resting easy as cattle will on full paunches.

Pretty soon Zack missed his Indian partner. He knew what Bert was up to, but the herd was quiet; he let the Indian sleep.

But every cowhand knows that the confidence a steer's got in the dark is mighty frail. About ten o'clock a train rounded the bend and blew two long blasts for the river crossing.

That kicked the lid off. The ground shook and every head of those wild steers was on his feet and headed for Mexico with his tail in the air.

Zack rode like hell, but what could one lone kid do with a stampeded herd of Mexico cattle? He might just as well have tried to stop a cyclone with a wave of his hat. The herd left him like he was backing up.

Off to his left he heard a wild hollering. He quit the herd then and cut in that direction.

It was his sleeping Indian friend Bert Freshmeat. But by now Bert's boogered horse had dragged him far enough on the end of that forty-foot rope to wake him up. The faint moonlight showed him sitting up out in the middle of a burnt-off patch of grass stubble, trying hard to free his foot from that rope. But his horse was watching him close; every time Bert made a move to reach his foot, the horse would snort and leave out again, making a drag out of Bert.

Zack didn't know what to do. That was a goosey horse Bert was riding; he hadn't been under saddle half a dozen times. He wouldn't let Bert cut loose from the rope, and every time Zack started toward him, he'd run again.

It was a proposition, all right. Camp was a couple of miles away. The boys would come soon; they were bound to have heard the stampede. But would they come soon enough? If that booger-hunting horse of Bert's ever whipped the Indian around a rock or stump, there'd be one more red man ready for happy hunting grounds.

The only out Zack could see was to run Bert's horse down and do it quick. Bert would just have to stand a little fast dragging.

Zack hooked spurs to his own horse and cut him down both hips with his rope. Bert's horse whistled keen as a deer and left out. The race was short, but the squalling of that Indian dragging by one foot turned Zack's blood to ice-water.

Zack caught the horse in less than a hundred yards. He cut the Indian loose and led his own horse back to help Bert mount. Bert was sure a sorry sight to look at. The grass stubble had cut his garments to strings and raked off patches of hide a foot long. The fire-blackened ground had him streaked and smudged till, back in the light of the campfire, he looked like a tattooed Negro. As for working cattle, Bert was fed up.

'I think,' he told the hands, 'that I tell the Indian agent tomorrow he can put another Indian to work here.'

And that's what he did. He didn't even stay to help round up the herd he'd let scatter to hell and gone in the timber along the river.

Bert was strong on all Indian tradition. He believed, as did many others of his tribe, that when a brave stumbled and fell while running for the Sun Dance pole, he'd never live to see the next Sun Dance. That year, during the Sun Dance ritual, Bert lost his footing and rolled in the dust. Immediately, he got ready to die.

'I never live to see the next Sun Dance,' he told Zack.

And he didn't. A few months later, the horse Bert rode stepped into a prairie-dog hole and piled up, with the Indian under him. When the horse got to his feet, Bert still lay there, the life crushed out of him.

Things like that, Zack says, they never printed in the books he read. He always figured that what he learned from the Indians would lay any schoolbook lessons in the shade.

2

COWHAND FROM THE EMERALD ISLE

JIMMY MOORE was the man who taught Zack most of the things a ranch kid thirsts to learn. Jimmy was a blarney little cowhand from the Emerald Isle, stoop-shouldered, with eyes bright as a squirrel's. He rode humped in the saddle like it hurt him to straddle it, but he could stay there longer and tire a horse less than any rider on the 101.

Nobody ever knew much about Jimmy's past. He would talk a blue streak when the notion struck him, but he didn't make a habit of airing his paunch about personal affairs. He'd come from Dublin. He'd served a couple of years in the United States Army back East somewhere. Then he'd decided to become a cowhand, so he'd caught him a west-bound train out of New York and ridden it to the end of the line.

The why's and wherefore's of these moves were anybody's guess; Jimmy never took the trouble to explain.

It was in 1880 that he caught that west-bound train. And the end of the line proved to be Hunnewell, Kansas, where G. W. Miller and a crew of his hands were in town, shipping out some steers.

Broke and hungry, Jimmy left the station and followed his nose across a street to the 101 chuck wagon where the hands were squatted around, polishing off a beefsteak dinner. The little Irishman stopped, sized up the men and the grub, then hit up Zack's father for a job.

22

G. W. motioned toward the dutch ovens. 'Eat,' he said. 'Then we'll talk business.'

Jimmy ate. He tucked away the third helping of beefsteak before he pitched his tin plate into the dishpan and backed off, satisfied.

Grinning, G. W. invited him to have more.

Jimmy Moore shook his head. 'Thanky, sir!' he said gravely. 'Me stomach could be holding no more.'

He confessed right there that he didn't know a cow from a sheep; but G. W. signed him on.

'Anybody,' G. W. declared, 'who can eat that much beef at one squatting is bound to have the makings of a cowman. We'll put you to wrangling horses.'

Miller's prophecy proved correct. Jimmy was quick to learn; he was a natural with a rope. By the time Zack was big enough to go out to the ranch, Jimmy was boss of the 101 outfit whenever G. W. was gone.

Jimmy took Zack under his wing from the start. He rigged his boss's son out in cowboy boots and a Money-Weight Stetson, a straight-brimmed, flat-topped hat popular with cowhands in those days. The hat would exactly balance a twenty-dollar gold piece on the scales and sold for that price. Jimmy put Zack to roping goats, chickens, fence posts, anything a rope would go on. He went further than that; he taught Zack how to use his head in sizing up his catch.

'Now, Dogie,' he'd tell Zack, 'when you set out to be roping a steer, think which way you'd go if you was the steer. Keep that in mind and you'll be letting few of them get away.'

He took time to show Zack how to set a saddle. That saddle had to sit where it belonged, with the cinch drawn up just right. Jimmy Moore wasn't taking any chances on letting a green kid or a careless cowhand beefsteak the back of a good horse.

He loved a horse, Jimmy Moore did. He'd never crowd or whip a tired one or allow any of the hands to do so. 'Faith and he'll get along as fast as Godamighty wants him to under the circumstances!' he'd say.

Let him catch a hand misusing a horse and Jimmy Moore's short temper exploded like the joints of the blue stem grass in a prairie fire. 'Faith and be Jasus Christ!' he'd begin, and from there, he'd dish out to the guilty one a brand of cursing that for violence and sting had no equal on the Salt Fork range.

'It peels the hide off in shoestring widths,' one cowhand described it.

No show-off rider ever spurred a horse in the shoulders twice around Jimmy Moore. 'Listen here, you son-of-a-bitch,' he'd say. 'That horse belongs to you only from the saddle cinch back. Everything in front of that belongs to G. W. Miller and I'm after looking out for his interests. You do that again and bedamned, mon, if I won't settle with you in an Irish way.'

And the man took it. Jimmy Moore was a dead shot with a six-shooter and he never rode without a rifle in his saddle scabbard, with the butt turned back, handy to his reach. He never shot a man; he never had to. No man ever raked up the nerve to call his hand.

Maybe Jimmy Moore knew the meaning of the word 'reincarnation' — likely he didn't. But that's what he believed in. He'd finish tonguelashing a man for spurring a tired horse and always wind up with 'Faith, and in the next life, it'll be a sore back you're wearing and you'll be the horse!'

Jimmy Moore named all his horses 'Baby' something or other — Baby Blue, Baby Black, Baby Joe. He babied them all and there was hell among the yearlings any time he caught a man riding a horse that belonged in Jimmy's own string. He even had pets among the horses in the strings of other riders.

Old Bird Ass was one of these pets. Bird Ass was an old stove-up cowpony with sand-burnt scars all over both hips. In times past, he'd been as good a piece of horseflesh as a man ever threw a saddle on. But age and hard work had stiffened his knee joints and now he was used mostly to mount outsiders and kids on. But Jimmy Moore still loved him.

One day a telegraph messenger named Frank Taggart walked up to the Salt Fork camp from Ponca Station. He said he had a telegram for a trail-herd outfit camped on Yellow Bull Crossing. He wanted to borrow a horse to deliver it on.

G. W. was down in Texas on a cattle deal at the time, and Jimmy Moore was out riding the pastures. Uncle Doc Miller, G. W.'s younger brother, who had come to live at the ranch, roped out and saddled old Bird Ass for the messenger.

'Now you take care of that old crow-bait,' Uncle Doc warned. 'And have him back in camp tomorrow night. He's a prime favorite of Jimmy Moore's and if that Irishman was in camp now, he'd never let you have him. He thinks that Bird Ass is a down-the-road horse and he'd work up a big lather if you lost him.'

Taggart promised to take care of the horse and rode off. That afternoon a chunk-floating rain fell. By night the Salt Fork was on a rampage; but the rain stopped, and the flood-water began falling the next day. However, neither Taggart nor the horse showed up at camp that night.

The third night passed and still they didn't come. Jimmy Moore rode in for supper on the fourth night of Taggart's absence. Uncle Doc was worried; he told Jimmy about lending old Bird Ass to the messenger and how long they'd been gone.

Jimmy Moore gave Uncle Doc a hard look. 'You'll not be seeing the mon nor the horse alive again,' he said roughly and went off to bed.

Next day at noon some men from Ponca Station drove up in a spring wagon. They came and ate with the 101 crew and finally one of them got around to asking if anybody'd seen or heard of Taggart.

'Sure, and I never heard a word out of him,' Jimmy Moore said grimly, 'but I know right where he is. When dinner's over, I'll be taking you there.'

The men gave the little Irishman puzzled looks; but Jimmy Moore wasn't a man to question when he was in a bad humor. And it was easy to see that he was in one now. In fact, for the last couple of days, he'd been in such a sour-tempered frame of mind that the cowhands had taken to stepping light and talking easy whenever he showed up in camp.

The men fed in silence, then followed the little Irishman off down the river to the mouth of a creek. There, when the river got up, a whirlpool formed, trapping logs and trash. The creek mouth was always boggy.

And out in the middle of the bog, the body of Frank Taggart hung partly over a log, buried to the armpits in the suck-hole. There was no sign of Jimmy Moore's beloved pet, old Bird Ass. The mud had already closed over him.

The men stood on the bank and pitched a rope over the dead man's head. But when they pulled, the rotten body parted in the middle, leaving half of Frank Taggart in the bog. They hauled the rest into town, wrapped in a slicker, and buried it the same way.

'When did you first find him?' Uncle Doc wanted to know.

'Sure, and I seen him when the water went down the other morning early,' Jimmy Moore said.

'Then why in the hell didn't you tell somebody?'

'Faith, and be Jasus Christ!' snapped Jimmy Moore. 'It was no good you could be doing him then. You should have stopped the fool before he rode the best horse on the Salt Fork into a suck-hole grave!' He puffed short angry whiffs of smoke out of his little stub pipe and added: 'Sure, and he didn't have half-human intelligence or he wouldn't have forced a good horse into water like that!'

After that, the creek was always called Dead Man's Gulch. It's called that today.

Jimmy Moore was a born gambler, and a good horse-race could take his heart, liver, and tongue. He liked bust-head whiskey, Lipton's tea, and Climax chewing tobacco. He didn't chew the tobacco; he shaved it up with his knife and smoked it in a little clay pipe where it popped and fried and went out almost as soon as he took a lighted match from it. Around ten o'clock in the morning and four in the afternoon was teatime, and nothing short of a fist fight or a prairie fire could keep Jimmy Moore from calling a halt on what he was doing and making tea. He brewed it in a little fire-blackened tomato can that he always kept tied to a saddle string, and drank it from the same thing. For his tea fire, he wanted dried cow chips. He'd rather have them than the best of seasoned oak. He claimed cow chips gave off a more even heat and brewed a better-flavored tea.

The year that the 101 outfit ran cattle on the Osage Reservation, about thirty-five miles out from Tulsa, Jimmy Moore usually sent Zack into town with a pack mule for grub. There were only two stores in Tulsa then, a plank one and another built of cottonwood logs.

'Now, Dogie,' Jimmy would advise Zack, 'you go to the plank store and buy a little. You'll be tying up and sleeping there and it's only right that you trade some with this mon. But you'll be buying most of your stuff from the mon at the log store. He's the better merchant; he keeps Climax tobacco and Lipton's tea.'

Around camp, Jimmy Moore's chief amusement was arguing with Zack's Uncle Doc Miller. Uncle Doc was a medium-sized, brown-haired man who hung out at the ranch as if he were hiding from somebody. He never went to town; he never went anywhere. He just stayed out at the ranch headquarters, spending most of his time cooking.

A time or two, Zack got the idea that it was a woman

Uncle Doc was dodging; he never did know. But Uncle Doc was always powerful bitter about women for some reason or other.

One day he caught Zack thumbing through a copy of a *Police Gazette*, Jimmy Moore's bible. Zack had located the picture of a New York beauty and was sizing up the shape of her bared leg. Uncle Doc crawled Jimmy Moore's hump about leaving that magazine around.

'Don't you know,' he stormed, 'that an eleven-year-old kid ain't got no business looking at the pictures of naked women?'

Jimmy Moore handed him a one-sided grin. 'Sure,' he said, 'and let the lad admire them. Be Jasus, if I'd had one of them papers to look at twenty year ago, I'd be knowing a hell of a lot more about she-stuff than I do today!'

They'd argue over horse-races. They'd argue over prize-fighters, Jim Corbett and John L. Sullivan. Somehow Jimmy Moore had come by a copy of Dante's *Inferno*, and they'd take sides on the question of whether or not there was a hell.

From there, the argument would drift off into religion. Neither of them had any more religion than a billygoat, but they'd take sides and argue on it. They'd heard about a rider with a cow outfit farther down the Salt Fork who'd had his cods horned out by a bad steer, and Jimmy Moore swore and bedamned that such a man could never be entering the Kingdom of Heaven. And when Uncle Doc took issue with him on that, Jimmy Moore would rear up on his hind legs and shout at him.

'Faith, and it sure as hell says so in the Bible, and I've seen it there! "A mon," it says "who's lost his stones and privy member cannot enter the Kingdom of Heaven." '

Uncle Doc would tell him that he was a damned fool, that there'd be no men or women in heaven, that they'd all be angels. And then Jimmy Moore would pounce again.

'Be Jasus, and would you be telling me then,' he'd want to know, 'why they'll bar a mon without cods at the Pearly Gates if the good Lord didn't aim for mon to play with women in heaven?'

They'd keep up that sort of thing half the night, with listening cowhands laying bets as to which one of them would be the first to get mad and go off to bed and sulk.

Zack never did know if Jimmy Moore's quotation came from the Bible, from Shakespeare, or from Jimmy's own fertile imagination; but he was convinced of one thing: he was sure going to be careful and not let a bad steer fix him up like that ruined rider down the Salt Fork. Zack felt mighty sorry for that man.

Carrie Nation was getting around in those days, beating up the bars with hatchets and raising hell in general. Uncle Doc backed every move she made. Uncle Doc would drink whiskey now and then, but drinking was against his principles. Mostly, though, he championed Carrie's crusade against the demon rum because he knew how Jimmy Moore loved his juice of joy and hated anyone who interfered with its making or his drinking.

Jimmy always declared that hypocrites and women had no business tampering with liquor, in any way. He got fighting mad every time he heard about some new batch of good whiskey Carrie had destroyed.

'Sure,' he'd snarl viciously, 'and they ought to bile the

bitch in ile and put her in the pot while the ile is still cold!'

Either Uncle Doc or Jimmy Moore would have been miserable without the other; but it looked to Zack as if they tried to make life as miserable as possible for each other. They were always just at the point of fighting, but never quite got around to it. One time they shaved it close, though.

It was on the Fourth of July. Some of the boys had slicked up and let their spurs out to the town-hole notches and ridden into Hunnewell to celebrate. They rode back in to the Deer Creek headquarters just about sundown, loaded to the gills and waving a jug they still hadn't emptied.

Zack was out at the well, pumping water into a hollow-log trough for the horses. Jimmy Moore was squatted in comfort on his spurs in front of the dugout wasting matches on his Climax shavings. Uncle Doc was up on top of the dugout, hoeing out a patch of onions he had growing on the roof. The boys passed up Zack, gave Jimmy Moore a drink, then called to Uncle Doc.

'Come on down, Doc, and have a drink.'

There were times when Uncle Doc could be a prince; there were also times when he could be as cranky as a hungry bear. This time was the latter. He and Jimmy Moore had just finished wearing themselves down to whispers on a Carrie Nation argument and Uncle Doc was in a sod-pawing mood.

'To hell with your damned whiskey!' he snapped. 'I won't touch a drop of it!'

This was an insult to a celebrating cowhand. 'You'll either come down and take a drink,' one declared, 'or we'll come up there and pour one down you.'

Uncle Doc invited them to come have a try at it any time they felt able — and they felt able right then. They rode up to the back of the dugout and onto his onion-patch roof, roped him and stretched him out. They stamped down most of his onions in the scuffle, but they poured about a pint of whiskey down Uncle Doc.

By the time Uncle Doc started rustling up a bait of supper, that whiskey in his empty stomach had taken hold. He was higher than a kite, ready to give somebody a horse or back him in a poker game.

While he was working up a batch of sourdough biscuits, Uncle Doc looked out the dugout door and saw his pet dog Kaiser romping with a bear cub belonging to Jimmy Moore. Kaiser was a big brown shepherd dog with a ring of white around his neck. Zack used him a lot to pen goats with. The bear cub, Jimmy Moore had caught up in the Glossy Mountains one time while on a trail drive. He kept the cub chained to a cottonwood tree near a hollow log into which the bear could crawl for shelter. Both men set great store by their pets and the pets loved each other.

While Uncle Doc was looking, however, he saw the bear grab old Kaiser up to him in a hug tighter than the cub meant it to be. The bear was coming a three-year-old now and stronger than he knew. Kaiser gave one strangled yelp. The cub let him go. But it was too late. There was no more Kaiser to play with; he'd been smashed flat.

Uncle Doc's whiskey flush bloomed a bright red. Without a word, and with the biscuit dough still clinging to his hands, he reached and took his Winchester down off a wall rack. Taking dead aim, he shot the bear between the eyes, racked his Winchester, and went back to his biscuit-making.

The sudden quiet among the boys there in that old dugout was thick enough to slice with a knife. Every eye went to Jimmy Moore. Every man knew the little Irishman's love for animals in general and for this cub bear in particular. They also knew what a hair-trigger temper he had. Zack sat there shivering, afraid to draw a good breath. A killing could come of this!

Maybe the whiskey he'd drunk had mellowed Jimmy Moore for the evening. Or maybe he thought what an empty life he'd lead without Uncle Doc to argue with. Zack never did know. The little Irishman kept squatting there on his spurs, staring at Uncle Doc. Just squatting there and staring and sucking on his stubby pipe, making the Climax shavings pop and fry.

The tension built up till the men were ready to stampede. Then, with a casual movement, Jimmy Moore reached for the whiskey jug and tilted it toward the sunset.

'Ay,' he said calmly, when he had set it back down. 'A fair exchange is no robbery. You lost a dog and I lost a bear. Come have a drink, Doc.'

Uncle Doc came and had a drink and went back to put his biscuits in the dutch oven. He said nothing. Jimmy Moore said nothing more. And if the two of them even mentioned the incident again, nobody ever heard it.

Hard as he was, Jimmy Moore had a keen sense of humor and could appreciate a joke on himself as quickly as on the next man. The 101 hands were trying to pen some wild steers at Hunnewell one time when the train engine popped off a batch of steam and stampeded the herd.

Hard riding stopped the steers before they got far; but

hard riding, hell, nor high water couldn't put them back in those pens. Once in sight of the gate, they'd cut back and high-tail it for the prairies, ready to horn any horse that tried to head them off.

The hands turned them toward the pens time and again. Each time, the steers would cut back a little farther from the gate. In about three days, a man could have combed Oklahoma and half of Texas and not rounded up enough cowhands to pen those steers. The wild bunch had the crew backed off out on the prairie so far that they had to shade their eyes to see the corral gates.

Jimmy Moore was up a tree. His reputation as a cow-hand was at stake. Something had to be done.

Then one of the hands hatched off an idea. He said the thing to do was to get a cow with a young calf, separate them, putting the calf in the pens and the cow out with the steer herd. That way, the calf would bawl to its mammy and the old cow would hear and start toward it, bawling. And the steers would see her heading into the pens where her calf was, and that would take the scare out of them and they'd follow. He claimed he'd heard of that trick being pulled down in Texas.

Jimmy Moore was doubtful. But by now he'd have been ready to try calling in the steers with a turkey yelper if anybody had thought of it. He was ridden down, trying to pen those steers. So were his horses and his men.

He sent a cowhand to Hunnewell to locate a cow with a young calf. The hand got one from a widow and brought her boy along to handle the animal. They put the calf in the pens and drove the cow down to the steer herd. The calf started blatting. The old cow began to bawl and headed for the pens. And the steers did just what the cowhand said they would. They started following the cow, bawling every time she did, and trailed her right into the pens as if that was where they thought they belonged.

Jimmy Moore shut the gate on them.

'And what'll you be asking for the use of your cow, lad?' he wanted to know.

The tall, lanky kid stood digging a bare big toe into the dirt and studied awhile. Finally, he said: 'I guess $21.65 would be about right.'

Jimmy ducked and blinked. That would have been a high buying price for the cow and calf, and he'd only wanted to pay for the use of them.

'Now how in the hell, lad,' he said, 'would you be arriving at such a figure?'

'Well, I'll tell you, Mr. Jimmy,' the kid said. 'I owe George Avery $21.65 and he keeps dunning me for it and I want to get it off my mind.'

Jimmy Moore leaned back in the saddle and laughed till his face hurt. 'Faith,' he said at last, 'if that's not the best damned reason for holding a mon up I ever heard!' and he gave the boy his price.

Every time Jimmy Moore got together a thousand dollars, he made a trip back to Dublin. He'd go down to Hunnewell and buy a round-trip train ticket to New York and leave fifty dollars cash with the ticket agent to hold for him till he got back. In New York, he'd buy a round-trip steamer ticket to Dublin and leave with the steamship agent fifty dollars to hold till he got back. That way, he could go to Ireland, blow in every cent he had, and still make it back to the 101.

He always came back broke. Part of his money he blew in on two old-maid sisters and his father back in Dublin. The balance went for whiskey and a trunk-load of presents he'd bring in for everybody from the swamper to his boss, G. W.

G. W. would always bawl and roar around every time Jimmy got the money for another trip. He'd tell Jimmy that he was fired, that the 101 didn't have any room for a fiddle-footed hand who had to sack his saddle and take a prowl every year or so.

But Jimmy Moore never paid any attention to it. He'd just grin at G. W.'s paw and beller and go right ahead fixing up to take his trip. And when he got back, he'd catch up his string of horses and start to work again without bothering to see if G. W. wanted him on the payroll again.

But G. W. always did. Zack guessed his father thought nearly as much of Jimmy Moore as he did.

3

HORSE TRADER

AT AN AGE when most boys are swapping taw marbles and broken-bladed pocketknives, young Zack was already horse-trading. G. W. Miller saw to that. G. W. was a trader from the ground up and tops when it came to judging livestock. He could look at a bunch of hogs, lump them off, and judge their weight within a few pounds. Many a time he'd go out into the feed lots at Winfield where there'd be maybe three to five hundred head of cattle, with hogs among them. He'd walk through once, make an offer on the whole outfit, and buy them at a price that left room for profit.

'Son,' he used to tell Zack, 'when you ride through a herd of cattle one time, buy them — or turn them down. You go back for a second look, and nine times out of ten you'll beat yourself.'

And Zack listened. He was a chip off the old block; trading was in his blood. He'd trail G. W. like a pet dog, all eyes and ears to catch every trick and turn of the deals. He'd already made himself a promise a good while back: one of these days he'd be as sharp-witted as his father about dealing in livestock.

And every chance he got, G. W. shoved his son Zack out into the middle of a deal. Once down in Texas on a cow-buy with his father, Zack ran onto some spotted Spanish goats, the first he'd ever seen. Zack thought they were sure pretty things and bought one off the owner for four-bits.

When he came riding into camp with it, G. W. said: 'Why in the hell didn't you buy the whole bunch?'

That one was easy for eleven-year-old Zack to answer. 'I didn't have enough four-bit pieces,' he pointed out.

G. W. went to his buckboard and put some money into a morral and handed it to Zack.

'I'm making you a loan,' he said. 'Go buy the balance of the goats if you want them.'

Zack wanted them and he bought them. But by the time he'd peddled goats all over Kansas, trying to pay back that loan, Zack was hating the sight of a Spanish goat.

Some of these goats, he traded for horses. And then G. W. started siccing horse traders on the boy, trying to teach him the game. It was G. W.'s contention that the quicker his son got taken for a few good cleanings, the sooner he'd get his eyes open to the fact that anything goes in a horse-swap.

And the theory held good. It cost Zack a few horses to learn; but by the time he was twelve years old, he could tell a snide just about as far as he could see one. He learned to feel the socket over a horse's eyes to find out if he was really young or if some slicker had pumped that socket full of air just to make the horse look young. He knew that a carefully compounded mixture of permanganate of potash and water would hide a blazed or roan face when a buyer was looking for a solid-colored horse. In selling horses to the Government, traders had learned that the army bought only solid colors; a white-faced horse would make a natural mark for an enemy to shoot at. That paint job, done right,

would last till the horse shed his hair in the spring. Zack
had seen beautiful horses ruined by distemper, and then
seen the owners put sponges in such an animal's nose so
that he could breathe naturally. Of course, a horse doc-
tored up that way would choke down at the slightest exercise. But then there was always the chance that someone
not in the know would come along and buy him without
first taking the precaution of running him.

Then there were always buckers, biters, kickers — outlaw horses, spoiled by accidents or poor handling. Some
were natural stumblers. Some were cinch binders —
they'd rear up and fall back on a rider. Some had been
Indian broken and couldn't be mounted from the left side.
Some would balk. Some were runaways that turned cold-
jawed and couldn't be stopped short of running head-on
into a tree. Some would fall sideways, hoping to pin a
rider against the ground and roll over him. It took a
shrewd man with his eyes wide open to come out on the
long end of a horse trade.

A little way outside of Arkansas City one time, young
Zack came upon a gypsy camp down in a creek bottom.
Zack was mounted on a moon-eyed roan that some slick
trader had put off on him at Winfield. The roan was a
good enough horse, all right. He was well set up, clean-
limbed, and had a good saddle gait. But every so often he
went blind in one eye. He'd stay blind for a few days, then
the eye would clear up, only to turn blue a little while later
and go blind again. Today, his eye was clear.

Tied at the edge of the gypsy camp was one of the most
beautiful gray horses Zack thought he'd ever seen. Judging
from the horse's build, there was a touch of Arabian in his

blood. He was a young horse and stood proud; he lifted a fine intelligent head at Zack's approach.

Zack pulled up and sat in his saddle, looking the horse over. A big, smiling, dark-faced gypsy sauntered out from the camp, studying the roan Zack rode. Almost at once, he bounced Zack for a trade.

That aroused the boy's suspicions, but he still couldn't see a thing wrong with that beautiful gray.

'Is he broke to ride?' Zack wanted to know.

The gypsy nodded. 'And he leads and is bridle-wise,' he said. 'He has only one little trick — he'll buck sometimes when you first get on him.'

To Zack's way of thinking, that was nothing against the gray. According to cowhand opinion, any young horse with enough life in him to be worth riding liked to pitch and romp a little when first saddled. Zack thought this was a mighty good chance to get rid of his moon-eyed roan.

The gypsy demanded fifteen dollars boot. Zack offered five. They settled for nine dollars and fifty cents.

The gypsy helped Zack to saddle the mount. 'Just hold him up a little and he'll give you no trouble,' he said.

He pulled the gray's head around by the cheek of the bridle and held it till Zack had mounted and caught up the reins short. The gray snorted and crab-walked a little when the gypsy turned him loose, but didn't offer to pitch. And once lined out down the road, he traveled in the running-walk gait that is a pleasure to any rider. The twelve-year-old Zack turned to wave good-bye to the gypsy. He guessed he'd taken that bird for a real cleaning, putting off that moon-eyed roan on him.

Turning to wave his hand was a mistake, however. In

doing so, he gave the gray a little rein slack. The gray was set and waiting. With a bawl, he bogged his head and went after it, pitching the hardest and fastest of any horse Zack had ever been on up to then.

Zack made a ride of it. But it wasn't a ride that a man would want to brag about later. Sometimes he was in front of the saddle, and then again behind it. He swears that he rode every square inch of that gray, from the roots of his tail to right up against his ears. And all the time, he was clawing leather and mane with both hands and wishing he had a couple more hands to grab holds with.

When he finally got the gray's head pulled up, Zack couldn't tell which was more surprised to find him still in the saddle — himself or the horse.

But if Zack thought that one ride was all of it, he had some more thinking to do. He'd meant to stop in Arkansas City to eat; but when he rode up to a hitch rack and started to get off, the gray got more slack and Zack had it all to do over again. By the time the two of them had put on a good show for the hooting and yelling mob of cowhands lining the sidewalks, Zack had lost his appetite and decided to stay in the saddle.

It was fifteen miles from there to his home in Winfield. Zack might have made it pretty good if a gradual urge hadn't built up to make him more uncomfortable by the minute. The urge got worse and worse as he rode along. He didn't know what to do. He knew that if he took care, he could hold the gray up long enough to get off and relieve himself. But how in the hell was he to get back on him again without the gypsy to help?

Nature finally solved the problem. The water ran down

inside Zack's pants leg and collected in his boot, where it sloshed and gurgled with every movement of the horse. That relieved Zack of his suffering for the time being, but long before he reached Winfield, he had other pains; riding in those wet pants set up a friction, galling the inside of his leg.

That was the longest and most miserable fifteen miles Zack ever rode. He held the gray up short and fell out of the saddle at Winfield and could just barely stand. The ride the gray had given him had him black and blue all over, and the inside of one leg had rubbed to the raw and was bleeding. All he needed now to make him a cripple was a handful of lead pencils.

With all the pitch knocked out of him by a 101 bronc peeler who knew how to get the job done, the gray finally made one of the best cutting horses ever to set foot on the ranch. But Zack never was right certain who took whom to a trimming in that horse trade with the gypsy.

It was another gypsy, ribbed up by G. W., who got the swaybacked snide off on Zack. The gypsy hit Zack up for a trade in Winfield. The horse the gypsy rode looked a little potbellied to Zack, but the animal had a good eye, sound feet, and a gentle single-foot gait. Zack rode him in the gypsy's saddle to make certain his action was good. He offered the gypsy a runty mule and fifteen dollars for the horse, and the deal was made. Then the gypsy pulled off his saddle and started counting the blankets and quilts under it.

'One,' he said, laying aside the saddle blanket.

'Two,' he counted, pulling off a comfort quilt.

'Three,' he said, pulling off a second quilt and grinning slyly at Zack.

There were four quilts and a saddle blanket in all and when they'd been removed, the horse looked as if he'd been cut in two from his withers to his hips. The traders standing around roared their laughter. Zack knew he'd been sucked in on a good one.

'Now,' said the gypsy, 'I'll give you the mule back for him if you're not satisfied.'

'What about the fifteen dollars?' Zack wanted to know.

'I keep the fifteen dollars.'

Hot anger flooded young Zack's being. 'You'll play hell!' he said resentfully. 'I'll keep him. I'll get him fat and ride him.'

Zack brought his swayback home. He took the ribbing and rawhiding his father and the cowboys handed out. But he fattened his swayback and rode him, just like he'd said.

In the fall, he caught a Winfield trader by the name of Benny Fuson with his pants down and put the horse off on him, getting in exchange a fair horse and forty dollars to boot. Then he went back home and had the laugh on his father and the hands.

Benny Fuson traded the swayback to a horse trader named Young Yates, who was looking for just such a snide. Yates took up right where the gypsy left off. He'd saddle that old horse with all his blankets and quilts and trade him for any kind of an old crow-bait, so long as he could get cash to boot. Then he'd pull off the saddle and quilts and give the man back his horse, but keep the money. He kept this up for years, trading all over the country, picking up on the average ten, fifteen, maybe twenty dollars a day.

When the swayback became too well known in Oklahoma, Yates drifted down into Texas and then on into Louisiana. It was down in Mooringsport where the pay-off came. Yates traded his snide to a Louisiana planter for a mule and twenty dollars. Then he uncinched his saddle and started counting off the blankets and quilts.

The look on the planter's face was too much for Young Yates. He whooped and he hollered. He slapped his leg with his hand and bawled his laughter till the tears came into his eyes. When he could finally get his breath, he said to the planter: 'Now, that you've seen him naked, I'll give you your mule back for him.'

'Like hell you will!' snarled the planter and drew a six-shooter and shot Young Yates right between the eyes, then shot the horse, dropping him on top of Yates's body.

Being a native, the planter got away with the killing, his money, and his mule, too.

Old Blue was the best horse Zack ever owned. He picked Blue up from a neighbor named Alderman. That was along about the time Zack started shaving. He'd been down to the Dinkey Market in Ponca City where all the horse traders gathered of a Saturday. It was a year when there was hell to pay and money was scarce. Horses were a drug on the market.

There was a man at Dinkey's with ten head of ponies he wanted to sell. He claimed he was leaving the country and was ready to give his stuff away. He wanted thirty dollars for the whole kit and boodle.

By the time he'd worked the man down to fifteen dollars,

Zack saw that he could go further. So he made him an offer of eight.

'My bottom price is ten!'

'How about splitting the difference?'

Zack bought the ponies at ninety cents apiece.

On the way home, he passed old man Alderman's outfit. Alderman came running out, wanting Zack to catch up a wormy horse for him. Alderman had started in the live-stock business too late in life ever to master the art of roping. Zack thought himself the world's best. So he threw his ninety-cent ponies into an empty corral and rode into the next one to show the old man how it was done.

The wormy horse was a yearling past, a mouse-colored *grulla* with a black stripe down his back and legs. He was set up right, with a short-coupled body, trim legs and feet, and the long neck that Zack's father always demanded of a good horse.

'He's got to have neck enough to reach the grass,' G. W. always said.

Zack liked this *grulla*'s looks. But the horse was in bad shape right then. Somebody had castrated him recently, then let the blowflies get to him, and now the screw worms had a knot the size of a tub swelled under his belly.

On impulse, Zack hit the old man up for a trade. 'What'll you take for him?' he demanded.

Alderman shook his head. 'I'd hate to put an animal like that off on a borrowing neighbor,' he said. 'But then, of course, he can be cured up easy. What'll you give?'

Zack could tell the old man thought the *grulla* would die. Zack wasn't too sure but what Alderman was right. But on the other hand, the animal might be saved, too.

'I'll give you the pick of them ponies I just corralled,' he offered.

Alderman waited long enough to make a show of giving the matter serious consideration, then grabbed at the offer.

Up at the Salt Fork pasture that night, Zack led his blue colt out into the river till the water came up past the horse's belly. A few times he'd seen range hogs soak screw worms out of themselves that way. Maybe it would work with a horse. The way it looked to him enough medicine to kill the worms would kill the horse, too. This was his only out.

Somebody had rolled a wagon out into the water to soak up the wheels and tighten the tires; Zack tied his horse to the wagon and left him there overnight.

He never did learn if the water cure would work; the minnows beat him to it. During the night, they went to work on Blue's wound. They ate every worm out of him and picked off a patch of proud flesh as big as a Mexican's hat. By daylight, they had that wound cleaner than a country doctor could have scraped it.

Zack led the horse out of the water and threw a couple of handfuls of slaked lime on the sore. It healed right up.

He threw Blue into the saddle-horse trap where he could get to him. Zack petted him till he was a four-year-old, then broke him to ride and trained him to come to his whistle.

While Zack was breaking him, Blue developed a set-fast on his withers. Zack cured that with Sloan's Liniment. From then on for the next twenty-five years, every time Zack stripped the saddle gear off him, Blue would roll, spraddle, and shake himself, then go squat beside Zack to have his back washed and Sloan's Liniment rubbed on.

That Blue was a fast horse and he could turn on a dime. Plenty of times when wheeling to head a cut-back cow, he made Zack grab for the nubbin to stay with him. Zack could ride him through ten bands of loose horses at night and Blue would pay no mind; but the minute they passed a horsebacker, Blue would nicker a soft warning. Zack had him trained so that he could touch him on the ankle with the toe of his boot and Blue would lie down and stay there till Zack told him to get up.

A dog bit Blue once, and from then on he was plenty shy of dogs and wolves. Zack could never make him chase a coyote; and nights when Zack lay out on the prairie and turned Blue loose to graze, the horse would stay close, ready to come to him at the first scent of a prowling wolf, stamping and snorting like a government mule.

Zack could take Blue out on the darkest kind of night, give him the reins, and Blue would take him to the nearest 101 gate.

There was a night when Zack went to sleep in the saddle while riding across the range. When he awoke, he didn't know straight up from where he was. He turned the business of direction-finding over to Blue till finally they located a fire off in the distance. Zack tried to swing Blue toward it. Blue didn't want to go. He'd keep bearing off to the right. Zack would pull him back on the course, but Blue would start swinging to the right the moment he got rein slack. Finally, Zack used good judgment and let Blue have his head. Blue took him home.

The next day, Zack found that he'd been trying to ride Blue toward the campfire of some of the Witherspoon bunch, a cow outfit the Millers were having trouble with right then.   Like many another good cow-horse in those days, Blue had more sense about some things than the man riding him.   If he hadn't, the chances are Zack would have got his head shot off his shoulders that night.

Zack rode Blue for twenty-five years.   He showed the horse at the San Francisco Exposition in 1915.   Finally, old age caught up with Blue; his teeth got bad and he couldn't eat rough winter feed.   Zack sent him back to the ranch then and had him fed ground corn.   Blue died there on the 101 with a bell on, daddying a bunch of mule colts.

For a ninety-cent horse, Blue was worth the money. Zack couldn't have spent nine hundred dollars and bought a better piece of horseflesh.

4

BOOKLEARNING

IN SEPTEMBER of 1890, G. W. sent Zack to Marmaduke Military Academy at Sweet Springs, Missouri. Zack stayed till spring, rooming with Ples Porter, whose father was then chief of the Cherokee Indians. But Zack didn't like school. There wasn't enough room. There wasn't enough freedom. There was always something to be done on schedule and somebody telling him to do it. So when his father sent him back there the next fall, he stayed only a couple of months and then ran off. He went to Texas where Jimmy Moore was feeding out a bunch of 101 steers at Walnut Springs.

This was more to Zack's liking. Here, he could loaf around camp, ride a good horse when he wanted to, and watch the Negro bullwhackers hauling cottonseed to feed the steers.

But he hadn't been there a week before his father came riding into camp.

G. W. didn't say much; he just called Jimmy Moore off for a confidential talk. He told him Zack might come nearer earning his keep by driving one of those seed wagons. Then he pulled out for Oklahoma again.

Zack took over the driving of an ox team the next morning. He soon learned to pilot those big dumb brutes, all right. He'd already learned from Jimmy Moore how to pop a sixteen-foot blacksnake whip so that it sounded like a pistol shot. And he'd watched the Negro bullwhackers till he knew most of the commands that an ox would pay any attention to. If he shouted 'Whoa-ah, come!' loud enough and cut the hair off the rump of the right-hand ox, the animal would lunge to the left, shoving his mate over, and the wagon would turn left. 'Histe!' and a hard cut with his blacksnake on the rump of the left ox would swing them to the right. 'Whoa-ah, back up!' was the command to stop and the one the oxen spent all their time listening for. All Zack needed to make him as good a bullwhacker as the Negroes was a little brushing-up on his profanity. And that came easy enough after a few hours of fighting the stubborn oxen along.

It was the mud that got Zack. If he could have ridden the seed wagon, he might have made it. But there was no riding a wagon and driving oxen at the same time. So he waded in the mud. Sometimes the mud was ankle-deep and then again it was up to his knees. It was three miles of mud to the gin where he loaded his seed, then three miles of mud back to the feed lots where he unloaded. He and the Negro bullwhackers made three trips a day. And after the last one, Zack would fall into bed at night, too tired to eat supper or take off his muddy clothes.

Zack lasted four days and then told Jimmy Moore he guessed he was ready to go back to school. The Irishman grinned and told him he thought that was a good idea, too. He inquired about the amount of spending money Zack had. Zack said he was broke. He said the school wouldn't let him have more than a dollar and a quarter a week for spending money. He said they'd take it out of a boy's mail if anybody sent him more.

Jimmy Moore got ringy about that. 'Faith, and be Jasus Christ!' he exclaimed. 'A young mon can no be getting along on that pittance. You be looking up a girl you can trust when you get back and send me her name and address. We'll be seeing about this expense money!'

Zack went back and fixed it up with the school authorities about having run off. It wasn't much of a job; they were willing to overlook a lot as long as a student's parents paid the bills. Then he found a girl for Jimmy Moore to write to. From then on, the little Irishman sent Zack five dollars a week.

In those days, that was a lot of spending money for a schoolboy. It made Zack the envy of every kid in the academy, but it still didn't make him like school. There was too much book work. There was too much reciting, too much marching and drilling. Not enough excitement. Zack began to look for some.

Old Colonel Halderman, commandant of the school, had a cavalry horse whose mother he'd picked up on the Solomon River in Kansas back in Indian campaign days. This horse was an appaloosa, a big spoiled devil, hard to manage mainly because he was kept up in the stables too much. He'd pitched off several of the stable grooms and was a general hell-raiser and trouble-maker around the barns. Zack thought he'd like to ride that horse. It'd give him a chance to shine a little in front of the other boys.

But getting a chance to ride him was something else. The problem kept him stumped for a few days, then he thought he had an idea. Maybe the colonel would let him ride the appaloosa after the mail every day; that would give the spotted horse the exercise he was spoiling for.

Everybody was afraid of the colonel, including Zack. The colonel was a big hard-bitten man, used to giving orders and having them carried out without question. Would he listen to the hair-brained idea of a kid? Zack doubted it, but finally raked up the courage to make a try.

The colonel listened to Zack's story. He looked Zack over as if he were a bug of low order, and snapped, 'No kid can ride that horse!' Then he turned to his desk and Zack knew the interview was closed.

He left, but he was riled. He didn't like the colonel's insinuation. He thought he'd topped out worse horses than the appaloosa and he was ready to prove it.

One day, he heard that the colonel was in town. That looked like his chance. He went down to the stables and told the man in charge that the colonel had given him permission to ride his big spotted cavalry horse. The stable man looked doubtful. The colonel wasn't in the habit of letting strangers ride his horse, especially school kids. But Zack made his story sound good and the man finally led the horse out.

Zack saddled, cinching that old McClellan down tight. Then he took an extra blanket, folded it tight, and tied it down across the saddle just back of the fork where it made a swell to get his knees under. A good bucking roll like that might come in handy, in case this spotted horse got any moon-chinning ideas. And it looked as if he might, judging from the way he kept snorting and shying away and rolling up the whites of his eyes. Just to make sure, Zack wound up the job by tying down his stirrups. He was ready then, he figured, for high riding.

A couple of Negro stable hands led the horse out to the

parade grounds and held him. Zack stuck a foot in the stirrup and went up. The Negroes turned loose their grips on the bridle. The appaloosa swallowed his head with a grunting groan, and the show opened.

He went straight up with Zack, rattling every leather in that old army saddle and rattling Zack's bones with them. He came back to earth, landing one foot at a time, giving the 101 kid four separate jolts. Zack was sitting off on the appaloosa's ribs when the horse started climbing for the second jump. A third jump would have spilled Zack. But the appaloosa never made it. He'd been bluffing from the start and when two hard jumps didn't empty the saddle, he threw up his tail and called off the party.

Zack straightened himself back in the saddle, shook loose a fistful of mane and circled the parade ground a couple of times, giving everybody a good chance to see him. Then he brought the big horse back to the stables at a hard run, proud of the showing he'd made.

He wasn't so proud, however, when the colonel sent word right away for him to come to his office. The colonel hadn't gone to town, but had stood at his office window watching Zack's show-off ride. Zack was scared sick. And the stormy session that followed didn't do much to cheer him. The colonel gave him a hide-scorching lecture on being headstrong and misrepresenting facts.

Then he topped it by offering to let Zack ride the horse and carry the mail!

Zack had ridden his luck hard with that stunt and he should have been satisfied not to crowd it further. But, boylike, he couldn't let well enough alone. He'd been carrying the mail for about a week when one rainy day he overstayed his time downtown. He was making a hurry-up ride back to school when he sighted the colonel's surrey rounding a street corner several blocks ahead.

That meant they'd meet and Zack would have to get down off his horse and stand at attention while the colonel passed. Zack didn't want to do that. The street was sloppy wet. He'd get his shoes muddy and he didn't have time now to get them cleaned up before supper inspection. It looked to him like a good time to pull off a runaway.

He waited till the colonel's surrey was a couple of blocks away, then hooked spurs to the appaloosa and hauled back on the reins. The horse snorted and reared, slinging his head and fighting the pull on the bits. He came down, running hard.

They tore past the colonel like a glory-bound bat. It had been no trouble to make a show of trying to hold that old horse. Zack was putting all the strength he had into that very thing. He had him a lot better runaway started than he'd bargained for.

From there to the school, they split the street traffic wide open, giving ground to no one.

Where the driveway to the school quartered off from the street, a plank bridge spanned a small creek. That bridge stopped the runaway in short order. The appaloosa's feet hit the rain-wet timbers and went out from under him as if he'd stepped on ice. He piled up in the middle of the bridge, slinging Zack completely over the rail into about a foot of water below.

That was a teeth-shaking jolt, and for a long minute Zack was too stunned to lift his head. And when he finally managed it, he put it right back down in the mud again.

Yonder went the appaloosa, bucking and snorting. And here came Colonel Halderman, whipping his surrey around in the middle of the street and heading back for the school on the run!

The set-up called for fast thinking. It was a certainty now that Zack could never get ready for supper inspection. And what could he tell the colonel? Zack knew it had better be an airtight story. And he'd need time to think up one.

From every angle, it seemed to him that his best bet was to lie there, badly hurt. If he was so badly hurt that he couldn't talk, then he wouldn't have to answer any questions.

He was practically unconscious when the colonel lifted him out of the mud and water and hauled him off to the hospital in the surrey.

It was nice there in the hospital. No lessons, no orders to obey. All a man had to do was lie still and have the nurses bring him what he wanted. Zack enjoyed it for three whole days, lying there with a back so badly hurt that the only time he could sit up was when they brought him his meals.

Likely he could have lasted longer in the hospital — even if the doctor was suspicious — if he hadn't got so tired of the hush and quiet and inactivity that one evening he sneaked out of bed to visit a sick friend. There, the doctor caught him dead to rights.

There was no use in playing 'possum any longer; he put on his clothes and went back to face the music. It was plenty hot; and after that, he didn't carry the mail.

But there was still trouble to get into. Zack was made

powder monkey for the artillery squad who fired the cannon at sundown each evening. He'd pack powder out to the cannon in a little silk bag and a boy by the name of Stewart Alexander would ram it home. Tom Hutton did the firing.

It was Stewart Alexander who got to wondering if one of the little balls from the school bowling alley would go into the mouth of the cannon. He said it looked like it would just fit. Zack was ready to bet that it would, too, but Tom Hutton swore it wouldn't. Tom said he'd have to see that ball put in the cannon before he'd believe it.

That night they stole one of the smallest balls from the bowling alley and hid it in the grass at the base of the cannon. The next evening after Stewart rammed the powder home, Zack picked up the bowling ball and eased it into the cannon's mouth. It was a neat fit, just small enough to roll to the bottom.

Stewart Alexander looked at Zack. Zack looked at Tom Hutton. The gut was in the fire now; it was too late to back out.

The flag came down. Tom Hutton touched off the cannon. The bowling ball whistled out of the cannon and knocked half a side out of the cavalry barn. It killed one horse and stampeded the rest.

The school had quarters on the third floor for boys like the three in its artillery squad. It was a place of hard bunks, short rations, and little heat. Fifteen boys landed in there on account of the shooting. The authorities knew who'd put the ball in the cannon; they'd seen Zack do it. But nobody knew a thing about how that bowling ball happened to be lying out there so handy for the purpose. Every day for a week, Colonel Halderman went up and dragged them all over the coals again, trying to dig out some information. The bunch was as shut-mouthed as a group of convicts.

The colonel tried putting them on a diet of clabber cheese. It was clabber cheese for breakfast, dinner, and supper.

They stood it for three days, then hunger sharpened their wits. Some of them climbed up into the attic and brought down some boards. They tied the boards together with short lengths of ripped-up bed sheets, making a ladder.

Around midnight, they climbed down the fire escape, taking their ladder along. It just barely reached from the fire escape to the ground. But they made it. Then they prized up a window and entered the kitchen.

They were tucking away butter-bread and jelly at a fast pace when Fritz, the head cook, came in. At the sight of them, Fritz's eyes got as big as saucers; then he got resentful.

'I've got you!' he declared. 'I'm going right now to tell the colonel!'

But they ganged him first. He fought hard, but he didn't have a chance. They stretched him out on the kitchen table and one of the boys thought that while they had him, it might be a good idea to feed him a batch of the clabber cheese he'd been dishing out. The rest agreed. They dragged out a whole tubful of the stuff and invited Fritz to get started. Fritz was bashful about it, so they helped him along. Two held his hands, two held his feet, and Zack used a big spoon to stuff cheese in his mouth. When Fritz refused to swallow, Zack held his nose to choke him down and make him.

Fritz struggled, begged, and finally cried a little. But

they stuffed him till he wasn't likely to need any more clabber cheese for the next year or so, then promised him that if he told the colonel, they'd make him eat a whole tubful of cheese the next time they caught him.

Fritz crossed his heart and hoped to die if he told. Fritz had had enough cheese.

Next day, the colonel lined them all up and worried them again, trying to find out this time who had raided the kitchen. Fritz had reported the raid, but he didn't have the least idea who was guilty.

None of them had any more idea than Fritz about it. The colonel kept them confined to quarters three more days, then came to the conclusion that he was forced to expel Zack Miller, Tom Hutton, and Stewart Alexander.

The three had packed and were standing around in the academy lobby, waiting for a cab and enjoying the envy their disgrace had stirred up in the rest of the boys when a fire broke out inside Fritz's kitchen. The alarm went out and Colonel Halderman rushed in, calling for a bucket brigade.

Zack and his two friends went outside and waited around to watch the excitement, finally to join the brigade that extended from the creek to the academy building.

That was a mistake. The colonel saw them helping and called them back into his office before they could get away.

'Well, boys,' he said, 'I watched you helping to save our old school from fire. It's possible that I've misjudged you. I'm ready to knock off all the bad marks and start over again!'

It looked like Marmaduke was a hard school to get away from.

The boys stayed, and the school paper ran a long piece about them under the heading of 'Barriers Burned Away.' They talked it over and agreed that that was the only time they'd ever suspected you could become a hero by dipping water out of a spring branch!

Zack didn't waste any time grieving when he finally left Marmaduke. He'd learned to drink and swear and hold authority in contempt. That was about all the booklearning he could lay claim to getting at Marmaduke.

5

ON THE CHEROKEE STRIP

FROM 1880 TO 1890, Zack's father trailed thousands upon thousands of longhorn cattle out of Texas. He followed for the most part the trail blazed earlier by Chisholm — and Zack can show you the scars of that old trail across the prairies today. Miller fattened his cattle on the Strip, drove them to the nearest railroad points, and shipped to Chicago markets. The profits piled up; Miller expanded operations. He was building up a cattle empire and making it a big one.

But the thing was too good to last. Other cowmen were taking advantage of the cheap grazing on the Strip, some paying leases to the Indians, others pushing in and grazing by right of the Winchesters they packed across their saddle bows. Then came the Man with the Hoe, the sod-busting nester who couldn't rest till he'd stuck a plow into the rich brown earth of that Strip. He wanted to own the land outright. And he meant to get it.

In the bitter wrangle that followed, nobody considered the red man who owned the land. He was a heathen; he didn't count.

Pressure brought to bear upon the Secretary of Interior won the fight for the nesters. In 1893, President Grover Cleveland issued the proclamation that broke up all the big cow outfits that had become established there. Acting on the advice of his Secretary of Interior, he forbade grazing on the lands of the Cherokee Strip and ordered all cattle to be removed immediately. And the Indians, with all revenue gone from their holdings, were forced to sell the land to the Government at little less than half the price offered to them by the cowmen. That is, all except the Ponca tribe, which G. W. Miller had helped to settle ten years before between the prongs of the Salt Fork and Arkansas Rivers. The Poncas kept their land.

Surveyors were put to work chopping the Strip up into hundred-and-sixty-acre blocks in preparation for throwing the land open for settlement in 1893.

Cleveland's order was a blow to the plans of Zack's father. The backbone to all of G. W.'s fast-building fortunes was the grassland he controlled on the Strip. The big cowman bawled his wrath at government interference till he could be heard half across Kansas; then he rode down to the Salt Fork Ranch to talk it over with Jimmy Moore.

'Faith, and why be leaving good graze when there's more ways to skin a cat than one?' the little Irishman demanded. 'Sow a wee bit of pocket money in the right places, and we can always be a trail herd out of Texas, bound for Kansas. There's no law against that yet, now is there?'

It was a bold move, but G. W. Miller had made plenty of them. He told Jimmy Moore to have the fences pulled down and rolled up, like the Government had ordered, then to put riders with every herd and tell them to start moving the cattle north at the first sight of government soldiers.

'We'll try that awhile,' he said, 'and wait to see which way the cat jumps.'

The first soldiers showed up in the spring. Zack and Jimmy Moore had prowled off from the Salt Fork camp on-to the Big Flats to the west of Pond Creek. Jimmy Moore was searching for cattle that might have bogged in the soap-holes and twelve-year-old Zack had an eye out for a newly born antelope kid. He kept several milk goats at the ranch all the time; on their milk he could raise his antelope pets that he always hoped would stay when they got older, but never did.

Jimmy Moore borrowed Zack's telescope and almost im-mediately spotted an antelope giving birth to a kid. 'If we'll ride fast, Dogie,' he said, 'we'll be there in time to catch it when it's dropped.'

The weakened antelope mother left in a wavering gallop at the approach of the riders. The kid lay where it had dropped, still wet and shiny. No fear showed in its large eyes as the little Irishman picked it up, wiped off the cling-ing blades of dry grass, and handed it up to Zack. Zack held it across the saddle in front of him. Jimmy Moore mounted, and they rode toward Pond Creek.

They had ridden about a mile when Jimmy Moore glanced back over his shoulder. 'Faith, and be Jasus Christ!' he exclaimed. 'Buffalo soldiers!'

Zack looked back. Six Negro soldiers were trailing them at a gallop! 'Buffalo soldiers' was the Indian's word for the black soldiers of the frontier forts because of their color and kinky hair.

Jimmy Moore hooked spurs to his mount. 'Would you be whipping up a little, Dogie?' he urged. 'We've got to beat them into camp or somebody's tail is in the crack!'

They left out in a high run, with the Negro soldiers

spurring after them. Jimmy Moore set a pace that put Zack to riding for all he was worth. Zack's horse leaped a gully; the antelope kid slipped out of his hands, but he didn't pull up to get it. There wasn't time. The soldiers were mounted on good horses and it looked as if they were gaining. Zack's heart hammered; he could feel his breath choking off.

The crossing on Pond Creek was right at its mouth where it ran into the Salt Fork River. The trail pitched sharply down into the creek between high clay banks and swung out through another steep gut on the opposite side. During the spring rains, the crossing was always boggy.

Jimmy Moore called back over his shoulder, 'Sure, and I'm fixing to play me a Christmas joke on them blackbirds! You tail me close, now, Dogie!'

They piled off down the slant at breakneck speed. At the bottom, Jimmy Moore swung sharply away from the crossing and rode up the creek bed a ways, missing the bog, then cut back down the other side, still screened from the soldiers by the high banks. He took his time going out on the far side; he wanted to make sure the soldiers saw him. He grinned back at Zack as they went out on top again.

'Be Jasus,' he said, 'and this ought to be worth twisting your neck to look at.'

It was. Just as Jimmy Moore had expected, the soldiers thought he'd crossed the creek at the regular crossing. They took their horses out into the bog at a hard run; the animals went in up to their bellies and were floundering beyond hope before the soldiers quite realized what had happened.

Jimmy Moore led off toward camp at a slower gallop,

grinning happily. 'Sure, and why not?' he said. 'Didn't the Indians play the same dirty trick and drive the buffaloes into that very bog? Yonder lie the bones of the poor dumb beasties they trapped and slaughtered in a like manner.' And he pointed to the heaps of bleaching buffalo bones around a little sand hill upon which the red men in times past had dried their meat after the butchering in the bog-hole was done.

Charlie Pierterson, one of the 101 hands, was at camp when they rode up on blowing horses.

'Charlie,' said Jimmy Moore, 'would you be hitching up the wagon and driving down to the mouth of Pond Creek? There, I think, you could be of kind service to some of Uncle Sam's boys!'

Charlie Pierterson hitched a team to the spring wagon. Before he drove off, Jimmy Moore cautioned him. 'Sure, now, Charlie,' he said, 'and if there's any talking to be done, this Irishman will do it. We'll no be wanting to mix our stories.'

So Charlie drove down to Pond Creek and helped the Negro soldiers drag their horses out of the bog-hole and brought them on back to camp without saying a word. 'I played it deef and dumb, to be on the safe side,' he told Zack later.

Jimmy Moore did not give the Negro soldiers time to ask any embarrassing questions. He beat them to it. He asked them if they had a white captain with them and they told him yes, that he was in camp on Doe Creek.

'Then send your captain down,' Jimmy Moore told them, 'and I'll do my talking to him.'

The soldiers rode off. Jimmy Moore got to sizing up the

log houses of the Salt Fork camp and decided it wouldn't look so good for a trail crew to be living in such comfortable quarters. So he had the hands round up everything they could haul and put it in the chuck wagon. When the white captain with a detachment of soldiers found the 101 outfit the next day, Jimmy Moore had them camped on the ford at Salt Creek.

'Sure, and we're a trail herd bound for Montana,' Jimmy Moore assured the questioning captain. 'Just laying over to give the poor horses a mite of rest. We camped in our old quarters last night; the shelter was good and the water handy. But we'll be long gone for the Kansas line, come morning. Faith, and we never had the intention of staying on the Strip.'

Maybe the captain believed this and maybe not. He stayed for dinner, however, and during the meal, Jimmy Moore questioned him about his family.

'You got a kid that's riding size? Sure, and we got some of the finest spotted ponies and we'd be glad to present the little one with your pick of them.'

He sent the horse wrangler out to rope up a pretty little black-and-white spotted Indian pony. The captain accepted. And just before he rode off, Jimmy Moore called him aside for a farewell handshake and accidentally had five twenty-dollar gold pieces in his hand.

'Captain,' the Irishman said, 'the grass is good here on the river; our cattle are poor. It would no be too great a strain on your good nature if we moved back into the house and stayed a month. Now would it?'

The captain fingered the gold pieces and looked at the spotted Indian pony he was taking back as a pet for his boy and couldn't see any reason for the trail crew to rush right on through.

'Just don't be here when I come back in thirty days,' he told Jimmy Moore.

'Sure, and we'll be well on the trail by that time,' Jimmy Moore assured him.

When the captain had been gone about a month, Jimmy Moore moved the outfit forty miles up the river to the west.

Along in the fall, the 101 had another visit from the captain. Jimmy Moore told him: 'The big boss has been here since you were gone and he is thinking this is a wonderful place to winter. It's going to be cold up in that northern country, you know, with our cattle not used to it. Sure, and we'll take a big loss if we move.'

Jimmy Moore rustled around and found a hundred dollars more and the captain decided there was nothing in his orders limiting the time it took a trail herd to cross the Strip. Just to make certain on that point, he'd write headquarters about it, he said.

Evidently, headquarters was in full agreement with the captain's decision. The cattle stayed all winter and got fat. The outfit had regular monthly visits from the captain, who always had use for a good horse or an extra hundred dollars.

Along about this time, bald-faced Hereford cattle began to first show up in South Texas. G. W. heard about them, saw a few, and got plenty concerned. He had Shanghai Pierce, 'The Beefsteak Baron of Texas,' on contract to ship the 101 outfit five thousand head of Texas steers each year for three years, and he was convinced that he didn't want any of this new-fangled Hereford stuff included in these shipments. He wanted longhorns; they'd already proved they could rustle for themselves, fatten, and make a man money.

Just to make certain that longhorns was what he'd get in the next shipment, G. W. took a trip down to Shanghai's outfit at Pierce's Station in Wharton County, Texas.

Shanghai met him at the door, his fog-horn voice roaring a welcome that sent all the catch-dogs on the place in a yelping run for the brush.

'Come into this house, man!' he bellowed. 'What the hell you doing down here in this sea-lion country?'

G. W. followed him into the house, took a long drink out of Shanghai's bottle, and told him.

'Shanghai,' he said, 'I come to get a matter straightened out. I won't have any of them hothouse Herefords in the steer herds you send me. And if you're putting any of them bald-faced bulls with your cows, our deal's all off.'

Shanghai was outraged at the idea of anybody's thinking he'd stoop to tampering with the blood strains of the Texas longhorn. He shouted and swore and took another drink.

'G. W.,' he bawled, 'when I deliver my next herd, you can depend on it: you won't get a frosty roan, a natural pacer, or a cherry red in the whole goddamned bunch. They'll be pure-bred sea lions, mossbacks, and swamp angels, just like you've always got!'

G. W. was satisfied, and before he'd left had agreed to winter four thousand head of Pierce's BU stuff for him up in Oklahoma.

The man Shanghai sent to Oklahoma to oversee the grazing of his BU cattle was the big man's nephew, Abel

Borden. Borden was about twenty-two or -three. He knew his cattle, all right, but he was a cocksure youngster and mighty impatient about getting things done in a hurry. He hit the Deer Creek Ranch a day or two in advance of the herd that was being shipped in by rail.

Zack was alone at the camp dugout the day Borden showed up. Zack heard the camp dogs barking and went outside to see a dark-haired young man drag his saddle gear out of the back-end of a buggy and pay off the man who'd driven him out.

'Where's everybody, boy?' the newcomer demanded.

'They're out prowling,' Zack told him.

The man said, speaking in a short-clipped voice: 'I'm Abel Borden. I'm a Shanghai Pierce man. I want a horse.'

Zack was thirteen then and about the only horse the 101 hands would let him keep around camp was an old stove-up pet called Possum. He started to let Borden have Possum, then thought better of it. Borden was too short-spoken to suit Zack: he acted like the kind of man who might be rough on a horse. And Zack's Possum was too old to stand the gaff.

'I'll saddle,' Zack said, 'and round you up a horse.'

He saddled and rode off while Borden pulled on a pair of bull-hide chaps and stood slapping his quirt against one leg. Zack could tell that Borden was in a big hurry to get started wherever he aimed to go.

Borden had his rope off his saddle and a loop shook out by the time Zack ran four horses into the corral. Borden stepped into the pen, whipped his loop over his head once, and latched onto the best-looking and meanest horse in the outfit. That was old Falling-Back Bob, a cinch binder, who could get a lot of satisfaction out of rearing and falling back and trying to pin a rider between the saddle and the ground.

'Mr. Borden, I wouldn't ride that one,' Zack advised. 'He's got a trick that'll hurt you if you don't know him.'

Borden looked insulted. 'Hell, I can ride him, kid. Forget it!'

Zack didn't forget it, but he kept quiet. The way Borden had cut him off had made Zack about half mad and he didn't bother to tell Borden how the only safe way to mount old Falling-Back Bob was to put a foot in the stirrup and crow-hop along beside him a piece before stepping across. He guessed he'd just let this smart-aleck scissorbill learn about that the hard way.

Old Falling-Back Bob had a way of swelling out big when a man drew up the cinch on him so he'd have plenty of breathing room later on. He didn't get by with it this time, though. Borden caught him at the trick and set a foot against the horse's ribs and yanked the latigo strap up to suit himself. He paid no attention to the way the horse backed his ears and showed the whites of his eyes. He just chucked a foot in the stirrup and went up without even bothering to untrack the horse.

That was a bad mistake. Falling-Back Bob was ready for him. He snorted and went straight up, then came on over backwards.

The South Texas brush-popper hit the ground flat of his back, with the full weight of Falling-Back Bob in the saddle on top of him. The horse rolled to one side and onto his feet and left out, bawling and pitching and flopping loose stirrups high.

And the Shanghai Pierce man lay there on the ground with one leg broken between the knee joint and the hip.

'Catch my saddle!' he yelled to Zack.

Zack had heard that cry more times than he could remember. A cowhand's saddle was the first thing he thought of when a horse threw him. The horse belonged to the boss, but the saddle was his, and he hated the idea of letting a horse get loose with it. The saddle might slip down and get under the horse's belly where he'd kick it to pieces. And a new saddle could cost a man several months' good wages.

Riding Possum, Zack crowded the bucking horse into a fence corner and caught him. He came leading him back and then just sat on Possum, staring down at the white-faced man. He wished now that he'd told the stranger how Falling-Back Bob would act.

Borden barked at him. 'Well, goddammit! Do something! My leg's broke. I've got to git to a doctor!'

Borden's high and mighty ways rubbed a raw place on Zack again and he didn't much give a damn if the man's leg was broken.

But it was up to him to get Borden into town. He unsaddled Possum and Falling-Back Bob, then went to the corrals and caught up old Frank and Crappy and hitched them to the spring wagon the boys used for hauling salt to the cattle. Zack brought the wagon up beside Borden, and he had to give the man credit for having guts. Borden had crawled to the dugout, knocked a dry barrel apart and splinted up his broken leg the best he could with the staves, using strips of old torn canvas for binding.

How to get the man into the wagon was a problem.

Borden could catch to a wheel and pull himself up with one leg, but Zack wasn't big enough to lift him on in. The man's face was pasty-white from the pain and effort, and beads of cold sweat broke out all over him.

'Maybe we better wait till some of the hands come in,' Zack panted.

'What time'll that be?' Borden wanted to know.

'Around the middle of the evening.'

'Hell's fire!' flared Borden. 'We can be in Hunnewell by that time.'

They tried again, and by straining his limit, Borden got his one good foot off the ground and onto the hub of the wagon. Zack gave him a push and he rolled in, hitting the bed of the wagon like a beef carcass.

It was twenty-eight miles to Hunnewell. The road was nothing but a rough trail. Zack started out driving slow, trying to make the trip as easy for the man as possible. Borden couldn't stand that.

'Goddammit!' he said. 'Whip up them old crow-baits and get me into town.'

Zack whipped up the horses. The crippled man began to bounce and slide all over the bed of the light vehicle.

'Hell's fire!' he roared. 'Slow up a little. You trying to break my other leg?'

It was like that all the way to Lige Smith's dugout, ten miles down the road. There was no driving fast enough or slow enough to suit Abel Borden. Zack turned off at Lige's place to get water for the man and hit Lige up to take Borden the rest of the way.

'If I drive fast,' Zack said, 'he gives me hell. And it's the same thing if I drive slow. I can't drive to suit him!'

'The thing to do,' said Lige, 'is to drive to suit your own self. Goddamn him, he brung it on hisself and if he keeps hollering, git out, give him the lines, and tell him to have at his own driving!'

But Zack didn't have to do that. Abel Borden had listened to Lige Smith's advice and evidently decided to leave the driving up to Zack from there on. He lay back in the wagon bed and bit the blood out of his underlip, while he watched his leg swell till it nearly broke the splints. But he didn't say another word.

They pulled into Hunnewell late at night and Zack delivered the Shanghai Pierce man to the Hale Hotel and turned him over to a doctor. And the 101 hands had to handle the BU cattle when they came through.

That leg kept Borden in bed till late in the winter. Shanghai had had no word from his nephew; so he came looking for Borden. He, too, caught Zack alone at the Deer Creek dugout.

It was in the dead of winter now. A big snowstorm had come up. The cattle had turned tail to the storm and drifted south till they'd piled up against the south Deer Creek fence and broken through. They were still drifting, and every man from the cook to the horse wrangler had ridden out, trying to check them before they reached the Salt Fork. That is, all except Zack. They didn't think a boy his age, and the boss's boy, at that, ought to be out in weather like this. So they'd left him at the dugout with orders to keep a pot of coffee on the fire and warm grub ready for them when they returned.

Early dark was coming on. Outside, the snow kept falling and the wolves howled lonesome from the high places. Zack felt very much alone. He'd eaten an early supper and banked a batch of biscuits in the skillet against the chance of the boys riding in later. He sat on a roll of bedding in front of a roaring fire in the dugout chimney and played with the fur of a big black house-cat curled up between his legs. Rubbed the wrong way, that old cat's fur would pop and crackle and shoot off quick bright sparks.

A heavy pounding started at the dugout door and a voice bellowed at him: 'Open this damned door!'

Zack jumped to his feet, but hesitated to lift the bar from the door. He knew the Millers were running cattle on the Strip illegally. They'd been ordered off by the Government, like all the other cowmen; but they hadn't gone. That might be soldiers out there. Zack was afraid of the soldiers. He and the crew had been chased by soldiers a lot, and the hands had told it plenty scary about what the soldiers would do if they caught him. They'd put out the scare talk to keep Zack from riding off from camp in their absence and maybe getting lost in just such weather as this. But Zack didn't know that. All he knew was what they'd told him; that if the soldiers came, he was to get inside the dugout and bar the door. And under no circumstances was he to let them inside.

While he hesitated, the man outside kept shaking the door as if he would tear it off its rawhide hinges. He roared like a bull.

'Open this goddamned door, I said!'

Zack peeked out through the cracks. He saw a huge man bundled in a snow-covered coat that just might be a soldier's overcoat. But he had on a cowman's hat, a big white Stetson. Zack peered closer. In the gathering darkness, he made out the blur of a white man's face; so he wasn't likely to be a soldier. Most of the soldiers were Negroes.

'Open this door before I kick the goddamned thing in!' bellowed the voice.

Scared, Zack lifted the bar and let the door swing out. The man stepped inside, shaking the snow from his coat. Zack had known from looking through the cracks that the man was big, but not just how big till the man completely filled the wide doorway.

'Where's Abel Borden!'

The man's bawling tones frightened Zack so badly that he thought the man said he was hungry. Zack rushed to the grub warming at the fire and started rattling pots and pans, trying to throw a meal together.

'You all by yourself?'

Zack admitted that he was. 'The boys are out after drifting cattle,' he said. 'They'll be back tonight or to-morrow or sometime.'

Then his stomach muscles tied themselves in knots, he was wishing so bad that he hadn't said that. No telling what this big, bawling-voiced stranger might do, now that he knew there was no one else here. Zack was a scared boy.

Then the man spoke again. 'I'm Shanghai Pierce, boy!' he roared. 'And I'm hungry as a bitch wolf. Move out of the way; I'll wait on myself!'

He moved closer to the fire. The light fell on his face and Zack recognized the features of the big, braggy-voiced Texas cowman who liked to introduce himself to strangers as 'Shanghai Pierce, the Daniel Webster of the cow business, by god!'

Zack was so relieved he could have cried. He dragged out grub for Shanghai to eat and poured him a scalding cup of coffee which the big man swallowed at a gulp.

'Where'd you say Abel Borden was?' he asked again.

Zack told him.

Shanghai snorted. 'Goddamn him,' he said, 'he always was like that. He thinks he can do anything that anybody can. But he's a brush hand, down in my country, that boy is. They say a South Texas brush hand ain't nothing but a damned fool on a race-horse, which may be right; but it takes men like Borden to handle the goddamn moss-horn coasters I grow. Hell, you can scare one of them swamp-angel steers, and it takes two good men to see him — one to say here he comes, and the other to say there he goes!'

His mind at ease now, Zack backed up against a bedroll and sat there, letting Shanghai eat and talk.

'This grub,' said Shanghai, 'hits the spot. Puts me in mind of the way old lady Ward used to feed me. That was down on Trespalacias Creek, in the Matagorda Bay country. I was just a young rooster then, working for Bing Grimes. Breaking horses for four-bits a day. There was some slave nigger riders on the place, but I got all the bad horses. Old lady Grimes done that for me. She showed up at the corrals one morning when one of them prize buck niggers was topping out a salty one and she sure gave Bing a going-over. She wanted to know what Bing meant, risking the life of a thousand-dollar nigger on a bad horse when a fifteen-a-month damn Yankee like me could take the risk just as well?

'Well, she don't have to hit Bing over the head for him to get the point, and from there on, they put Shang on the bad 'uns; them niggers is worth too much.

'I'm too pore to buy decent clothes, so I ain't allowed in the polite part of the house. I eat in the kitchen and sleep out in a shed. And the only time I'm ever treated like white folks is when I take a ride over to old lady Ward's, up the creek a piece. Old lady Ward, bless her soul, knows I can eat more than a whole livery stable, and when I come, she piles flapjacks before me up to my chin, with plenty of butter and lick to go with 'em.

'By god, a better woman never lived than old lady Ward!'

Zack had had plenty of grub cooked up for the entire Deer Creek crew, but if they'd made it back to the dugout that stormy night, they'd have found slim pickings. By the time Shanghai sat back and pulled his shirt-sleeve across his mouth, there wasn't enough meat and bread left to have given the cat a full bait.

But Zack didn't worry. He just built up the fire and kept listening to the talk of the big Texan who, at the age of nineteen, had stepped off a boat at Port Lavaca, Texas, without a dime in his pockets and then worked up till he now controlled better than a million acres of Texas cow country.

It was 'way in the night when that braggy, rumbling voice finally put Zack to sleep.

During Zack's boyhood it was the custom around cow camps for any kids on the crew to hold the cut while the grown-up riders ate. Just as it was back at home where the youngsters had to stand around with their mouths watering while the old folks got the pick of the grub at the first table-setting.

This galled Zack. He looked forward to the day when he

could get a meal on time instead of having to hold the cut. He hoped he'd grow a paunch with the capacity of Shanghai Pierce's. The amount of chuck that big Texas cowman could get around was a sight to pop a kid's eyeball.

With the years, Zack grew the bread sack, all right. It could never hold as much as Shanghai's, but it was sizable. Only, by then, it was too late. By then, folks were leaning to the opinion that their offspring amounted to more than dogie calves and ought to come first — even at the table. Zack was just born too early — or too late. Circumstances trapped him in a time of change that left him holding the cut both early and late. He's still hoping the time will come when he'll get to eat at the first table.

It was having to wait while the rest of the hands ate that caused him to pull his first drunk. Spotted Face Maxwell helped him pull it. Together, they threw a woollybooger.

The 101 spring roundup wagon was camped up on the head of Bird's Nest Creek. They'd made a big cow-gather there and were working the herd in weather hot as hell with the blower going, according to Charlie Orr. G. W. rode in from Winfield right at dinner time; he ordered Zack and Spot to hold the cut while the rest of them went back to camp to eat.

Spot and Zack hadn't had a drink all morning and were spitting cotton, they were that thirsty. But they couldn't afford to leave the herd long enough to ride in for water. The milling, bawling cattle might mix, and all the morning's work of cutting would be lost. So they endured, and finally G. W. led the main crew back out and took over.

Zack and Spot high-tailed it for camp at a lope. They found the camp cook stretched out under the wagon tongue, sweating and snoring. They hunted up the water bucket and when they found it, understood how the cook could sleep with the hot sun beating down upon his face. That big cedar bucket was better than half full of blackberry wine!

This was a find, considering the fact that it was against the law to be caught with intoxicating liquors on any of the Indian reservations. But what threw them was the fist-sized chunks of ice that G. W. had left floating around in the wine. In those days, ice in town was something special. Out in a cow camp, it was as rare as a pretty woman.

Zack and Spot took to that cold wine like panting dogs to a water-hole. One downed a tin cupful, then the other. They finally stopped for a short breather, then Spot said, 'Let's have another one'; so they had another one.

They backed off into the shade of a tree then to take comfort on their spurs and Zack suggested they have another one, and they did.

They squatted there in the shade and kept pouring wine in on empty stomachs, and it didn't take long for the cows to come home. In thirty minutes, they had the big goose hanging high. They didn't care if the peaches never got ripe; they'd eat theirs out of a can!

They drank and grinned at each other and drank some more.

The ice was still in the bucket when the wine played out. Zack looked at Spot.

'Maybe we better eat,' he said.

Spot looked toward the wagon. 'Eat, hell!' he yelped. 'Yonder's a jug, setting under the wagon. Bring the ice and come on!'

Spot got up and started toward the jug. Zack was like an old horse; he made one try, then decided it wasn't worth the effort.

'You bring the jug to the ice!' he told Spot.

Spot wandered around over a whole lot of territory and finally waded through the campfire coals getting to the jug. He picked it up and was taking a short cut back to the shade when he stopped to hammer the bottom of the jug with his fist to force the cork. The cork wouldn't come; he had to pull it with his teeth.

This was a mistake. Maybe he pulled too hard. Or maybe the weight of the cork overbalanced him. He fell flat of his back in the grass and lost the jug.

He didn't try to get up. He just listened till he located the gurgling sound the wine made pouring out of the jug. Then he rolled up on one shoulder, puckered his lips and lay there, drinking easy, as the wine flowed out.

This was too much for Zack. It looked to him like Spot was making a hog of himself. He guessed he'd better get up and do something about that.

It took the third try for Zack to get up, but he made it. He weaved toward Spot. He bent down to pick up the jug and it seemed like the jug and the ground just rose up and hit him in the face.

He managed to set the jug up so no more of the wine would spill. Then he saw a couple of cowhands riding into camp.

'Get up, Spot,' he said. 'Come on, we've got to get to our horses.'

Spot tried to get up, but couldn't — with Zack lying across him. And Zack couldn't get off him because he wasn't able. And they couldn't have caught their horses if they'd been able to get up — because their horses, the wagon, the two riders, and the whole prairie was doing a ring-around-the-rosy at an eye-blurring speed.

Zack remembered when one of the cowhands caught him by the heels and dragged him under the wagon; if anything else happened, it didn't matter.

They were sure sorry sights when the crew rode back to camp along in the shank of the evening and woke them up. Spot resembled the losing end of a dog fight and felt worse. Zack had a headache built for a horse, and the first drink of water he took came close to turning him wrong-side-out.

The cowhands gathered around to rawhide the pair. One offered Spot a little hair of the dog that bit him and Spot didn't need even the first drink of water to make him unload.

'Grab his spurs, boys!' shouted one of the hands. 'Spot's fixing to puke up his heels and them spurs'll cut his throat, sure!'

'Judging from their looks,' remarked another, 'that wine on the way up ain't got the flavor it had going down!'

The crew rode them hard, but it was the sort of good-humored hurrah that made a kid feel that he was one of the bunch.

What was so rough to take was G. W. Miller's silence. G. W. rode in, looked the young drunks over, then went to eating his supper without saying a word.

The sick Spot and Zack were afraid to look Miller's way. They knew they were due to catch hell and were dreading it plenty. At the same time they were anxious to get it over and done with. They kept waiting for the fireworks to start; but they didn't. And they never did.

That's what hurt them so bad. If G. W. had torn up their tail-ends with the double of his catch-rope, as they were expecting, they could have soon forgotten the whole thing. But like it was, he just let them sweat it out. Neither of them ever had a thrashing to hurt him as bad as the suspense and the big cowman's silence.

Those were good times Zack knew there on the Cherokee Strip, back when he was just a boy — the sort of good times a man can't live long enough to forget.

6

BROKE--FLAT AS THE PRAIRIES

G. W. had to have grass located for his herds before the opening of the Strip that was to come in the fall of 1893; so in the spring of '92, he sent his oldest son Joe down to the Ponca Reservation to make a trade for grazing rights on the Ponca lands. Joe had no trouble carrying out the mission. White Eagle, head chief of the Poncas, hadn't forgotten how Joe and G. W. had helped to find land for him and his people when they were homeless. The Millers and the Poncas had been friends ever since and now White Eagle was glad for a chance to return a favor. At his recommendation, the Government agent for the Poncas leased one hundred thousand acres to the 101 at one cent an acre a year, payment to be made when Miller took over. White Eagle went further than that. He promised that the lease could be renewed for years.

Jimmy Moore was pleased when he heard about the lease. 'Faith,' he said, 'and we'll be holding that for winter grazing and keep right on running cattle on this good free grass till the fall roundup.'

So he 'trailed cattle across the Strip' till G. W. ordered the fall gather in September.

When the count was made at the Big Pens on the Salt Fork, it fell thirty short of the five thousand steers that should have been on that part of the range. That wasn't a big loss out of five thousand head of steers on the range, but Jimmy Moore wasn't satisfied yet to mark those steers off his books.

'Dogie,' he said to Zack, 'strap on your hot-roll and saddle up. We'll be going to look for them steers.'

They rode toward Black Bear Creek, some twenty miles from the Salt Fork camp. It was a hot afternoon, and at four o'clock on the dot, Jimmy Moore called a halt beside a clear pool of water. It was teatime.

Zack helped gather dry cow chips for a fire, then sat back in the shade of a cottonwood while the little Irishman brewed his tea in his tomato can and sipped it between puffs on his little clay pipe. Not a breath of air stirred, and even in the shade, the sweat kept breaking out on a man. Jimmy Moore eyed the pool of water. Finally, he lifted a hand and sniffed at one armpit, then snorted.

'Sure, and it's rank as an old billygoat I'm smelling,' he declared. 'In a clear pool like yonder, a mon might be washing some of the sweat off his body.'

He got up and hung his tomato can back on the saddle, then shucked out of his clothes. The skin normally hidden under his clothes gleamed white in comparison to the blackness of his sunburnt neck and face. He tested the water with one toe to make sure it wasn't too cold, then stepped in.

Zack got up and was stripping to join him when he heard the little Irishman shout. He wheeled in time to see Jimmy Moore falling all over himself in waist-deep water and knocking sheets of it high in the sunshine.

'Faith, and be Jasus Christ!' Jimmy Moore said, getting up. 'And now what would a mon be stumbling upon out in this clear pool?'

He reached under the water, caught hold of the object that had tripped him, and lifted it up. It was the head of a steer.

'Sure,' he said, 'and somebody's been helping himself to G. W.'s beef, like I been suspecting all along.'

He felt around on the bottom and dragged out nine steer heads. He scrambled out of the pool, dressed, and mounted.

Zack had his clothes back on now and mounted with him.

Jimmy Moore said: 'Being one of the Irish and knowing my kind, I think we'll be paying a visit to the grading crew working on the railroad dump across yonder.'

He led the way across the prairies till they hit Skeleton Creek. They followed it a way. In a grove of hackberries, they ran onto the remains of a camp. The little Irishman rode a wide circle around it and located more steer heads, with hides to match them this time. The hides bore the 101 brand.

'Faith, and the trail scent warms fast!' Jimmy Moore said.

They quit the creek, crossed a rise, and rode down to where a crew of men and mules sweated in a deep cut, dragging dirt to the top of a high railroad dump with sliding scrapers.

A big double-fisted Irishman stood upon the dump, directing the work. Jimmy Moore reached for his Winchester and laid it across the bow of his saddle.

'Might you be the boss?' he demanded of the man.

The big Irishman studied Jimmy Moore's Winchester a moment, then lifted his eyes. 'Sure, and it's the right mon you've found.'

'Ay,' said the little Irishman. 'Jimmy Moore's my name. I'm repping for G. W. Miller and I've come to collect the meat bill!'

The man on the dump stiffened. 'And what might you be meaning by that, Mr. Moore?' he demanded.

'What I'm meaning,' said Jimmy Moore, 'is for you to be writing me out a check for the 101 steers you've eaten — at thirty dollars a head.'

The big Irishman stood on the dump and stared down at the little one on the horse. Neither seemed pleased at what he saw. Jimmy Moore swung the business end of his Winchester around and gave the other man a chance to look down its bore.

'And how many steers, Mr. Moore, do you think that would be?' the big man asked.

'Faith, and be Jasus!' flared Jimmy Moore. 'You'll be knowing better than I. It's a check I'm waiting for, mon. And the patience of the Irish is short, as you'd well be knowing!'

Zack caught himself trying to swallow a dry frog in his throat. He watched the eyes of the big Irishman and he could tell by their expression that the man was weighing his chances against Jimmy Moore and that rifle.

Evidently, he didn't think they were good. He turned his back suddenly, then waved a hand for them to follow.

Jimmy Moore trailed him to a little tent down below the dump. Zack trailed Jimmy Moore. The man waited for them at the tent entrance, then led them inside where he wrote out a check for nine hundred dollars. He handed it to Jimmy Moore.

Jimmy Moore pocketed the check with a grave nod. 'It

would have been bad,' he said, 'to have had to shoot one of the boys from the auld countree.'

The other nodded just as gravely. 'Ay,' he agreed. 'It would have been that.'

'Would it be a Dublin mon ye are?' Jimmy asked.

Some of the wariness left the big Irishman's eyes. Zack thought he was going to smile. 'I am that!' he said.

Jimmy Moore grinned, shifted his Winchester to the left hand and stuck out his right. ''Tis good to see a mon from Dublin,' he said.

The other shook his hand and grinned back at him.

On the ride back to camp, Jimmy Moore was in high spirits, half the time singing his little pet song about how 'If there'd been no whiskey made, in Ireland I'd still be!'

Being forced off his holdings on the Cherokee Strip was an aggravation to Miller and a disruption of some well-laid plans. But he would have been the first to admit that he wouldn't be bad hurt financially. He was ready to move over onto the Ponca lease he'd arranged for before the big opening. And if he hadn't been able to manage for that, there was still open range to be had. He could have gone west, or south into Texas, and found grazing for his herds.

What did hurt him, however, was the business depression that hit the United States in the spring of 1893. The panic was like a big kill-hungry wolf on the prowl. Its range was wide and its attack deadly. It gobbled up the 101 outfit at one grab and licked its bloody chops for more.

It takes big money to operate a cow outfit the size of the 101, and Zack's father had been using big money. Even at that, if he'd stuck to his earlier habit of dealing in hard cash only, he might have weathered the storm. As it was, he'd been borrowing money to branch out, and he'd put too many of his eggs in one basket.

The J. J. Campbell Commission Company of Kansas City was acting as agent for him in all his cattle dealings. G. W. had a $300,000 credit on the books of this company when the big squeeze came, but no money in his pocket. In the fight to keep their own heads above water, the head men of the commission house had been giving Miller credit for cattle shipped to them, but they'd failed to pay off a bunch of notes that they'd sold to a Boston banking firm — notes against the 101 livestock, amounting to $100,000. And in spite of all the juggling of accounts they could do, the Kansas City commission company went into the hands of a receiver. And the 101 was left with credit in a bankrupt commission house and $100,000 outstanding against 101 cattle.

In the last days of July of that year, the Boston banking firm holding the notes sent a man named Claypool down to the 101 to take over the livestock. A United States marshal came along to back up the man's authority.

Claypool found Jimmy Moore and Uncle Doc Miller at the Salt Fork Ranch. He told them who he was, the outfit he represented, and what he'd come for. He said he was ready to ship now and called on them to furnish hands to make the gather.

Jimmy Moore sent Claypool and the hands to the East Pasture, but he and Uncle Doc stayed at headquarters. For once, the two men could agree on something. Both thought G. W. Miller was getting a raw deal here. And both were ready to stand back of him to the finish, in case

he wanted to make a fight of it. G. W. was due at the Salt
Fork sometime that day and they wanted to be on hand
when he showed up.

They were eating dinner when G. W. rode in. Zack
came with him.

'Where'n the hell is everybody?' G. W. demanded.

Jimmy Moore told him how the land lay. ''Tis rounding
up the cattle that the mon Claypool is doing now,' he said.

Zack saw his father rear his head like a bull scenting
trouble. 'I'll be goddamned if they ship them cattle now!'
G. W. roared.

'Faith, and I see no way of preventing them, short of a
gun fight,' Jimmy Moore said.

He lifted a loaded Winchester from under the table and
laid it gently across the top. His eyes looked hopeful.

'Then, by god, it'll be a gun fight!' bawled Miller.
'But this isn't the place to start the shooting. Saddle your
horses. We'll head them off at the East Pasture gate!'

This was one time Zack's Uncle Doc Miller didn't hang
back to putter around camp. He followed Jimmy Moore's
lead, reaching a Winchester down from a rack over the
doorway and thumbing shells into the magazine. Zack
felt sort of proud of his Uncle Doc right then.

The four of them were waiting at the East Pasture gate
when Claypool and the marshal rode up, pointing the herd
of steers the 101 hands were driving.

G. W. wasn't one to whip the devil around the stump.
He came right to the point. 'Claypool!' he shouted.
'These cattle won't go. They're too thin. Throwed on
the market in the shape they're in now, they won't clear
me with them blue-bellied Boston bastards!'

Claypool was a tall, dark-haired man with a quiet manner. Calmly he looked Zack's angry father over, studying him close. 'Then you aim to put up a fight?' he asked.

'If I have to,' Miller said. 'But I'll meet you halfway. We've had a good rain lately; these cattle will put on fifteen dollars a head more fat by the first of October. Leave them till then and you can come ship them without any trouble from me. Or we'll start shipping them for you — and cut them right. You haven't cut them right to bring the best money!'

Claypool took his time and thought that over while he twisted a cigarette and lighted it. Then he turned in his saddle and shot a look at the marshal.

The marshal was uneasy. Even Zack could see that. The marshal wasn't liking the bright hard shine in Jimmy Moore's eyes or the way Uncle Doc kept patting that .44 Winchester he held across his horse's neck. He wasn't liking, either, the way the 101 hands were pulling away from the edges of the herd behind him and riding up, with plenty of hardware in sight.

Zack's father said: 'Whatever it takes to stop you, Claypool, we've got. I don't like the idea of fighting with a five-dollar-a-day man like you. If this resorts to shooting, I'd rather start with that nest of Boston damn Yankees. But be damned certain of this: if you try to throw these cattle on the market now, the shooting will commence!'

Claypool looked at the marshal and flashed a sudden white-toothed grin. 'All right, Mr. Miller,' he said. 'We'll turn them loose and I'll go telegraph for orders.'

G. W. waved a hand toward his riders, letting them know the matter was settled. 'Turn 'em loose, boys.'

He said to Claypool: 'When you send that wire, you tell them I don't aim to beat them out of a dime; that I'll ship ever' steer when he's ready to go. But not before. We'll have them all there by the first of December. And I won't listen to any other trade or compromise. I'll use any method I think best — but you'll not ship a steer off the 101 till the first of October. Or I won't be here, one.'

Claypool turned and spoke to the marshal as if he were the only man there. 'I've about come to the conclusion,' he said dryly, 'that we're not shipping any cattle right now. Let's ride.'

He swung his horse around and rode off. The marshal took out a bandana handkerchief, wiped the sweat from his face, lifted his hat and wiped the sweat out of it, then followed Claypool.

Jimmy Moore looked disappointed.

Nothing was heard from the Boston company for some time. Then one day word came that the company was sending Shanghai Pierce out to try to talk Miller into letting the cattle go. Uncle Doc met and waylaid the big Texas cowman at Ponca Station.

'Shanghai,' he told Pierce, 'G. W.'s still on the prod and I don't blame him. If you go out there to the ranch, one of you'll be going back on this train tonight packed in ice. The best thing you can do is catch a train to Texas and stay out of this.'

Shanghai Pierce knew cowmen and he knew G. W. Miller. He took the hint and caught a train to Texas.

September came, date of the big opening of the Cherokee Strip. Nesters, boomers, land sharks, cowboys, store clerks, and land-hungry farmers gathered at the starting lines, ready to dash in and grab off choice pieces of land the moment the soldiers guarding them fired their guns at twelve o'clock sharp. Along the Kansas line and in southern Oklahoma they crowded in, twenty-five to fifty persons deep. They were not allowed to run from the Osage Reservation on the east. They came in wagons, buggies, gigs, surreys, hacks. Some rode bicycles. Hundreds were afoot.

The 'sooners' were already on the one hundred and sixty acres they'd picked out. They were hidden in the timber, hoping to avoid the eyes of the roving bands of soldiers sent out to comb the brush and gullies and arrest these illegal entrants.

Zack and Jimmy Moore were with the 'sooners.' Like most oldtime cowhands, Jimmy Moore looked down upon nesters. And he hated farming. But he said he just as well get a piece of this free land as the next one.

'It'll do to bury me on,' he told Zack.

Zack was too young to own land; so the little Irishman put him on the one-sixty he'd chosen, with instructions to set up a flag the moment he heard the guns and start waving everybody else off the land. Then Jimmy went up and hid out on the Chicaski and waited till the rush started.

The guns of the soldiers touched off the land-maddened rush of humanity. They poured out onto the Strip like stampeding longhorn cattle, wrecking wagons, killing horses, and shooting each other for a chance to jump a choice claim. It was the wildest show that young Zack ever hoped to see. But that didn't keep him from putting up his flag the moment the first of the mob raced up out of the horizon.

He started waving them aside and nobody stopped to question how he'd got there so soon or whether or not he was old enough to file. And Jimmy Moore made it there with the first comers and took over. Together, they held and got deed to the one-sixty tract that Jimmy Moore was to will young Zack when he died.

Uncle Doc Miller made his run for land from the southern line. He was a little slow and all he managed to get was a tract of high prairie land that nobody else seemed to want. Jimmy Moore and some of the other hands hurrahed Uncle Doc about his land, but it later proved to be the center of the Tonkaway oil fields.

Only, Uncle Doc never got any benefit from it. There were two ways of filing on the Strip. One was to get on the land first and set up stakes of possession. The other was to go to the land offices and file first, then go out and put up the stakes. By law, the first man to file or the first to put up a stake got the land. The wild joker in this deck, of course, was the fact that one man might be putting up stakes on the same tract that some other was filing on, back in the office. That very thing kept the courts blocked for years afterward, settling these contest cases.

And that's how Uncle Doc lost his land. Another managed to prove in court that he had filed on the tract before Uncle Doc had taken possession.

Zack's older brother Joe lost half of his tract in a like manner. Joe pulled a fast one at the Perry land office. He arrived there, aiming to file through the office, and found something like a hundred people in the waiting line ahead of him. So he pulled out some old telegrams, erased his own name from the envelopes, and wrote in the name of the land commissioner there at Perry. Then he crowded up ahead and got past the guards by insisting he had to get the commissioner's signature for the telegrams. Once inside, he filed on the tract he'd picked out. But he was contested on it for years by a man who claimed to have been in possession of the tract before Joe filed. The two finally settled out of court, dividing the land between themselves.

Some of the big cowmen on the Strip tried to hold onto a part of the land they had controlled before the Government turned it over to the nesters. They had every man on the payroll to homestead a hundred and sixty acres, with the promise of buying the land from him once the title was clear. But Zack's father didn't bother with this. He and his hands had their work pretty well cut out for them, moving the 101 cattle onto the Ponca Reservation lease and shaping up the herds for fall shipment. Anyhow, the way G. W. saw it, a man couldn't operate a cow outfit on little quarter-sections of land that would likely be scattered. He needed his grass all in one piece.

Claypool came down on the first of October and they began cutting out and shipping fat steers. The work ran on into November before the last of the stuff went on the cars. When they were done, the 101 was out from under those $100,000 notes that the Boston banking firm held. But G. W. was cleaned out, his last tail-feather plucked.

Claypool waved a hand toward the cull stuff that still remained in the pens — eighty-eight old lame horses and a handful of runty, lump-jawed, and crippled steers.

'G. W.,' he said, 'you've played fair with me and come through without making trouble, the way you promised. You take this shirt-tail full of junk here and say nothing about it. It's worth damned little, but you can maybe salvage something from it.'

That was all G. W. had left. A couple of hundred dollars in the Winfield National Bank. No cattle or horses worth the grass they'd eat. Not an acre of land except his lease on the Ponca Reservation — and where in the hell was he to get the thousand dollars to pay the next year's lease? Or cattle to put on it if he did?

G. W.'s face was gray and drawn as he left the shipping pens, Zack with him. Riding across the empty range, Zack heard his father growl in disgust.

'Broke!' he said. 'Flatter than the goddamned prairies!'

Zack wished he knew something to say to his father that would make the loss easier to take. But a sixteen-year-old boy never has fit words for saying anything. Zack kept silent.

They rode toward Winfield.

7

UP FROM SCRATCH

Luck had ridden Zack's father with a sharp-roweled spur.
In one broad swipe, his big 101 outfit had been cut down
till it was on a par with the little greasy-sack cow spreads
that operated on pure hope and had to wildcat for meat.
It shook G. W. Miller. It would have shaken any man.
But G. W. didn't let it throw him. He wasn't cut out to
let a stroke of bad luck prey on his mind.

He took stock of what he had left. There were a few
cull steers and eighty-eight horses, most of them too old
and stove-up for saddle work. His bank account was down
to a couple or three hundred dollars, and he owed the
Government a thousand if he hoped to keep his lease on
the Ponca Indian lands. He had a home in Winfield. He
had three boys, all of them big enough to work, a daughter,
and a wife who'd stick with him from here on out. He
guessed he wasn't so bad off. Many a man had made a
good start with less.

First, he had to get hold of money. Then horses. A
cowman without a good horse is like a honkytonk dancer
with one leg missing — he's bad crippled. The problem
now was where to make the first move.

Joe Sherburn had a government contract to furnish beef
for the Ponca Indians. G. W. went to him.

'Joe,' he said, 'I want to show you where you can give
me a big boost and make a little money on the side. You

95

get eight cents a pound for the cattle you deliver the Poncas. I've got enough cattle to fill your beef issue contract and I can let you have them for three, provided you'll let me deliver them dressed. They're cull stuff and they won't pass inspection alive.'

Joe Sherburn was interested, but there were complications.

'The Indians will raise hell,' he said. 'They want the beef issue delivered on the hoof. You know they always want to do their own butchering.'

'I can make it right with the Poncas,' Miller said. 'I'll bring them down to the butchering pens where they can gather up the guts and blood while the butchering's going on.'

Joe Sherburn thought that might work; he was willing to give it a try.

They butchered at the Big Pens, with the Ponca Indians on hand to collect the entrails. Zack did most of the shooting; he knew how the Poncas wanted it done. They wanted an animal lung-shot so that the lungs would fill with blood before it died. Those blood-filled lungs made good eating, to the Poncas' way of thinking. The livers they ate raw, dipping the warm slices in the bitter gall. That was their greatest delicacy, short of an unborn calf.

The squaws helped with the butchering and skinning so they could select choice morsels for their men. All ate from the raw side of the fresh hide that had been spread out in the shade before the men, like a white woman's picnic cloth.

A bum showed up at the pens while the butchering was going on. Zack guesses he was a bum; he was afoot. To a cowman, in those days, anybody who amounted to anything rode a horse.

The bum came up and hung his elbows over the fence awhile, watching the slaughter. He saw the bloody hides hanging on the fences. He watched the squaws and children tying up the paunches and entrails in other rawhides. He watched the Indian bucks squatted around a rawhide and gorging themselves on raw liver dipped in gall. He shuddered and moved over toward Zack and Joe Sherburn.

'Them blood-eating bastards!' he said, full of scorn. 'Damned if they ain't worse than cannibals!'

Zack and Joe Sherburn had a lot higher opinion of the Indians than they did of a man who'd tramp around the country afoot.

Joe Sherburn said: 'My friend, you hadn't ought to have said that. These Poncas understand English; they know every word you said.'

Startled, the bum swung around to face the nearest group of Indians. Every one of them was staring at him — as they would have at any stranger.

The blood drained out of the bum's face. Before he could say a word, a Ponca friend of Zack's called to him from another group, rawhiding him in the Ponca tongue about making a bad shot on one of the beeves. Zack replied, with much grunting and sign-making.

Then he turned to the bum. 'That Indian,' he said, 'is ready to kill you for what you've just said. I've talked him out of it, telling him that he didn't understand, that what you wanted was to come eat with them. Now, if you think much of your scalp, you better go do it.'

'But, my god!' the bum yelped. 'I can't eat that stuff.'

'Then you better develop an appetite for it mighty quick,'
Joe Sherburn said, 'or get ready for knocking on the gates
of hell!'

Between them, they convinced the bum that it was eat
that raw meat or get shot. They led him, trembling all
over, to the first group of Indians.

They didn't feed him raw liver dipped in gall. Zack
knew that wouldn't taste bad. He'd eaten it lots of times
with his Indian friends. For some strange reason, beef
gall gives a fine flavor to warm raw liver, while it spoils
any other meat it touches. So they had one of the Indians
slice a chunk of raw steak from one of the slaughtered
beeves and dip that in gall. That's what they fed the bum.

He choked and he gagged, but under the solemn stares
of these savage heathen, there was nothing he could do but
swallow it on down and hold it.

By now, the Ponca men had caught on — and nobody
loves a good joke better than an Indian. So Zack carried
the thing farther. He told the bum that he was doing all
right, but that it was a custom with the Poncas to have
any stranger who ate with them tell a funny story or sing
a funny song before he left.

The bum was scared now till he could barely talk. He
said he didn't know a funny story or a funny song. Zack
spoke to one of the Indians, and the man reached for a
rifle propped up against the corral fence behind him. He
laid the gun across his knees and stared hard at the stranger.

The bum thought, then, that he could sing a funny song!

He tried. He tried hard. But facing the dead-pan stare
of every Indian there was too much for him. His voice
cracked on the first high note, choked off, and died completely.

'Run, man!' Joe Sherburn hollered at him. 'Run for your life!'

That was all the bum needed to stampede him. He wheeled and ran for his life. The Indians all raised a big howl at the sight, and the sound made the bum throw on a new batch of speed. Just before he reached a barbwire fence a couple of hundred yards away, the Indian with the rifle planted a couple of shots to one side of him and he dived through that fence as if it weren't there.

When Zack and Joe Sherburn could quit laughing long enough to see again, all the sign left of the fast-footed bum was just little puff-balls of dust hanging in the air and marking the course of his escape.

They learned the next day that the tramp was still running when he went through Bliss.

Meat was meat to the Poncas; they paid no attention to the class of cattle Zack's father butchered for them. They gathered up the guts and blood and took them back to camp; and G. W. delivered the dressed meat to the Ponca Agency, where it passed inspection, was weighed out on the wagons, and paid for.

That little deal fixed Miller up for wintering expenses. What he needed now was a thousand dollars to pay the lease on the Ponca grazing — and some livestock to put on the grass. So he rounded up every head of horses in the 101 iron, cut out two carloads of them and called Zack aside.

'Son,' he said, 'I'm shipping these buzzard-baits down into Louisiana. I haven't got time to go with them. I'm fixing to talk Willie Otis of the Winfield National Bank into backing me in a little project that just might put us back in the money. So I'm sending you. Now, here's what you do. You sell them damned horses, trade 'em, or give 'em away. But come back here with a thousand dollars. We got to have it to pay off our lease on the Ponca Reservation.'

That was a big order, but Zack didn't hedge or ask a lot of questions. He understood the situation and he was proud that his father felt safe to put such a responsibility onto his shoulders. He loaded his horses on the cars and pulled out for Louisiana.

Zack landed in Alexandria, Louisiana, on Red River, and put his fifty head of horses in the feed barns of a man named Hirsch. He hit a streak of luck the first day and swapped off twenty of his best horses for a carload of two year-old steers which he shipped back to the 101. If his father did manage for grass, Zack figured those steers could make some money.

But then it looked like he was stuck. He'd topped his herd to get the cattle, and the rest of the horses made a hard-looking bunch for a man to expect to get a thousand dollars out of. And that's what Zack had to get. A thousand dollars to pay off that lease.

Hirsch also had some cull horse stuff he needed to get rid of. He and Zack talked it over and agreed that their best bet was to put on a Saturday auction sale. That way, they could clean up the stables.

Zack was to do the auctioneering. Zack was sixteen years old. He'd had plenty of experience in horse-trading. But when it came to standing up before a crowd and fast-talking men into buying horses that weren't worth the

powder and lead it would take to shoot them — well, that
was a stiff proposition for a kid to tackle.

But the 101 had to have that money and have it soon;
so Zack screwed up his courage and went at it. He shouted
and raved. He begged and he cried. He waved his hat in
the air and pounded boards with his fists. He talked those
horses up till he had them able to do just about anything
short of piano-playing. By sundown, the sweat was running down into his boots and all the sound he could manage
was a hoarse whisper. But he'd sold horses.

He hadn't sold them at any fancy prices, but he'd sold
them. And he'd kept the average up to around thirty-five
dollars a head, which was more than they were worth.
He took his money and brought a bank draft for a thousand
dollars. That left him fifty dollars to pay up here at Alexandria and get home on; but Zack guessed that when it
came to putting horses under the block, he could hold his
own.

He didn't feel so good, however, when he went down to
settle with Hirsch for the feed bill. He offered the stable
owner the thirty dollars he figured he owed, and Hirsch
told him he'd made a mistake in calculations.

'Boy,' Hirsch said, 'you owe me thirty dollars for feed
and three dollars a head for every horse sold through my
auction ring. The bill is a hundred and twenty dollars!'

Zack was hot, sweaty, and worn out, his temper on a
hair-trigger set. 'I'll be damned if it is, you old bastard!'
he croaked. 'All I owe you is a thirty-dollar feed bill.
You can go to hell for the rest. I sold your horses right
along with mine out there, and I won't pay you a cent for
that!'

'Oh, but the law!' said Hirsch. 'The law says you'll pay, and you will. Or I'll have you arrested!'

'Go get your law!' Zack dared. He threw thirty dollars on the man's desk and walked out.

Zack was about ready to pull out home that night when Hirsch came running up. With him was a constable with a big gun and a bigger chew of eating-tobacco.

The constable pulled a paper out of his pocket and, between spits, read it to Zack. It was a warrant Hirsch had sworn out for the boy's arrest on the charge of carrying concealed weapons.

Zack had an old six-shooter along, all right. He'd seldom worn it; he'd mostly just kept it tucked away in his war bag. But he guessed Hirsch could make the charge stick if he wanted to.

Hirsch grinned slyly at Zack. 'Pay me ninety dollars, boy,' he said, 'and we'll tear up the warrant.'

Zack stooped and picked up his valise. 'We'll go see a lawyer,' he said. 'It's going to take more than that warrant to make me dig into that bank draft.'

It was long after dark now. His train was ready to pull out, but he had them take him to the home of an Alexandria lawyer by the name of Joe Bachelor. Zack didn't know Joe Bachelor from a prairie wolf, but he'd heard he was a lawyer and guessed one lawyer was about the same as another.

He guessed wrong there. Joe Bachelor was far above the average. At their knock he came to the door in his nightshirt, packing a candle in one hand and a loaded Winchester in the other.

'What the hell you mean getting a man up this time of night!' he growled.

Hirsch told his story, making it sound as favorable to himself as possible. Joe Bachelor stood barefooted in the doorway and peered down a long nose at Hirsch and the tobacco-eating constable. Finally, he turned to Zack.

'Let's hear your side of the story, boy,' he said.

Zack told him. Joe Bachelor went straight up. He cursed Hirsch and the constable in a voice that had neighbors throwing up windows all over the block.

'Hirsch,' he finally wound up, 'you dirty, blackmailing son-of-a-bitch! You take this boy over to the Rapids Hotel and put him up for the night. I'll stand his bond. And first thing in the morning, I'll have you slapped so far back in jail for attempted blackmail that they'll have to shoot beans at you with a sling-shot. I'll make it my business to railroad you to the pen for this, or my name ain't Joe Bachelor.'

Hirsch wilted and started shaking in his boots. 'Now, wait a minute, Mr. Bachelor,' he said. 'It's not all that serious. I can make it right with the boy.'

'All right!' stormed Bachelor. 'I'll give you a chance. Tear up that fool warrant. Go pay that boy's hotel bill for him and then his train fare home. After that, if you don't ever wake me up in the dead of night like this again, by god, I may let it ride!'

He slammed the door in their faces before Zack could thank him. The constable didn't wait for Hirsch to tell him to tear up the warrant; he just spat and rolled his cud to the other cheek and started tearing it up on his own hook.

Hirsch took Zack by the arm and rushed him over to the Rapids Hotel, where he got the best room in the house for him.

The next morning, Zack's train ticket was waiting for him at the hotel desk when he checked out.

Zack went back to Winfield, ready to strut a little with his thousand-dollar bank draft.

But there was bad news waiting for him when he pulled in home. Jimmy Moore had sung for the last time his little song about 'If there'd been no whiskey made, in Ireland I'd still be.' He'd gone into Ponca City one night, taken on an overload of his juice of joy, and died before morning in his room in the old Planters Hotel. When Zack got back, they'd already buried the little Irishman in the 101 burial lot at Winfield where today a big granite shaft, with carvings of empty saddles and coiled ropes, marks the graves of many a good 101 cowhand.

All his worldly goods — his one-sixty homestead, seventeen hundred dollars, and a good span of mules — the little Irishman had left to 'Dogie,' his favorite among the Millers.

Zack felt mighty lost and lonesome when he learned that Jimmy Moore was dead.

William E. Otis had decided to take a long chance and back the project G. W. Miller had laid out before him. It was wheat-raising. G. W. had thought that one up when he got to recollecting how he'd coined money out of wheat on the Chicago stock market in years past. Why couldn't he grow wheat on the rich prairie lands of Oklahoma? Labor was cheap. There were nesters all over the Cherokee Strip now, crying for cash to tide them over till they could prove up on their homesteads. With any luck, a man just might make a killing in wheat-growing.

Down near the Ponca Agency headquarters, on the

south bank of the Salt Fork River, G. W. was building another dugout. Uncle Doc and Zack's older brother Joe were helping him. This was to be the new 101 headquarters. Zack pitched in and helped with the work till it was done.

The thousand dollars Zack brought back from Alexandria paid off a year's lease on the Ponca land. Then, using money he'd borrowed from the Winfield bank, G. W. hired nesters to break sod for fifty cents an acre. The nesters' teams were poor and weak; they had no grain to give them strength. But the nesters could plow for a few days, then go home and rest up their teams before coming back to plow for more coffee and sugar money. They turned the rich brown earth with old wooden-beam plows, and their camps were strung along the bank of the Salt Fork like a bivouacked army. They broke sod and seeded in a little over two thousand acres of wheat for the 101 that year.

But a binder never touched the crop; the chinch bugs beat them to it!

Uncle Doc walked out and stood staring at the blackened ruins of the wheat fields. 'If this keeps up,' he said to G. W., 'we'll soon all be down to hunting and roasting terrapins with the red heathen.'

G. W. swore, then threw up his head. 'We'll put in another crop,' he said grimly. 'We've got the land and the tools. I'm going to tell Billie Otis that all he can do is throw some good money after the bad. He'll come through.'

Putting in that second wheat crop was a big gamble for Zack's father. In a way, it was even a bigger gamble for the banker Otis. It wouldn't take too much of this kind of money-lending, on nothing but a man's word, to suck the bank in, along with the 101 outfit. But Otis knew Miller. The big cowman would pay when he made it. And Otis figured he was bound to make it after a while if he kept trying. He let Miller have the money.

The 101 put in the second wheat crop. They worked short-handed, early and late. Their only alarm clock in that old sod-covered dugout there on the Salt Fork was G. W.'s bawling: 'Roll out of it; I can see the mawning star!'

A lot of times Bert Colby beat him to it. Bert had hired on with the 101 there a few months before, and he and Zack's father had made a sort of little game out of seeing which could wake up first in the mornings and holler out the hands.

On top of his second gamble in wheat, G. W. took a high-flyer in watermelons that year. Up in Kansas City, he'd run onto nearly half a carload of watermelon seed that the claim agent said had been shipped and refused because the buyer said it was too late to plant them. G. W. bought them all for about what the freight was worth and brought the seed home. He bought fifty little hand corn-planters that operated something like post-hole diggers and started planting watermelon seed with them. He had the crew plant them in rows close to a mile long and keep planting till the seed ran out. When they'd finished, the 101 had a little watermelon patch that covered about eighteen hundred acres.

They never did cultivate the melons; it rained too much. But at ripening time, a man could stand at the edge of that field and see sixty- and seventy-pound watermelons just as far as his eye was good.

Old man Alderman, the neighbor who'd sold Zack his little *grulla* horse he called Blue, raised a little saddle-blanket patch of watermelons that year between the 101 outfit and Ponca City. He put up a sign in his melon patch. It read: 'Keep Out! $5.00 Fine for Stealing Melons!'

G. W. saw it and put up signs around his melon patch. G. W.'s signs read 'Help Yourself to a Melon. $10.00 Fine If You Don't Get One!'

Plenty of neighbors visited the 101 melon patch to keep from paying that ten-dollar fine.

Uncle Doc Miller took charge of the free-melon business when they began to ripen. He built up a brush arbor and roofed it with prairie grass. He built benches and tables under it. Anybody eating a 101 melon ate it in style.

Uncle Doc had only one rule about eating a melon. The visitor had to put the rinds in a barrel and wash off the table when he'd finished.

A great number of visitors to the Miller watermelon patch were Indians. Fred Roy was one of them. Fred was a young buck and a real dude among the Poncas. He always wore his black hair down his back in long, slick braids. He kept himself rigged out in full Indian dress and most of the time wore a little face paint.

He came down one evening for a watermelon and Uncle Doc told him to help himself, but bring the melon to the table. Fred brought a big one and put it on the table and Uncle Doc wiped off his special melon-knife to do the cutting. Zack, Spot Maxwell, and a little Indian boy all gathered around, ready to get in on the feed.

Maybe Fred Roy thought there were too many gathering around his own melon. Maybe he thought they aimed to beat him out of the best part. Anyhow, when Uncle Doc laid open the two big halves, the dude Indian grabbed quickly, ripping out the luscious heart from each half with his soiled hands.

To Uncle Doc, this was the height of bad manners. 'Goddammit!' he swore, grabbing up a melon half, 'if you like melon so well, I'll let you wear this one for a hat the rest of the day!'

And he slammed the melon down over the dude Indian's grease-shined hair, crushing the flesh till the juice streamed down over Fred Roy's face and shoulders.

The Indian was mad as hell. He slung the melon-half off his head and stalked haughtily away, claiming he'd never come back to this melon patch again.

And he never did — not till his belly got empty again.

G. W. sold melons to anybody who'd buy them, but the bulk of the crop went to the Robert Nicholson Seed Company, a wholesale seed outfit at Dallas that's still in operation today. They bought no melon weighing less than fifty pounds; but the wagon trains from the Miller patch, loaded with fifty-pound melons, were longer than anything that ever set out across the continent in the '49 Gold Rush to California.

But big and good as this melon crop was, it was on the wheat crop that year that Zack's father got well. The 101 harvested seventy-five thousand bushels of grain off two thousand acres.

That was the year that Joe Leiter cornered the wheat market and ran the price up to a dollar and a quarter a bushel. G. W. sold his crop on contract at that price, before it was ever harvested. By the time it was delivered at Bliss, wheat was down to seventy-five cents. But Miller collected his dollar and a quarter and the crop brought him better than ninety thousand dollars.

They'd shot at the moon and hit. The 101 was back on its feet again — with money to burn!

8

BUSHWHACKER

FROM THE TIME Zack took those crow-bait horses to Louisiana, he was spoiled for anything but trading. He was a born trader, like his father before him. Circumstances had given him the necessary background and knowledge, and that one real success at Alexandria had whetted to a keen edge his appetite for making his way in a game that was all wits and fast thinking. It was a game he was never to grow tired of, and a game that earned him the title of 'Bushwhacker of the 101.' Any time one of the Millers smelled out a trade, Zack was ready to go and make the killing.

Half the fun of trading to young Zack was the chance it gave him to prowl in new places, seeing new faces and bumping into odd situations.

In 1895, after he'd cleaned up on wheat, G. W. sent Zack down into Alabama, Florida, and Louisiana on a cattle-buying trip to stock up the new ranch on the Ponca Reservation.

Zack ran into some queer deals down in that country. He was in Flomaton, Alabama, once when he heard of some good steer cattle belonging to a Negro living about thirty miles south, deep in the backwoods. Zack was tied up on a cow trade at the time; so he sent another man down to look at the stuff, giving him the authority to buy if the cattle were what they were put out to be.

The agent traded for the steers, all right, but he had to come back without them. 'That nigger!' he said. 'He won't take a check. Won't even take paper money. He's got to have gold.'

'If the cattle are right,' Zack told his man, 'we'll give him gold for 'em.'

Zack went to look at the cattle in a buggy, taking his agent along. They carried the gold in a sack under the buggy seat. They made it to the Negro's place by daylight the next day. The darky had his four-year-old steers in a trap close by. While the Negro was showing them, Zack located a hundred three-year-olds in a pasture just over the fence.

'What about these, Sam?' he wanted to know. 'Couldn't I make a dicker for them, too?'

'No, suh, boss,' said Sam. 'I raises steers to pay my taxes and my merchant with. I keeps them till they's foah yeahs old.'

'I'll pay you the same price for them I'm paying for your fours,' Zack insisted.

'No, suh, boss,' said Sam. 'I sells these foahs and I get money to pay mah debts this yeah. I sells them threes, too, and comes next yeah, Ise got no debts-money and no steers nuther. I keeps 'em till they's foahs. Next yeah, you buy 'em.'

So Zack contracted to buy the Negro's steers for the coming year at the same price he would have paid him then.

The Negro had his daughter come out and count the steers as he ran them through the gate. Evidently, ten was as high as the girl could count; for when ten steers had come through, she'd slam shut the gate and hold it till Zack had paid off her father in gold coin, then she'd open the gate for the next batch.

The Negro helped Zack and his agent drive the steers back to town. There, Zack took Sam to the bank and had the banker explain to him that Zack's check would be good when he came back to trade next year.

The banker took great pains. He showed the Negro the check blank which Zack would give him. It was the regular 101 Ranch blue check with a yellow steer lithographed on each side.

'Now, Sam,' said the banker, 'when Mr. Miller gives you a paper like this, you bring it to me and I'll give you money for it. That way, Mr. Miller won't have to carry gold around with him and risk getting robbed.'

Sam studied it over, examined the check blank again, then nodded. It was fine with him.

But when Zack came after Sam's cattle the next year, he'd used up all of the regular 101 check blanks except the last, which was smudgy with pencil marks and figurings on both sides. Without thinking, Zack wrote the Negro another draft and handed it to him.

Sam took the check and looked over both sides, then handed it back to Zack. 'Yessah, boss,' he said. 'It's sho a purty papah. But that banker man done told me to git the papah he shows me, the blue one with the big yaller ox on it. He say that papah good. I flat out don' know what to do.'

Neither did Zack for a little bit. Then he remembered that last pencil-marked check blank. He drew it out, carefully erased all the figures and wrote out a check for Sam.

Sam was so tickled he'd have wagged a tail if he'd had

one. 'Nowsuh, boss!' he crowed. 'Nowsuh, you's gittin' me paid right, suh!'

While mule-trading in Monroe, Louisiana, Zack kept his stock in the barns of a trader named Hartley. The head man around Hartley's barn was a boozehead Negro called Snow. Snow liked to make side deals on livestock when he could, but Hartley had made it a hard-and-fast rule that none of the traders around his barn were to give Snow extra money.

One day Snow came to Zack. 'Mistah Zack,' he said, 'if I sells that white mule you got for seventy-five dollahs, what do I git?'

'Well, what do you want, Snow, besides money?'

'Well, now,' said Snow, 'I could sho' delight with all the Live Oak whiskey I can drink at a settin'.'

'All right, that's a bargain,' Zack told him.

A couple of hours later, Snow came back with a fistful of money. 'Heah's yo' seventy-five, Mistah Zack,' he said. 'When do I gits mah hooch?'

Zack gave Bill Gans, a trader working for him, two dollars. 'Go buy Snow a couple of quarts of Live Oak whiskey,' he said. 'If that don't fill him up, we'll buy him some more.'

Gans brought Snow two quarts of his favorite brand and the Negro took it to bed with him on top of a pile of hay behind the barn.

About three hours later, some Negro crap-shooters came hunting Zack. They told him they didn't like the look on Snow's face. The crap-shooters led Zack and Bill Gans to the hay pile. There lay Snow, flat on his back, with the two empty whiskey bottles beside him. Zack shook the Negro and got no response. He raised one of the black man's eyelids and tickled it with a straw. There was no reflex.

'Snow's dead,' he said.

Bill Gans thought he was joking. The trader gave Snow's body a shove. It slid down off the hay, stiff as a board, with both hands held in the same position they'd been in while he lay on his back. Snow was dead, all right. Rigor mortis had already set in. Snow's delight in all the whiskey he could drink at one setting had been too much for his heart.

The Negroes who buried him the next day told it around that Snow's belly was still hot from all that whiskey when they shoveled the clods on him.

Zack felt sorry about the Negro, but that didn't keep him from using Snow's death as an axe over Bill Gans's head. For weeks, Zack had been trying to keep Bill Gans on the road with him. Bill was a top-notch trader. But he liked the bright lights too well. A couple or three days out was all he could take. He had to get to some big town then, where he could booze up and tomcat among the women.

After Snow died, Zack framed it with Hartley and together they brought the news to Bill that the sheriff at Monroe was packing a warrant for Bill's arrest on the charge of murder. It had been Bill who'd actually given Snow the whiskey that killed him.

For the next two months, Zack had no trouble keeping Bill on the road. He kept Bill thinking all the time that he was just about one jump ahead of the sheriff.

'Maybe I'd better pull out for Oklahoma,' Bill suggested

one day. 'This ducking and dodging the law is getting me jumpy as a cat on ice.'

'Now that,' said Zack, 'is the worst thing you could do. The sheriff at Monroe has already contacted the law at Winfield and Hunnewell. Both those places have warrants out for you. You better stay right here and keep bushwhacking for me where I can keep on the lookout for the law and put you wise.'

By this time, Zack had already spread the story among the other traders, who helped to keep it going. Every time Zack got about ready to move to another place, he'd have one of the traders call Bill off for a private talk and warn him that the law had cut his sign again.

Zack even tried to put Bill on a diet to change his looks, so that the law wouldn't recognize him. But Bill was too hearty an eater; Zack didn't have much luck there. Bill claimed he was willing to dodge the law, but he'd be damned if he could keep on the dodge and starve himself at the same time. He'd rather go to jail.

Bill kept trading for Zack and dodging the law till he finally made him and Zack both some good money. A couple of years later he died under the name of Bill Frazier. He still thought the law was after him for the killing of old Snow.

It was down around Branford, Florida, that Zack ran into what he considered the damnedest methods of cow work he ever hoped to see.

He'd been talking trade with old man Tom Peter Chair who ran a cow outfit near Old Town. Zack went down to look over the cattle, and John Valentine, Chair's foreman, met Zack at Fort Fannin, about six miles from the ranch.

Zack always took his own saddle along, a double-rigged Frank Meanea with a high goose-necked nickel-plated horn slanted right for good dally work, and a Cheyenne roll back of the cantle board. And when he pulled the sack off his saddle there at the Fort Fannin Station, he thought John Valentine's eyes would pop out of his head. That Florida rider had never seen a double-rigged saddle with an iron horn.

Zack looked at Valentine's saddle and guessed his own eyes stood out on stems, too. Valentine rode an old McClellan army-style saddle without a sign of a horn on it. How in the hell, Zack wondered, could a man do rope work on a saddle without a horn?

What burned Zack, however, was the fact that the horse Valentine had brought for him to ride was a mare with a sucking colt. Zack had come from a cow country where it was a disgrace for a man to ride a mare, much less one suckling a colt.

Zack wouldn't be caught out in the middle of nowhere on a dark night riding a mare with a sucking colt.

'That all you got for me to ride?' Zack wanted to know.

The Florida rider colored. 'That's a damned good saddle mare,' he said defensively.

'I'll bet she is,' Zack said.

John Valentine looked at the Oklahoman queerly. Zack felt like a fool. But he still didn't aim to ride that mare. He'd just as soon pull off his pants and walk down the main street of town with his bare rump shining in the sun.

'We're gathering some cattle back in the woods,' Valentine said. 'We're ready to pull out when you are.'

Zack stood around looking uncomfortable. About that time, a mail hack drove up, hooked to an old horse wearing the D. Hanis iron from South Texas. Zack ran out and had the mail-driver stopped and bounced for a trade in less time than it takes to slap a blood-bloated horsefly.

'What'll you take for that D. Hanis cow-horse?' Zack demanded.

The mail-driver looked startled. 'Why,' he said, 'I dunno.' He thought for a moment, studying Zack closely. Finally he set a starting price that gave him plenty of room to come down in case Zack wanted to dicker. 'Seventy-five dollars,' he said.

'You've sold a horse!' said Zack, pulling out the money. 'Take him out of the harness.'

The horse was old and scarred up, but right then, Zack would have paid a hundred and seventy-five to keep from riding that colt-suckling mare.

'Why,' the man said, 'I can't let you have him yet. I've still got to deliver this mail!'

'Take him out of the harness,' ordered Zack. 'He's my horse. You just sold him to me!'

Likely, the mail was late that day. They unhooked the horse and Zack slapped his saddle on him, and the last the Oklahoman saw of the mail-driver, he was walking off toward town, hunting another horse and shaking his head.

Valentine led the mare and colt, and Zack rode beside him on old D. Hanis, as he called his horse.

D. Hanis hadn't looked like much back there pulling that hack. But once under a saddle again, his spirits seemed to take a rise and he stepped out in a smooth, clear-footed gait. As a cow-horse once more, he'd got back his pride and dignity.

They joined some other Florida cowhands down the road a piece and all rode toward the Chair Ranch. The hands didn't talk much; they just stared at Zack's saddle.

This was a marshy, coastal country of thick brush and towering liveoaks with long ghostly festoons of Spanish moss hanging to the ground. It was wild, lonesome-looking country to Zack, a poor cow country, to his way of thinking.

But there were cattle here. And wild ones. They jumped a little bunch in a clearing a few miles from the Chair Ranch. The cattle took to the brush like cottontail rabbits.

A man shouted: 'Heretic! Heretic!'

The men all put spurs to their horses and took out after the cattle. 'Where is he?' another man called.

Zack spurred up D. Hanis and reached to take down his catch-rope. He didn't know if the man meant a bear or an alligator — all he could see was cattle. But he aimed to be ready.

John Valentine shouted: 'There he is. That brindle bull!'

The bull cut off from the herd and came tearing through the brush past Zack. Zack put D. Hanis on the bull's heels. He waited for an opening, then whipped out a loop built to fit and tied on.

D. Hanis might have been old and scarred up. But he was still a cow-horse. When he saw Zack give his rope a flip to tighten up the slack loop around the brindle bull's horns, the old horse squatted to take the load, his forefeet wide apart and braced. The brindle bull hit the end of the rope and turned a wildcat.

Zack quit the saddle and was on the bull before the animal could get his feet under him. He grabbed the tail under the bull's hind leg and held him. When the bull tried to roll to his feet, D. Hanis backed off, tightening the tie-fast rope. Zack and old D. Hanis made a real team. Between them, they'd caught a bull.

Zack squatted there, pulling the bull's tail over his side, waiting for somebody to bring him a pigging string for a tie.

But nobody brought one. All the Florida riders did was ride up and sit with their mouths hanging open. They'd never seen the beat of this. A man catching a bull with a rope! And a horse that knew how to help his rider hold a cow brute down!

'Goddamnedest thing I ever seen!' John Valentine marveled.

Somebody finally brought a rope and they tied the bull's feet.

'He's your heretic!' John Valentine said. 'That's the law in Florida. Any man catching a heretic owns him. What's your mark?'

Zack blinked. Evidently, what he'd known all his life as a maverick was called a 'heretic' here in this glades country.

'I don't want him,' he said. 'We'll put him in Chair's mark!'

Zack helped work cattle in the Florida brush there eighty days on a straight, riding old D. Hanis every day and taking mighty good care of him. Zack was making certain he didn't have to ride a mare.

When he learned that the Florida hands did all their cow-catching by bulldogging or using a rope loop on a long pole, he couldn't believe it. But they couldn't believe, either, that an Oklahoma cowboy could ride in and pick up a steer's heels with a rope, even after Zack showed them how. So that made them about equal.

Zack had read in a book somewhere about the Mongols of northern China catching their horses with ropes on a pole, but he'd be damned if he'd ever thought a white man would pull a trick like that.

When Zack finally showed them how to throw a rope over a running steer's neck and pick up his forefeet, John Valentine was sold.

'You just name your leg,' the big Florida man said, 'and that Oklahoma kid can catch it for you.'

But even Valentine wasn't yet ready to believe that Zack and old D. Hanis could handle that Botterford steer.

According to the Chair hands, this Botterford steer was a brush-wild old sinner that hung out in the big thickets off Fishbone Point. They claimed he was wilder than a musk hog and twice as mean. He had a reputation, they said, of just shutting his eyes and running right over a horse when anybody got him cornered, which was seldom. Then he'd cut for the marshes where a man didn't dare follow with a good horse. They sure told it scary about that Botterford steer.

Zack said he believed he could get that steer, and Valentine laughed in his face.

'Boy,' he said, 'if you was to catch that steer and keep your rope tied to your saddle, he'd drag you and that horse both right out into the marsh.'

Zack was at an age when talk like that could get under his skin and keep burning. 'If I get him in roping distance,' he said, 'that steer'll get a good chance to drag us off.'

It was about three days later when they worked Fishbone Point. They choused a few cattle out of the brush and here came this bad steer. He was an orey-eyed old devil, mustard-colored, with widespread horns corkscrewing out to fine points. There was no doubt about it; if he took a notion to run at a horse, that horse had better give him room.

He didn't run at Zack's horse, however. He cut off in a lumbering, hock-rattling run for the marsh.

Zack reefed D. Hanis down both hind legs, and the chase was on. It didn't last long. All his hack-pulling hadn't taken from D. Hanis that explosive burst of speed that makes the difference in a common saddler and a top-notch roping horse. Old D. Hanis put Zack right up where he wanted to be and the Oklahoma rider latched onto those wide horns.

D. Hanis was just as quick to stop when the time came. He had his rump brushing the ground when the wild one hit the rope. The big steer swapped ends in the air and stood on his head. They had him bedded!

Zack piled off his horse and went onto him. He didn't bother with a pigging string for tying. He just grabbed each of the stunned brute's forelegs and hooked them up over the steer's wide horns.

The steer came alive and rose to his hind feet. He twisted his rump. He wrung his tail and he bawled. But his head was still on the ground with his forefeet hooked over his horns. The shape he was in, they could leave him till the moon changed — and he'd still be there.

Zack pulled off his rope and grinned at the Florida hands. 'Any time,' he said, 'you boys want to start taking roping lessons, I'll open up a school.'

Zack left the steer there and rode into camp. He came back in a little while with half a barrel-head which he hung over the steer's face. Then he let the animal up. The steer could see out at both sides, but not in front. Every time he tried to run off, he'd butt his head into a tree. He was a mad steer after a few tries, but when they put him with other cattle, they could drive him.

Zack had every cowhand on the Chair outfit practicing with ropes when he finally pulled out with the herd he'd helped to gather, then bought. Whether or not he started something new in the Florida cow business on that trip, he never knew for sure. But the next time he was in Lafayette County, Florida, some twenty years later, every cowhand he met packed a rope, same as an Oklahoman or a Texan, and knew how to use it. And the saddle he rode had a horn.

Before Zack left, he traded old D. Hanis off for two yoke of oxen. He always hoped the old horse didn't have to go back to pulling a mail hack or maybe a plow. That old D. Hanis — he was a damned good cow-horse.

9

LINE-CAMP ON BIRD'S NEST

G. W. made another try at giving Zack a school education the year his son was eighteen. He sent him to Spaulding's Business College in Kansas City. But it was a waste of time and money. Zack wasn't interested in books. All he had on his mind was cattle, horses, and mules.

Before long he was spending more time hanging around Guyton and Herrington's mule barns than he was at classes. He got to know one of the Herringtons and the man asked him why he didn't speculate a little while he was hanging around.

'If you can put up a little margin,' Herrington said, 'we'll let you trade like the other men do.'

Zack had a couple of hundred dollars. He put that up, and every day after school, he'd take a streetcar out to the barns and start buying. Herrington would pay for the mules and debit Zack's account, then credit him when he made a sale. Zack knew his mules and mule traders, and it wasn't long before he was picking up a tidy little sum every day.

One day he stayed out of school to pull off what he considered a big deal. He didn't complete it; so he stayed out the next day, too. That happened to be the day G. W. came to Spaulding's to pay him a visit. The instructors already had a line on Zack; they sent G. W. out to the mule barns. There he found Zack right in the middle of a mule buy.

'I thought you came here to go to school!' G. W. bawled.

'I did,' said Zack. 'But I stayed out today. I've got a big deal on.'

'What about yesterday?' G. W. stormed. 'You weren't in school yesterday, either.'

'No,' said Zack, 'but I made fifty dollars.'

G. W. studied that over a minute. 'Come on,' he said quietly, 'I'm taking you back to the ranch. I think you've graduated.'

G. W. put Zack to work riding the North Pasture when he brought him home. Zack lived in a tent up on Bird's Nest Creek with a Negro boy named Henry Clay and Henry's bulldog Jerry. Henry and Jerry slept under Zack's bunk every night. Zack strung wire around trees to make a horse corral and had Henry dig them a well in the bed of a creek for water.

Zack's job up there was to keep 101 cattle from straying onto the nester homesteads. The 101 was having trouble with the Strip nesters that year. The nesters would put fences around their fields that a scared boy could run through. Then, when some ranchman's cattle broke in and destroyed their crops, they'd raise a big howl and demand payment. All the nesters were short on money and some of them made a regular business of penning up ranch cattle and collecting damages. When the cattle didn't break in often enough to suit them, it wasn't too much trouble for a man to open his gate and toll them in with a bundle of fodder.

There was one 101 steer, however, that no nester ever tried to lure inside his fence. No nester had to. The steer came anyhow, any time he pleased — and left the same way. He was a big old Mexican stag and a bad one. He'd just as soon fight a man as a dog and did it whenever he ran onto either one. If a nester happened to get him penned along with other cattle, the stag stayed till he got ready to leave, then jumped the pen or tore it down.

All the nesters were afraid of him. They finally sent word to the 101 that if that outfit didn't come get the steer and keep him off their land, they'd shoot him.

Zack went after the steer. He jumped him in a creek bottom and started him back toward the 101. But he hadn't driven the stag more than a mile when he balked and went on the prod. Zack roped and jerked him down a time or two, hoping that'd take the fight out of him. Maybe it would have if he'd kept it up long enough. But after he'd done it four or five times, Zack's rope broke.

The steer charged, and Zack's horse was so played out by this time that he couldn't keep out of the brute's way. There was all hell to pay then, and no water hot.

It was a big yellow mastiff dog that saved them. Where he came from, Zack never knew. Suddenly, he was just there, tying into that charging steer's muzzle with his teeth. The dog swung down and back between the stag's forefeet. The steer's heels went into the air and he took a buster that jarred the ground.

The mastiff hung onto the steer till Zack hollered to let him go. Then the big dog came and reared up on Zack's saddle, wrinkling his black muzzle in a friendly grin.

The stunned stag got to his feet. Zack was able to drive him awhile, then he went on the fight again.

'Git him, boy!' Zack yelled at the mastiff.

The dog rushed in and had the bad one stretched out almost before the steer knew he was there. Whoever had trained that catch-dog had trained him right.

The steer balked once more on that drive. But when the mastiff was through with him this time, he was a broken steer. From there on, Zack might have been driving in a milk cow for all the trouble the Mexican stag gave him.

Zack never did know where the mastiff came from or whom he belonged to. He called him Friday because that was the day the dog came to him, and Friday turned out to be the best dog Zack ever had. He followed Zack everywhere Zack would let him, and no man with a grain of sense ever tried to put a hand on Zack's horse while Friday guarded him. Friday could catch a wild hog, stop a runaway team, or hold a herd of cattle in a fence corner all day.

Zack kept him six or seven years, then somebody stole the dog. A posted reward of one hundred dollars brought a letter from the sheriff in Del Rio, Texas, who claimed to have found him. But before Zack could get the dog, somebody stole Friday from the sheriff.

One day Zack rode into camp on Bird's Nest Creek to find one of the 101 cowhands, Kurt Reynolds, wallowing in the dirt, groaning and slobbering in mortal agony. He was too far gone to talk, but the sign was plain to read. An empty tomato can lay beside him — one that Zack had opened several days before. Zack had eaten part of the tomatoes, then left the rest sitting around in the can, in case he might want to season a pot of beans. Kurt had polished off that can of tomatoes and got him a big dose of ptomaine poisoning.

Here was a proposition. None of the hands were around and there wasn't a doctor closer than a day's ride. Something had to be done quick or Kurt would be dead.

Zack was scared sick, standing there and watching Kurt trying to fight off death and knowing the rider could never make it. Then he thought of White Deer. White Deer was a Ponca medicine man who lived across the Salt Fork. Maybe he could save Kurt and maybe he couldn't. But in a ground-hog case like this, anything was worth a try.

Zack saddled and rode like a drunk Indian for White Deer's lodge. White Deer listened to the boy's troubles without comment. But he gathered up his medicine bag of mystic charms and rode back to camp with Zack.

White Deer used none of his charms, however. He took one look at the writhing Kurt and turned to search among the tall weeds growing along the creek bank. He found what he wanted and began pulling the leaves from a plant resembling a common ragweed.

Back at camp, he poked into the chuck box till he located a side of fresh bacon. He cut six slices of meat, put them in a skillet, and fried out the fat over the campfire coals. He cooked the plant leaves with the meat. Then he forced the poisoned cowhand to swallow the fat as hot as Kurt could stand it.

Kurt didn't miss much throwing that fat right back in the medicine man's face, but White Deer was quick and side-stepped it. He forced more of the fat down Kurt and this time the cowhand held it. Within a couple of hours, Kurt was feeling a lot better. By night, he was up and around camp with nothing worse than a fluttery stomach to remind him of the poisoning.

This aroused Zack's curiosity. After White Deer left, Zack went to the skillet and sampled White Deer's cure. The meat had a good flavor; the weeds had been some kind of wild sage. Zack liked the taste so well that he ate all six slices of meat and wished for more.

A couple of days later, Zack promised the hands a prairie-chicken dinner to vary the beef diet. He rode out expecting to knock over some chickens within an hour or two; the prairies were swarming with them. Only this time, of course, there wasn't a prairie chicken to be found.

It was time to get dinner and Zack reined his horse toward camp, disgusted at his luck. Passing a pond, he spied a snapper turtle sunning himself on the bank. He was a big old mossy-back turtle with a shell big enough to make a good horse trough. His head was the size of a man's doubled fist.

This wasn't prairie chicken, but it was meat. And it wasn't beefsteak, either. Zack drew a fine bead on the turtle's head and the bullet shattered it.

Back in camp, he cleaned the turtle, cut all the meat off the bones, and made turtle stew with dumplings. At the last minute, he recollected the flavor of White Deer's meat. He gathered a handful of wild sage and threw it in the pot.

He couldn't have done a better job of seasoning with that age if he'd known how to use it. The hands waded into the stew; they couldn't get enough. Best stew they'd ever eaten, they declared, and wanted to know what sort of meat was in the pot.

'I promised you prairie chicken, didn't I?' Zack said. 'The feathers are right down the creek.'

When they'd finished eating, Zack showed them the

'feathers.' One cowboy looked at that turtle shell and grinned.

'By god,' he said, 'if that damned stuff hadn't tasted so good, I'd organize a gang to whip your tail with a pair of chaps. When do you aim to turtle hunt again?'

The success of that turtle stew encouraged Zack to try the wild sage on other meats. It worked on them all. After the 101 established its packing plants years later, he used it to season sausage. He finally concocted a special barbecue seasoning with wild sage the principal ingredient. It hit the spot for taste, and every time the 101 had a barbecue, somebody would pack off all the basting sauce that hadn't been used.

In the fall of ninety-seven, the Yates brothers, Jerry and Jimmy, shipped in cattle from close to Del Rio, Texas, and leased a pasture near the 101 outfit. The brothers batched in camp and did all their cow-work themselves, and, according to Pete McDuleck, a 101 rider, they were both weaned on pickles. Pete said a man could ride from the Rio Grande clean to the North Star and not find another pair of cowmen that stingy.

It was the custom in those days of open ranges for neighboring cowmen to help each other out in roundup time. And when the Yates brothers sent out word that they were rounding up to ship, all the neighbors combed their ranges for Yates cattle that might have strayed and brought them to the Yates roundup grounds. Of course, then, there was the job of cutting Yates cattle from any others that might have drifted onto the Yates range, and the job sometimes took all day.

If it did, the Yates brothers let the neighbor hands work right on through till they were done, without a halt. Along about noon, one of the Yateses would ride off and be gone for a while. When he came back, the other would disappear for a while. Neither of them ever mentioned a meal to their help.

They pulled this trick three or four times and finally the neighbors got a full bait of it. One day the Yates brothers called for roundup help and the neighbors pitched in as usual. The gather was extra large this time and the work dragged on to around three o'clock in the afternoon and still wasn't done.

Suddenly, somebody noticed that both the Yates brothers had sneaked out to eat.

'All right!' Zack told the hands. 'We'll all ride over to my camp for dinner and see what happens to the Yates cut when we turn all these cattle loose.'

The whole outfit rode off, leaving the Yates cattle they'd spent all morning cutting out to mix with the rest. They ate dinner in Zack's camp on Bird's Nest, spent the afternoon playing saddle-blanket poker, then rode off home when night came.

The next day, Jimmy Yates rode into Zack's camp looking peeved. 'How come you men to quit us yesterday?' he wanted to know. 'It took me and Jerry till late this morning to cut out them cattle again.'

'By god, man!' exclaimed Zack. 'We got hungry!'

Jimmy Yates looked like he'd swallowed something that didn't set well. 'Why, me'n' Jerry,' he said, 'we was both down to camp rustling some grub. We'd a-been back soon as we finished, and held the cut while you gents et.'

Zack's conscience worried him a little the rest of the day. Maybe the two Yates men had just ridden off to get dinner, both of them leaving at the same time that way. He told Pete McDuleck about it a couple of days later.

Pete snorted. 'Hell,' he said. 'When I left Bird's Nest after dinner yesterday, I come back by the Yates outfit. Both them peckerwoods was piled up in their bunks like a pair of fat coons, and there wasn't enough chuck in sight to feed a rooster.'

From then on, when the Yates brothers needed help at roundup time, they had to hire it. And then they couldn't keep a man more than a day or two.

If there's anything a cowhand's strong on, it's eating.

The outlaw Ben Craven was operating in those parts while Zack was in that camp on Bird's Nest. Ben wasn't much of an outlaw as outlaws went in those days. He was just a sort of two-bit hijacker who went around sticking up grocery stores and things like that. Sometimes he'd show up on the 101, but nobody there ever bothered him. At that time, the 101 and most of the other big outfits practiced the policy of never interfering with the business of the outlaws or the John Laws following them.

Zack got into a couple of pretty tight shooting scrapes on Ben Craven's account, however.

The first time was up at Red Rock. Zack and another cowhand had made a ride up there on the trail of a little romance. It was night and they were hanging around Frank Swartz's store when in stepped Ben Craven and one of his henchmen, Bert Welty. Welty was dressed in woman garments; Zack never did know why.

Swartz was wrapping up some candy for the country gal Zack aimed to set. Welty dragged a six-shooter out of his dress and threw down on the bunch. 'Everybody here hold up your hands!' he ordered.

They were caught off guard and nobody was in a position to argue. They lifted their hands.

Ben Craven pulled his gun then and ordered Swartz to open the cash drawer. About that time, a man named Bill Bateman slammed through the back door, shooting at Ben Craven. Craven opened up on Bateman, and Zack was caught up in their crossfire. Hot lead whipped at him from both ways.

In the stampede that followed, the crowd inside Swartz's store just about knocked the wall boards out, getting away from there. Zack sure didn't hesitate about selling out to the gun-fighters. He went through the front door like a cat shot in the rump with a bootjack. He had to stoop and pull up his pants, though, before he could mount his horse. Either Craven or Bateman had shot his belt in two and that fast run through the door had Zack's pants slipped down around his knees, hobbling him.

He'd ridden five miles before the bullet burn started stinging. The hot lead had just barely marked his hide.

For all Zack knows, that country gal is still waiting for him to bring her that box of candy.

It was up in the Cheyenne country west of the ranch that Zack got into the second gun ruckus on account of Ben Craven. He and Bert Colby had left the camp on Bird's Nest and ridden up there looking for some stolen horses belonging to the Otoe Indians.

Zack and Bert were just crossing the South Canadian River when it happened. They were about halfway across a broad sand bar and hadn't reached the water yet when a shower of sand kicked up beside Bert's horse. Then they heard the whiplash report of a Winchester behind them.

A bee buzzed past Zack's ear and they heard a second gun crack.

They both twisted in their saddles. Behind and following them a couple of hundred yards back were two men in a buggy. One was standing up, sighting a rifle for a third try.

There was a big drift of logs and trash about a hundred feet from Zack and Colby. They were behind it and falling off their horses before the man could get in his next shot.

Colby snatched a Winchester out of his saddle scabbard and peered between the forks of a dead tree. 'Goddamn the crazy bastards!' he said. 'Let's kill both of them.'

'No,' objected Zack. 'We don't know what this is all about, Bert. Let's just set them afoot. You take the gray horse; I'll git the roan.'

Bert dropped the gray horse dead with his shot. Zack beaded a little too low and shot the roan through the shoulders. But the horse went down. The men quit the buggy like it was hot and hit for the protection of some near-by sand hills. They made the sand fly on that run.

Bert and Zack talked over whether to risk making a break now or waiting for night. They finally decided to wait till dark before exposing themselves crossing the river.

They put up with a nester that night and the next morning rode into Cantonment for breakfast. In the restaurant, they found a copy of the *Wichita Eagle* on the table. Across the front page was a big story about how George Foster, Deputy United States Marshal, and another man had pulled off a running fight with the Ben Craven gang on the South Canadian the evening before. The story said Foster and his man had lost both their horses, but Foster was certain he'd shot one of the outlaws.

It galled Bert and Zack, being mistaken for a little old picayune outlaw outfit like Ben Craven's. They didn't want people to know about it. They decided to keep shut-mouthed.

'Anyhow,' Bert pointed out, 'somebody might try to make us pay for them damned horses we shot!'

Zack wasn't right sure he ought to tell this yarn. He thinks maybe Bert Colby might jump him out about pawing over the bones of his past. But after all these years, Zack figures it won't do any harm to let people know the truth about Foster's big fight with that Ben Craven gang.

In those days, Oklahoma's most notorious outlaw was Henry Starr, a cousin to the even more notorious woman bandit, Belle Starr. Henry and his henchmen rode down to Ponca Station one day, aiming to hold up the south-bound Santa Fe when it came through a little after dark. The first man he threw a gun on was Zack.

Zack was at the station to meet his father who was due in from Kansas City. He'd dismounted in a dark corner beside the station and was tying up his horse when some-body shoved a gun in his middle and told him to reach.

Zack thought it was some kind of joke. He figured it was a friend of his named Jack, a pumper for the water tank.

'Go to hell, Jack!' he said. 'You can't scare me like that!'

The man in the dark jammed the gun so deep into Zack's stomach that it cut off his wind. 'Goddammit, I said git them hands up!'

Zack knew then that he'd called the turn wrong. He reached, and reached in a hurry.

The hold-up man took him inside the station and lined the agent and telegrapher up beside him, making them all stand with their hands locked over their heads. Zack got his first look at the outlaw then.

He was a little man, dark-complexioned, and quick-moving as a cat. Zack had never seen Henry Starr before, but he recognized him from descriptions he'd heard of the man.

'You boys just hold what you've got there,' Henry Starr said, 'and nobody'll git hurt.'

About that time, some of his men brought in several section hands they'd rounded up. They stood them beside Zack and the other two men. The newcomers got the same advice Henry had given the first and they took it without any fuss. Like Zack, they could see too many gun muzzles about belly-button level pointing their way. They didn't want to make an argument of it.

The train was a little late. And it stopped out beyond the stockyard instead of pulling on into the station. The outlaws started looking questions at each other; but they waited, holding their guns on the men.

After a time, the brakeman came down the tracks. Henry Starr swung his six-shooter around and threw down on him.

'What the hell's holding up that train?' he wanted to know.

The brakeman looked plenty scared, but he kept his head. 'Take it easy with that gun,' he said. 'The train'll come on just as soon as I wave it a light signal!'

'All right,' said the outlaw leader, 'get to waving it on.'

That's where Henry Starr made his second mistake that day. The first was in leading his armed band in sight of the station before dark. The dispatcher had already wired the train crew to be on the lookout; a band of heavily armed men had been seen hanging around the station. He'd told them to stop back of the stockyards and send a brakeman down to see if it was safe to come on in.

Under the eyes of the hold-up bunch, the brakeman got his lantern and stepped outside to signal the train. The engineer knew what that meant. Instead of pulling on down to the station, he backed his train up half a mile, then headed south again. He high-balled that train through Ponca Station with the whistle tied down and howling.

Too late, Henry saw his mistake. Cursing, he whipped a Winchester to his shoulder and took a crack at the engineer as the train roared by. But the light was bad and his target moving fast; he shot the gauge off the engine. He wheeled then and lined down on the brakeman who'd given him the runaround.

Right there, Zack thought he was going to witness cold-blooded murder. So did the brakeman. The man came close to fainting and nobody in the crowd blamed him. When Henry Starr got angry, there was a light in his black eyes that sent a little cold snake running down the crease of a man's backbone.

It was the Negro soldiers who saved the brakeman. They

came galloping up with their sabers rattling. They piled off their mounts between Henry's hold-up gang and their horses. Earlier in the afternoon an Indian had ridden past Ponca Station and seen this armed bunch of men and he'd reported it back at the agency where the Government had Negro soldiers quartered. The Indian agent had sent these soldiers out to investigate.

Henry and his men faded into the dark. They slipped around the depot and mounted the soldiers' horses and quit the country, stampeding their own horses as they went to keep the soldiers afoot.

Henry later told Zack about that ride. Somewhere in the get-away, the government horse Henry rode got cut up bad in some loose wire and went lame on him. Henry had to get another horse; so he cut for the ranch of old Hose Kaiser, who lived in the Osage country. Henry knew Hose's saddle stock was the kind to take a man yonder and get him back.

The outlaws pulled in at Hose's place a little after sunup. Hose was up on a new barn he'd built, shingling the roof. Three or four of his horses were grazing a couple of hundred yards out on the prairie. Henry's eye lit on a bay horse that looked like he had plenty of bottom. Henry hollered at Hose.

'Hose,' he said, 'I want that bay horse yonder. I'm dropping a hundred dollars here on the ground!'

Hose hollered back at him: 'Henry, you can't have that horse. You know what a hell of a penalty there is for aiding and abetting outlaws. If they catch you riding that bay horse, they'll hang my hide on the law fence alongside yours.'

Henry didn't have time to argue; he had to get out of the country and get out quick. 'Here's the hundred,' he said. 'I'm taking that horse.'

He rode his crippled mount out and ran Hose Kaiser's bay into a fence corner. He pitched a rope on the animal and started to switch his saddle.

Hose called down to a boy inside the barn. 'Bring up my Winchester, boy!'

The boy came running with the Winchester and skinned up the ladder with it. Hose laid the barrel over the peak of the roof and took a shot at the outlaw. But he was rattled; or maybe he was just a poor rifle shot. Anyhow, his lead kicked up dirt about four feet to one side of Henry Starr.

Henry turned then and fired from the hip through the unfinished roof. Henry was deadly with those hip shots, whether he was using a Winchester or a six-shooter. He got the old man in the knee.

Hose came tumbling down off the roof like a squirrel shot out of a tree.

'I hated to shoot the old man,' Henry told Zack, when the two got better acquainted. 'But I had to stop the old fool before he accidentally killed me.'

Zack thinks Henry was telling the truth about that, judging from what the outlaw did later. Henry and his men held up and robbed the Katy at Pryor, Oklahoma, and on his get-away ride, Henry pulled in at Hose Kaiser's house to see how the old man was making out with his crippled knee.

He found Hose and some neighbor men just sitting down to dinner. He stuck his head in at the door and said, 'Howdy, Hose!'

Hose almost jumped out of his chair. Then he braced up and invited Henry in to eat.

'Come in and set down, Henry,' he said.

Henry was cautious. There were too many men at the table to suit him. But he wanted to see Hose Kaiser so he came in and ate with one hand while he held a cocked six-shooter in his lap with the other. When he asked Hose how he was getting along, Hose shook his head.

'Damned bad, Henry. If I don't raise fifteen thousand dollars within the next couple of days, the Arkansas City bank's going to take this ranch and every hoof of stuff on it. And I don't know where a man could even steal fifteen thousand. It looks like I'm wiped out.'

Henry didn't want to talk in front of the others at the table, so he bided his time till the meal was over. Then he led old Hose out to where he'd tied his horse. There, he unrolled his slicker and handed Hose a shot pouch full of money he'd taken off the Katy train.

'Hose,' he said, 'you go up to Arkansas City and pay them bastards off and I'll be along in the next few days and take it away from them again.'

Hose didn't want to take the money, but Henry kept insisting. 'Get out from under that load while you got a chance, Hose,' Henry said. 'You're too old a man to make a new start now.'

So Hose took the money and paid off his debt and Henry felt better about having to shoot the old man off his roof that morning.

Enough such stories about Henry Starr made the rounds to make Zack believe at least a few of them. Henry had cowhand friends all over the country who swore there wasn't a mean hair on the outlaw's head.

Zack got to know Henry Starr well a few years after Henry stuck that gun in his belly down at Ponca Station. Every now and then, Henry would show up at some 101 cow camp. Zack learned to like the man and got after Henry to quit the outlaw game. And once Henry did quit for a spell. He married a squaw with plenty of money and promised Zack he'd track the straight and narrow from then on. But the next thing anybody knew, Henry was making long rides again, following the dim trails and watching back over his shoulder like a coyote.

Zack called his hand on it the next time Henry showed up at the ranch. 'Henry,' he said, 'why in the hell did you go back, after promising me you'd quit?'

The outlaw had the answer to that, all right. 'Zack,' he said, 'if you could get the kick I do out of shooting close to a man and watching him jump through himself, you'd know why I'll never quit. It gives me a feeling I can't do without.'

Zack guessed that's the way it was with Henry. Outlawing had got into his blood and he couldn't quit it. Just like hooch will sometimes get the upper hold on a man.

Henry wound up like most of his kind: with a bullet through his head. A trigger-jumpy bank cashier at Harrison, Arkansas, handled the gun.

As Jimmy Moore was always saying, Henry Starr had packed the same water pitcher to the spring too many times.

Men who weren't bosom friends of Zack Miller used to tell it around that he'd been arrested for everything from rape to train robbery. Zack says this isn't far from being a half-truth; he did rob a train one time.

The hold-up occurred during the time of a big Santa Fe Railroad strike. Zack and some of the hands had ridden down to Bliss to receive thirty cars of cattle his father had bought and shipped out of San Angelo, Texas.

The train rolled in about noon, right after the strike had been called and the station agent ordered to quit by his union. The train backed onto a siding and Mike Monahan, the section boss, and his crew were unloading the Miller cattle when the conductor came running down the tracks, hollering for them to hold up.

'Put them cattle back on the train,' he ordered. 'There's no agent here to deliver them to. We'll have to take them on to Arkansas City.'

The cattle had already been on the train for over thirty hours, when the time limit by law was twenty-eight. They were gaunt and drawn and bawling for water.

'Mike,' Zack yelled, 'don't turn them cattle back into the loading pens. They're our cattle and you're fixing to starve them to death.'

Mike Monahan was a friend of the 101 outfit. 'Well,' he said, 'if you're ordering me not to turn them back, then I won't.'

The conductor reared up on his hind legs about that. 'You get them cattle back on the cars,' he said.

Mike watched Zack slipping a Winchester out of his saddle scabbard and grinned. 'Not me,' he said to the conductor. 'The railroad don't pay me to do its rough fighting.'

The conductor wore false teeth and he started popping them like a mad hog. 'Go open up that switch, Jimmy!' he shouted at one of his crew. 'We're pulling out of here.

We'll leave what cattle have been unloaded, but we're taking the rest.'

Zack had his fur standing up now. 'Don't touch that switch, Jimmy,' he ordered. 'If you put a hand on it, bad luck'll overtake you as sure as I'm setting here in my saddle. If this railroad outfit wants to strike, they can have at it. But I'm not letting a good bunch of cattle starve to death on account of it.'

Jimmy sided with Mike Monahan. He said the railroad wasn't paying him fighting wages. He left it up to the conductor to throw his own switches. The conductor looked at Zack's rifle and decided to let the thing ride.

Zack hollered at the engineer to back up so they could unload the next car. The engineer bowed up then. He said he wasn't taking orders from the 101. He invited Zack to take a shot at him if he liked. 'Then who'll move this train for you?' he wanted to know.

He thought he had the bulge on the cowhands there; Zack began to think so, too. Then a red-headed rider for the 101 spoke up. He said he'd fired on a train and he could back the thing up to unload the cattle cars.

'All right,' Zack said to the engineer. 'Do you still want me to shoot?'

The engineer didn't. He came down off his engine and let the cowhand take over. They unloaded the cattle, the redhead backing the cars into place. Then Zack wrote out a check to pay for the freight and handed it to the conductor. The conductor wouldn't have it.

'I can't take a check for that freight!' he said. 'It'll have to be cash. We're trusting nobody.'

That left Zack up a tree for a minute, but Mike Monahan

came to his rescue. 'The railroad's just paid off a bunch of extra section hands in checks,' he said. 'I'll gather them up for you, then you can write your 101 check for each of the boys.'

The conductor refused to take these checks signed by the railroad company. He wanted cash.

Zack lost his temper completely then. 'Why, you bull-headed son-of-a-bitch,' he said, 'if them checks are no good, how come the company to issue them? You'll take them or get nothing. I've got a full bait of you and your whole damned outfit!'

He threw the handful of paychecks at the conductor and ordered his crew to turn the cattle out on the grass.

The strike was settled before long, and the station agent went back to work. The next time he saw Zack, he warned him.

'They're fixing to have you and your hands arrested for train robbery,' he said. 'I just got it over the wire.'

Zack went back to the ranch and told Joe about it. Dick Plunkett, the court crier for the federal court at Guthrie, was at the ranch at that time. Everybody liked Dick Plunkett for the way he always opened court proceedings.

'Hear ye! Hear ye!' he'd always shout. 'Now all you mully-grubs in the back of the courtroom keep your traps shut and give these swell guys up in front a chance to talk!'

Joe told Dick, who was also a deputy United States marshal, about the coming arrest. He told him, too, about the cattle being held on the train two hours beyond the legal limit.

'Why, now,' said Dick Plunkett, 'I think I'll have a word

with the district attorney about this tomorrow. I think when Jim Cunningham, the railroad's jackleg attorney, comes to the D.A., why the D.A. will have a word with him. And I don't think you'll have any more trouble out of the Santa Fe.'

Evidently, Dick Plunkett knew what he was talking about. Zack never was arrested for his train robbery.

10

WITHERSPOON TROUBLE

FRANK WITHERSPOON, a Texas cowman, came crowding in on the 101 with his Mill Iron outfit about 1898; but a couple of 101 riders with good outlaw connections shoved them right back off the grass before they had time to get a good hold.

It was a dog-eat-dog business from start to finish, with each side playing a fast and underhanded game.

The Witherspoons, with Lee Hiatt ramrodding, came in the year the 101 lease with the Otoe Indians expired. At that time, anybody wanting grazing rights on the Otoe Reservation had to submit a sealed bid to the Otoe Indian Agency at Red Rock Creek. The Millers submitted their usual bid; but the Witherspoons had bought off the agent. They turned in a blank bid, to be filled out by the agent after he'd seen the other bids. The agent raised the 101 bid by about a cent an acre and let the Witherspoons have the land.

This threw the 101 outfit in a bind. They'd had a good summer; their cattle were fat. But they'd been depending on that Otoe land for winter grass and had overgrazed their other leases. They managed to pull through the winter on short grass, but their cattle didn't put on the amount of flesh they should have.

That was rough. But what made it rougher was the high-handed ways of the Mill Iron crew. They considered themselves a tough outfit and weren't bashful about letting anybody know it. They packed guns and ammunition enough to make their horses swaybacked and were in the habit of throwing their weight around wherever they thought it would make a showing. The 101 hands were getting a bellyful of it long before the first trouble broke out.

This took place at the Bliss stockyards, where both outfits had cattle penned, ready to ship. It started over a steer with long winter hair making a dim brand hard to read. The steer was in the 101 gather. Ornsby Hiatt, Lee Hiatt's brother, spotted the steer and wasn't satisfied to let him go. He claimed that steer might be wearing a 101 brand, and then again, he might not. For all he could tell, from where he sat in his saddle, it might be a Witherspoon steer, Ornsby Hiatt insisted. He was all for roping and throwing the animal so a man could clip away the hair and make sure who owned him.

Zack's brother George was the baby of the Miller outfit, but he never was a hand to let a slur like that pass. He bowed up right quick. He said, dammit, the man who couldn't read that brand a hundred yards away ought to buy him a pair of specs. He and Ornsby Hiatt swapped a few compliments and George stepped down out of his saddle.

'Hiatt,' he invited, 'if you'll get down and throw that hog-leg six-shooter over the fence, I'll fist-whip you till you can't piss a drop!'

Hiatt was game. He got down. He unbuckled his gun-belt and hung it around the horn of his saddle and told George to have at that fist-whipping any time he couldn't hold off any longer.

They squared off and locked horns. It was a mean,

bloody fight from the start, with George holding an edge all the way, but one too slight to brag about.

Around it was none of the whooping and yelling and giving of free advice that generally belongs to a scrap where two cowhands are bent on settling a friendly difference. The onlookers were silent on both sides. They watched each other more than they watched the fracas.

George reached back to the ground and brought up a haymaker that came close to popping Hiatt's head off his shoulders. Hiatt piled up.

This was more than one lanky Mill Iron hand could stand. He reached for his gun. But he wasn't half fast enough. Spot Maxwell had him covered with a cocked six-shooter before his gun had cleared leather.

'All right, you long-shanked son-of-a-bitch,' Spot said, 'you git back on that horse and quit the flats. And don't you never look back one time.'

Zack had known Spot Maxwell from the time it had taken them both to climb on one horse. There wasn't a better-hearted man in Oklahoma. But looking at him right now, standing with that eared-back six-shooter rock steady in his hand — well, it gave Zack some idea of the loyalty a forty-a-month-and-found cowhand could feel for his outfit. It also gave him a mighty glad feeling that Spot was on his side of the fence. He could tell by the look on Spot's face that Spot was ready to kill that Mill Iron rider for the wrong turn of an eyelash.

The Witherspoon man had the sense to realize it, too. He climbed his saddle and wasn't slow about it. And the scenery ahead was plenty good for him to gaze at as he rode off.

George let Ornsby Hiatt get to his feet. They both looked as if they'd been dragged at the end of a rope. That was the only fist fight Zack ever saw his brother George take part in, but George was still on his feet and able to give advice. He gave it to the whole Mill Iron outfit.

'From now on,' he told them, 'I don't want ever to catch a one of you Mill Iron bastards on our land other than on roundups. You let us know when you're coming for a roundup and we'll let you come. Any other time one of your horses sets foot on the 101, he'll go back with an empty saddle.'

That little run-in there at Bliss set the Witherspoon tough hands back on their hunkers for a while. But it didn't last. Next thing they tried was rustling.

Zack was riding the North Pasture at that time and batching with a cowhand named Frank Potts. Potts rode the South Pasture. Potts was a big dark-skinned rider who had a grudge against the world in general. He was a good, dependable cowhand, but there was a look in his eyes that made a man sorry for the horse he rode, the woman he wanted, or the man he hated. He'd fight a man at the drop of a hat and drop it himself. Night or day, he was touchy as a teased snake, and G. W. was always cautioning Zack about Potts. G. W. said Potts was the kind of man who could get a kid into a bad shooting scrape.

Potts rode into camp one day and called on Zack to help him rope and doctor a wormy steer in the South Pasture. They rode down next to the south fence. Topping out a rise, they saw what looked like a group of riders gathered around something about a mile and a half down from the Miller line, on the Witherspoon lease.

In those days, Zack always packed a single-barrel tele-scope on his saddle. He put it on this group now and found two Indians, two white men, a wagon, and a steer on the ground. The men were butchering the steer.

Potts reached for the glass and took a look. 'I'll lay you two to one,' he said, 'that that there's one of old man Dolph-mire's steers.'

The Millers were grazing some black poll cattle for Dolphmire that year.

'Well,' Zack said, 'you know, Potts, that G. W. said for us never to go onto the Witherspoon spread without it's a roundup. He'd raise hell.'

'I'm going to see that steer!' Potts said flatly.

There was a steep-banked dry water-course running out of the 101 range down into the Witherspoon lease. The butchering was taking place just on the bank above. Potts said they'd keep to cover, riding down the bed of that draw, and be on the rustlers before they realized anybody was within half a mile.

He led off down into the draw, cut the dividing fence, and rode through. Zack followed, but he wasn't liking it. He knew G. W. was liable to get frothy about this.

'What'll we do when we get there?' he asked Potts.

'We'll do,' said Potts, 'whatever it takes to git the job done.'

He reached and dragged a .44 Winchester from his saddle scabbard and jacked open the breech to make sure there was a cartridge in the firing chamber. Zack was packing a rifle and six-shooter, like Potts, but he didn't want to use them.

'We'd better not do any shooting, Potts,' he cautioned. 'Unless we just have to.'

Potts handed him a twisted grin. 'Rest easy, kid,' he said. 'We'll let them make the first move, then take it up from there. I'll handle the situation; don't you bother about that!'

They rode quietly down the creek bed till they were opposite the men up on the bank. They could hear the men talking. They located a game trail leading to the top and rode out.

The men were less than fifty yards away.

'All right, reach, you bastards,' Potts said. 'Git them hands high.'

The men had left their guns back at the wagon, too far away to make a try for them. The white men lifted their bloody hands. The Indians stood and stared.

Potts started cursing the men then. Zack never heard such a cursing as those two Witherspoon hands got. Potts had a tongue with a cut to it like a blacksnake whip.

'I ought to shoot every damned one of you sneak-thieving sons-of-bitches,' he finished up. 'I ought to shoot them goddamned Injuns with you, throw you all in that there wagon, then burn it!'

Potts's anger was all out of proportion to the crime, it seemed to Zack. He wondered if the hard-bitten rider wasn't just trying to rib himself up to do a killing.

'Don't shoot 'em, Potts!' Zack started begging.

Potts paid Zack no mind. He cursed the men as if they'd been responsible for all the sourness and bitterness of his life.

The steer was half-skinned, with all the upper part of the hide lying raw-side-up behind the steer. Potts got down off his horse and flipped the hide over so he could read the brand. It was a black hide; the steer belonged to old man Dolphmire, all right.

The faces of the Mill Iron hands turned white when Potts looked up from that hide. The Indians started talking then. They were Otoes. They said they had traded for that steer in good faith. They said they had given two blankets to the white men for the steer. They pointed to the blankets hanging on the wagon. They said they hadn't known the steer was stolen.

Potts sneered at them and at the white men. He started toward the white men and there was a black, ugly look on his face that scared Zack.

'Don't shoot 'em, Potts!' He was almost screaming.

Potts stopped. He shot a quick look at Zack, then his mouth twisted up in that one-sided grin of his that had something wolfish about it. He bent and picked up the skinning knife lying beside the hide and cut the brush off the steer's tail. He handed this to one of the Mill Iron men.

'Now,' he said, 'you git on your horses and take this tail down to your camp and hand it to Frank Witherspoon. You tell him I sent it. You tell him to set down and count every hair in that tail. Then you tell him that when we've got a Mill Iron steer for every hair in that steer's tail, we'll quit stealing from him.'

The men took the steer's tail and rode off with it. Potts and Zack let the Otoes have their beef and hung the hide on the dividing fence between the Millers and the Witherspoons. That was to give anybody a chance to look at it who wanted to. Then they rode back to doctor their wormy steer.

That was the second time that the 101 outfit had made

some of the Witherspoon's tough saddle hands crawl in
the dirt. And that had been a big bluff Potts had just hung
up — about stealing those cattle. The way things were
shaping up, Zack looked for the lid to blow off any minute
now. Open range war could start from this, and killings
from ambush.

G. W. Miller sized it up about the same way. He made a
quick trip to Kansas City and came back with a dozen
brand-new .30–.30 Winchesters and a hundred boxes of
shells. Those were the first rifles of that caliber to be used
in the Salt Fork country; everything had been .44's and
.38's up to that time.

G. W. handed out the new guns to the pick rifle shots of
his crew and told them: 'Now, you take these guns and
don't be caught without them. Get used to the sights.
Shoot at everything you see. Shoot up every box of those
shells; I've got more ordered.'

In the next week or two, the 101 hands burnt up plenty
of shells. Around camp, somebody would empty a tomato
can and pitch it out on the grass and the rest of the bunch
would see how long they could keep it bouncing. They
shot jackrabbits, prairie wolves, dry-land terrapins, anything they could draw a bead on. The men rode in pairs
and nobody left camp without a six-shooter at his belt and
a Winchester in his saddle scabbard.

The Witherspoons had evidently taken Potts at his word
about that cow-stealing he'd promised. They set out to get
theirs first. They played it slick, too. They wouldn't
come out in the open and drive off a big bunch; but 101
stuff began to dribble away, one here, two or three there,
with the trail wiped clean behind them.

Potts was for riding right into the Mill Iron camp and calling for a six-shooter showdown, but G. W. checked him on that. So the black-humored cowhand bided his time and waited for the sign to get right; he aimed to do what he called 'a little arithmetic' of his own peculiar brand.

Thanksgiving time was right at hand. As usual, G. W. had promised the Salvation Army in Winfield a beef. He left orders with Uncle Doc Miller to cut them out a good fat one.

Uncle Doc looked the cattle over and let slip the remark that there wasn't a fit beef for butchering on the 101 range; the grass had been too scant for them to fatten.

This was excuse enough for Potts. 'Doc,' he said, 'you leave it to me. I'll git you a beef you won't be ashamed to strip a tarp off of when you git to Winfield.'

Uncle Doc was suspicious of only one thing: women. He thought nothing of Potts's remark. He told him to go ahead and get a beef. Uncle Doc was glad to shoulder the bother onto somebody else.

There was a carrot-topped cowhand on the camp pay-roll as Ida Red. That was the only name anybody knew him by and they'd got it from a song he was always singing about a girl named Ida Red. Ida Red was a bronc stomper, a hell-for-leather, spur-jingling sort of a rider who wore his hat slanted across his head at a hell-bent angle and was a banjo-picking fool.

Potts got Ida Red off to himself at dinner time that day and told him, 'Ida, you take a good long siesta this evening. Tonight, we're going to be up awhile, doing a little arithmetic.'

Zack heard what Potts told Ida Red, and he said: 'What you up to, Potts? What you boys got on for tonight?'

'Never mind, kid,' Potts said. 'You don't get in on this. Somebody might get hurt.' And that's all he'd tell Zack.

They pulled out after moonrise that night, Potts and Ida Red.

'You have your butchering outfit and wagon in the lot when we get back,' Potts told Uncle Doc before they left. 'We'll want it early in the morning.'

Zack stood outside the dugout and watched them ride off into the clear cold night. He'd about half wanted to go along; there was liable to be plenty of excitement. But Potts had said no and that's just what he'd meant. All Zack could do was stay there with Uncle Doc and wait for them to tell him about it sometime, if they ever got around to it. If he raised a row to go, Uncle Doc would catch on and queer the whole deal.

They told Zack about it later. Ida Red said they rode down to Red Rock Station where the Witherspoons had a gather of steers on feed. He said they left their horses at the feed pens and quiet-footed it up to the shack where the Mill Iron hands had their quarters. Right up at the house, a dog ran out at them, but Potts brained the animal with the butt of his Winchester before he could bark and tip their hands.

There was one little window in the shack and one door with a padlock on it. Potts and Ida Red looked in at the window. The Witherspoon hands were gathered around a poker table beside a sheet-iron stove. Potts reached for the padlock at the door. He pulled the hasp over a loop and locked them inside. Then he and Ida Red went back to their horses.

Down at the pens, chousing those steers around, trying

to pick out the fattest one, they made noise enough to wake the dead, the way Ida Red told it. He said they kept looking for some of the Witherspoon hands to show up, but none came. He said he didn't know whether they couldn't hear the noise or just couldn't break out of the shack.

The chousing spooked a bunch of steers and they made a run at the side of a pen. The timbers broke under their weight with a splintering crash. The steers poured through the gap.

Potts and Ida Red cut out three of the fattest ones of these. They knew a single wouldn't drive. They headed toward camp, driving the three.

Up on the head of a creek not too far from camp, they roped the steers and tied them up to some cottonwoods, then went for the butchering wagon. They dressed out the top steer, buried his hide, and hauled his carcass into camp. But what could they do with the other two?

They puzzled on that for two days. Then Potts thought of an Indian girl he'd been bedding up with now and then. He never had been able to give her old man a fit present; he guessed a good fat beef would just about fill the bill. An Indian got Ida Red's steer, too, and Ida Red added a couple of fancy blankets to his hot-roll.

Potts and Ida Red played it cautious, letting the Indians do their own butchering. They didn't want Uncle Doc Miller to catch on to what was up. They were worse afraid of Uncle Doc than they were of the law.

But Uncle Doc was a trusting sort of man; he never asked any difficult questions. And the Salvation Army got one of the fattest beeves in the history of Winfield.

Rustling three head of steers wasn't enough for Potts and

Ida Red, however. That was just play stuff. What they ached to do was make a real showing, pull off something that would cripple the Witherspoon outfit. So Potts looked up a few beef-rustling friends of his acquaintance who were butchering and hauling to Arkansas City and Pahuska. He invited them to help themselves to Witherspoon cattle, promising to give them good Winchester protection any time they needed to make a get-away across 101 range.

This suited his friends fine; their only complaint was a limited market. They claimed their buyers were little two-bit outfits and couldn't handle more than a good shirt-tail full of beef at a time. What they needed was a market that'd allow them to expand operations.

Potts came to Zack with the problem. 'Zack,' he said, 'you've knocked around some. You know any place a man could market a whole trainload of cattle without getting asked a lot of questions hard to answer?'

Potts pointed out that they couldn't ship to Kansas City on account of the brand inspectors there. If they shipped over the Santa Fe, they would be right under the noses of the Mill Iron outfit and they were bound to get curious. Then there was the Cattle Association in Kansas. It was a problem.

'I don't have any notion what you've got up your sleeve,' Zack lied to Potts. 'But there's a cattle buyer in Little Rock that's questioned me a few times about where he could buy some cheap beef. I'm shipping a carload of horses into Arkansas in a couple of days. You might ride down with me and see what kind of medicine you can make with him.'

Potts rode to Little Rock with Zack and looked up the

buyer. The two of them circled each other with some cautious questions a few times and finally came out in the open over a bottle of whiskey.

The cattle buyer told Potts he could handle as many as two hundred and fifty steers at a time, provided he could buy them for a cent and a half a pound. Potts told the buyer that he would likely have some to sell at that price, provided the buyer butchered in a hurry and forgot where the cattle came from. They killed the whiskey to clinch the deal and Potts went back to Oklahoma to get his cattle gathered.

He waited so long that Zack figured the deal was all off. Then one day, when some of the boys butchered a beef for some of the agency Indians, Potts cut off a chunk of liver and put it in his saddle pocket.

'What's that for?' Zack wanted to know.

Potts gave him a look hard to read. 'Sometimes, kid,' Potts said, 'you ask more fool questions than the law . . . Now if a man wanted bad to poison a wolf or something, where do you reckon he could locate the strychnine your Uncle Doc keeps?'

Zack said: 'Uncle Doc would sure paw up the sand if he caught you messing around that old private bunk of his in the upstairs part of the dugout. I'd hate to risk it.'

'He ain't catching me,' Potts told him. 'You go saddle a horse. We're taking a little ride to Billings this evening.'

Zack saddled a horse. Potts came from the dugout and the two of them headed toward Billings, the Rock Island Railroad terminal.

It was a twenty-two-mile ride to Billings. Potts wouldn't follow the road. He hung to the bank of Red Rock Creek, looking the country over, twisting in his saddle now and then to see how the landmarks stacked up behind him.

Billings was a little place with stockyards half a mile out of town. Potts stopped at the depot and had a confidential talk with the agent. He ordered ten cattle cars to be ready for loading at daylight two days later. Zack found out afterward that it cost Potts two hundred and fifty dollars to make sure the agent's memory would be short.

On the ride back to the 101 that night, Potts followed Red Rock Creek again, dropping off a bait of poisoned liver close to the house of each nester who'd settled there.

'A few friends of mine,' he explained to Zack, 'are fixing to ship some cattle and they aim to make a night drive along here. They claim it's mighty inconvenient to have dogs barking at you when you're making a drive over a new trail in the dark.'

When Zack rode into camp the next evening at sundown, he found Potts and Ida Red and five strangers piled up in the dugout bunks, all asleep. The strangers had the looks of a tough gun crew if Zack ever saw one. He got uneasy and woke Potts up.

'For god's sake, Potts,' he said, 'you're not fixing to rob that Rock Island train, are you? Don't get yourself tangled up in a mess like that!'

'Tuck in your shirt tail, kid,' Potts said. 'We ain't robbing no train. I'll give you the lowdown on this deal sometime when it's too late for the knowledge to hurt you, or us, either.'

That's what Potts did. He said they rode out under a quarter moon and picked up three hundred head of cattle wearing the Mill Iron brand, cut out two hundred and fifty of the best, and drove them down Red Rock Creek to the Billings stockyards. They penned at four o'clock in the morning. Not a nester dog barked along the trail.

They slept till the train pulled in at daylight, then loaded their cattle under the name of Billy Fox and billed them to the buyer in Little Rock.

There was a man in the country by the name of Billy Fox; Zack went up in the air about Potts having used his name. 'Dammit, Potts!' he said, 'you hadn't ought to have done that. They're sure to hop old Billy about them cattle.'

'Bound to,' agreed Potts, smiling his twisted smile. 'And when they do, they'll find that the signatures don't match. Then what trail can they take?'

Potts had a pass on the cattle train, but he was half afraid to take it. Finally, he went out and bought him a suit of tenderfoot garments, complete with pointed tan shoes, a choke-rope necktie, and a hard-shell hat. He rigged himself out in this, then caught another train to Little Rock.

The buyer wanted to weigh the cattle at the stockyards in Little Rock, but Potts said hell, no, they could guess them off close enough.

'The less people who have any dealings with these cattle, the better off we'll both be,' he told the man.

The steers would have weighed nine hundred pounds or better, but they guessed them off at eight hundred. This made them bring twelve dollars a head.

The cattle buyer tried to give Potts a check, but Potts was watching all corners. He shoved back his city-slicker coat to give the man a look at his six-shooter and told him he'd pay in gold, just like they'd agreed.

'Or,' he said, 'this'll be the last herd of cattle you'll ever buy, old man.'

The buyer paid in gold.

Back at the ranch, Zack saw Potts pay his tough hands two hundred and fifty dollars apiece for their part in the deal. Zack sold out cheap: Potts bought off his silence with a pair of bench-made boots.

The rest of the long-loopers wanted to make another haul of Mill Iron cattle, but Potts put his foot down. 'I ain't forgetting,' he said, 'about the water pitcher Jimmy Moore's always telling about — the one that was packed to the spring one time too many.'

Potts and Ida Red, however, continued to rustle a Mill Iron beef any time the opportunity came along. They'd butcher one or two at a time and sell to a Ponca City meat man who didn't demand to see the brand a steer wore if he could buy the meat right. Potts saved the hides till a buyer named Jake Goldsmith showed up at the ranch one day.

Potts propositioned Goldsmith: 'Goldie,' he said, 'if I was to ship you some good cow hides, could you forget where they came from?'

Jake Goldsmith had smelled rats before and recognized the scent. 'Sure,' he said, 'and I could pay for them hides by mailing money instead of a check. In case that would help.'

Potts agreed that would be a big help and next week shipped Jake Goldsmith some hides with the brands cut out. He shipped for a month before he got a letter from Goldie. With this letter was one to Goldie from George Foster, the same deputy United States marshal who had mistaken Zack and Bert Colby for the Ben Craven gang. Foster told Goldsmith that if he got any more hides shipped from Blackwell, to send them down to him; he'd be willing to pay good money for them.

Potts hated Foster's guts for some difference they'd had in times past. He had a hide shipment ready to go; so he took his hides down in a creek bottom out of sight and built up a brand fire. Then he spread his hides out and branded Foster's initials, 'GAF,' on every hide and shipped them all to Jake Goldsmith with instructions for him to send them all down to George Foster at Perry, Oklahoma.

About two weeks later, Marshal Foster was in a store at Bliss when Potts and Zack and some of the other cowhands walked in. Potts walked boldly over to Foster.

'Foster,' he said, 'I understand you're buying hides from St. Louis these days. We've been shipping some hides to St. Louis. Maybe we could just get together and save freight both ways.'

Foster took one look at the hard shine in Potts's eyes. Then he turned to the counter, bought a couple of cigars, and walked out without ever saying a word.

Zack said he was the only one of the Millers who knew where Potts got all his money to blow on swank clothes and fancy saddle gear. He said that by the time the Witherspoon lease was up on the Otoe lands, Potts was considered a cow-camp fashion leader by every outfit in that part of the country. The Indian girls thought he was sure pretty.

Also, by that time, Frank Witherspoon must have had a bellyful of Potts and his 'cow arithmetic.' Anyhow, the Mill Iron never did submit another bid for grazing rights there on that part of the Salt Fork.

That hurrahing, spur-rattling, banjo-picking Ida Red!
He had him a little song he used to sing about how Old
Trouble was always slipping up on the blind side of a man
when he least expected it. And that's how Old Trouble
came to him.

Ida Red wasn't looking for trouble the night it caught
up with him down in Missouri John Hutchinson's saloon in
Ponca City. Neither was Zack or Frank Potts, who rode
with him. All any of them had on their minds was to kick
up their Saturday-night heels around town a little, then
ride back out to the ranch for another week's saddle work.
But trouble came just the same.

They heard the fracas going on inside Missouri John's
while they tied up at the hitch rail. Ida Red cocked one
big ear toward the place and allowed it sounded like they
were shoeing a bronc on the inside. Then he shoved open
the bat-wing doors and went inside to see what the commotion was about.

Out in the middle of the sawdust floor a fist fight was
going on. It was a mighty one-sided affair, with two big
gun toughs holding one little man between them while a
third took his time and hammered the very face off the little
man.

It was the sort of setup few men could stomach. Ida
Red didn't say a word. He just waded in, both fists chopping like meat axes.

Ida Red wasn't a big man, but in a fist fight, he was a
hard one to shave. He started quick and was hell to stop.

Two licks, and he'd dropped two men like pole-axed
steers. He'd knocked the third up against the bar and was
fixing to give him a good working-over when in walked a

two-bit constable who thought he swung a big stick around town.

'Hold it, Red!' the constable blustered. 'Don't you hit him another lick. Hold it, in the name of the law, Red.'

Ida Red didn't even look around. 'You'll wait your turn,' he told the constable and kept right on at what he'd set out to do. To Ida Red, a constable's badge didn't always make justice.

Missouri John stood back of the bar and kept begging them to take it outside. Nobody paid any attention to Missouri John.

The first two men Ida Red knocked down were on their feet and sneaking out of the honkytonk by the time Ida Red finished off the third with a lick that crumpled him to the floor. Then Ida Red swung around to face the constable, grinning and licking his lips.

'Hand your gun to the barkeep,' he said. 'If you've still got something against me, we'll settle our difference outside. Missouri John'll give birth to a buffalo calf if we bust up many more showcases.'

He shoved his own six-shooter across the bar to Missouri John and stood waiting for the constable to do the same. The constable hesitated, then placed his gun beside Ida Red's.

Ida Red started toward the back door, going through a darkened hallway, the constable coming next. Frank Potts followed the constable and Zack was tramping hard on Potts's heels. Ida Red twisted his head and handed the constable a hard grin over his shoulder.

'I aim,' he said, 'to whip hell out of you before you can make up your mind to run!' Ida Red was still resenting the interruption of his brand of justice.

But the constable had other ideas; he reached under his coat for a second gun.

Potts saw the move and grabbed at the constable. 'Run, Red!' Potts hollered. 'He's drawed a hide-out gun!'

Ida Red ran. He leaped out into the dark with the constable's first shot knocking splinters out of the door jamb into his face. He headed straight for Zack's horse where he knew there was a six-shooter in one of the saddle pockets.

Ida Red could play a tune on a six-shooter, same as he could on that tight-strung banjo he picked. He played a tune now. Zack heard his gun bark and, over Frank Potts's shoulder, saw more streaks of flame stabbing the night. Then he and Potts were falling aside to duck the line of fire.

The constable shot once more, then went down with a strangled yell. He lay there in the dark, wallowing and pitching and making choking, rattling sounds in his throat.

Missouri John came rushing back then. Potts struck a light. The constable lay on his back in a puddle of his own blood, and it looked as if half his throat had been shot away. It was a sight to chill a man's blood, the way his throat looked.

Frank Potts called out into the dark. 'Take that gray horse of mine, Red, and don't look back. You've killed this bastard. You've shot his jugular vein in two!'

Ida Red took Potts's gray horse as he was told and pulled out. They could hear the quick hard beats of the gray's hoofs as he quit town, taking the rowdy, laughing, banjo-picking Ida Red down the outlaw trail.

Potts said that's where he was bound. He said that's all that could come of a shooting scrape with the law. Let common cowhands settle a difference with six-shooters, he said, and the winner could plead self-defense with a better-than-equal chance of getting in the clear. But not with the law.

'It's the lonesome trails for him now,' Potts said. 'Ducking and dodging, with the law and bounty hunters trailing him like a pack of wolves. If he lone-wolfs it, they'll git him; if he throws in with the wild bunch, they'll ruin him. Ida Red ain't the kind that can trail with the wild bunch.'

Frank Potts was bitter about the trouble Ida Red had got into. Frank Potts was a hard man, but Zack saw tears in his eyes that night when they lit the lamp back at camp.

11

FRESH SCALPS AND HEARTBREAK

THAT INHERITANCE Zack got from Jimmy Moore — it helped the 101 bushwhacker to make his first big killing in the game of buying and selling. It also turned out to be a wedge that almost prized Zack loose from his home and the 101, for good.

In the winter of 1900 Zack went up to Kansas City, looking around for a chance to turn one dollar into two. Out in the stockyards, he found Guyton and Herrington buying mules right and left.

'What's up?' Zack asked one of the barn men.

'Buying Boer War mules,' the man told him. 'Fifty-five a head for all that get the government iron, showing they've passed inspection. The same price goes for small cavalry horses.'

'Could I get the same price?' Zack wanted to know.

'If you can get the same mules,' the men said.

'How many can you use?'

The man smiled faintly. 'When you've delivered us thirty thousand head, we'll call a halt and take a look from there.'

Zack didn't know where he could get hold of one mule, not to mention thirty thousand. But he could see that at fifty-five dollars a head, there was some money to be made in mules if a man could locate them. He caught a train for the ranch that night, thinking hard. Where could he get his hands on some mules?

On the train he met old G. N. McCullough, who back in 1892 had helped G. W. to take a bad whipping on a sheep deal. McCullough was now in the dairy business in Needles, California.

'Mac,' Zack said, 'are there any mules in California?'

'Mules!' exclaimed McCullough. 'My god! The country's overrun with hardtails. They're giving away what they can and killing the rest. We've had a bad drought out there and the hay crop's failed. You can buy mules at your own price in California.'

Zack hit the ranch thinking fortunes in mule-buying. G. W. had other ideas. At the breakfast table the next morning, he told Zack about them.

'I've contracted for twenty-five hundred JAL steers in West Texas,' he said. 'I want you to go to Abilene to receive them.'

'Can't do her,' said Zack. 'I'm going to California to buy mules. This Boer War is making a big market for them.'

'Zack, you can't do that,' said G. W. 'I'm too busy to go after them steers; so is Joe. Anyhow, we've got no money to spare. That damned Boer War's liable to be over by the time you get them mules bought. Then we'll have them on our hands. And no market. You get on that train and go after them steers.'

Zack was young, and hot-headed as his father. 'Dammit,' he flared, 'if this mule business is half as good as it sounds, I'll make more money than you'll ever hope to make out of them steers. And if you don't think I've got sense enough to know what I'm doing,' he added, 'I'll use my own money. I'm going to California!'

'What money you talking about, boy?'

'The money I'm talking about,' Zack said hotly, 'is the money Uncle Jimmy Moore left me!'

The 101 was mighty near to breaking up that morning. G. W. walked the floor and bawled orders at his son. Zack bowed up, glaring at his father. Zack was twenty-two, headstrong, and stubborn as the mules he aimed to buy. It looked to him like G. W. didn't want to trust his judgment. Father and son were both fighting mad when they left the dugout. But Zack went to California.

He left with Jimmy Moore's seventeen hundred dollars in his pocket. He had also made arrangements to mortgage, for fifteen hundred more, the farm he'd inherited from the little Irishman if he should need the cash. Zack was hell-bent to risk every cent between him and starvation to show his father that when it came to trading, he was a grown man with both feet on the ground.

He rode the train to Bakersfield, California, where he wired McCullough to meet him at Needles. McCullough came.

'There's mules here,' the dairyman said. 'All we need to do is look around till we find what you want.'

They were taking breakfast in a restaurant when in came a scarecrow-looking man wearing high-topped laced boots.

'You know where a man could find any mules to buy?' Zack asked him.

'Well,' said the man, 'up the Colorado River here about forty miles is a hundred head of silver-mine mules. Fat ones, too. Been feeding on mesquite beans.'

Zack made a deal for the man to take him to the mine where the mules were. The three of them left out in a buggy. The Colorado River was flooded and they had to hire Indians to build a raft and put them across. They reached the mine at sundown, just as the mules were coming in to water. The mules were trailing a bell mare.

Zack sat there in his buggy, looking them over. He was recollecting the advice old Hezekiah Williams had handed him one time at Ponca Station where Zack wanted to plunge on a bull buy.

'Son,' Hezekiah had said, 'when it comes to trading for livestock, don't waste time looking at the good ones. They'll take care of theirselves. Spend your time looking for the hard ones. They're what'll beat you out of your money.'

He looked for the 'hard ones' now. He found only two; the rest were made to order if Zack knew mules. And he thought he did.

They ate supper with the mine superintendent that night. Zack hit him up for a trade.

'Well,' the superintendent said, 'there's a hundred and two in the bunch and they'll cost you fifteen dollars a head.'

'That's a good price on a hundred of them,' Zack said. 'But there's two I can't use. A one-eyed mule and another one with a crooked foot.'

The superintendent's mouth fell open. 'For a young duck,' he said, 'taking one quick look, you sure as hell don't miss much. But the rest are sound as a dollar. There's not a mule in the outfit over eight, and few that old. Cutting out the two you mention, my asking price still holds — fifteen dollars a head.'

'Delivered at Needles?' Zack crowded.

'Delivered nowhere, young feller,' the superintendent

said. 'When them mules go through that gate yonder, I'm done with them.'

They argued on into the night and at sunup the next morning, Zack paid the mine superintendent fifteen hundred dollars for one hundred mules, the bell mare, two saddle horses, and two saddles. The mine man threw in the two cull mules, but Zack had to deliver.

That didn't turn out to be much of a job, however, the mules being trained to follow the bell mare wherever she went. McCullough led her behind the buggy, and Zack mounted his scarecrow helper on a saddle horse to chouse up the drags. They made it down to the river crossing by night and pitched camp. They had no corral; so they tied the bell mare to a tree and the mules stayed.

It took some figuring to cross the flooded Colorado that morning, but they made it with the help of fifty Indians Zack hired. The deal he made with them was to pay them twenty-five dollars for crossing the mules, but to knock five dollars off the pay for every mule they let get away.

There were three islands still showing at the crossing on the flooded river. The Indians put the bell mare in a skiff and rowed her from one island to the next, swimming the mules behind her.

In every good-sized bunch of horses or mules, there are always one or two that can't swim. There were three in this bunch. But the Indians were ready for this, too. The red men rowed behind the swimming herd in shallow skiffs and when they came to a floundering mule, they'd grab his head and pull it over into the boat. One Indian would clamp his teeth on one of the mule's ears to keep him from jerking away, while the other man rowed the skiff.

That way, they swam the mules from island to island, resting them between swims. The middle island was boggy. Some of the mules floundered there, sinking up to their bellies where they gave up and didn't try to get out. These, the Indians lashed with willow switches, helping them to change their minds.

They made the crossing without losing a mule or a horse.

At Needles, Zack loaded his mules on the Santa Fe, thirty-three to a car, billing them for Bliss, Oklahoma, then wired for a Guyton and Herrington man to meet him there.

The buyer showed up as the mules were being unloaded for feed and water.

'Well,' said Zack, 'you wanted mules. Here's a hundred head; yours for the standard price!'

Up till now, Zack had been plenty bold and confident about his mule buy. But now, when the buyer started looking them over, he knew some shaky moments. The mules he'd bought, the freight on them, and the trip expenses had just about eaten up the last dollar of Zack's seventeen hundred. If his judgment was poor, he'd have to mortgage the land Jimmy Moore had left him.

It took the buyer two dragging hours to look the mules over, running five into the pens, then running them out before running in five more. When he was done, he wrote Zack a check for fifty-five hundred dollars and told him to bring more mules.

Zack caught a train for Winfield. He showed the bankers at the Winfield National how much he'd made in fourteen days and wanted to know if they'd let him have more money on quick notice, in case he needed it.

'If I find them cheap, how far can I go?' he asked.

'Go to the end of the road,' the bankers told him. 'Buy all you can; we'll back you.'

Zack went back for more mules. He had nine hundred head ready to go the next time his bankers heard from him, thirty carloads. But he'd overbought this time, getting four hundred and thirty of them cut back on him for over-size.

Zack wasn't hurt financially; he'd bought the mules right, at around twenty dollars a head. But he still didn't know what to do with four hundred and thirty head of mules. That many mules can run up a mighty big feed bill in a month's time. He left the mules at Bliss and went down to the ranch. Maybe somebody there knew where he could place some big mules.

G. W. was gone when he got to the ranch. So were Joe and George. Deck Chase was in charge, prizing up hell because the wheat crop was going to the bad for lack of binder teams.

'G. W.'s off up in Kansas somewhere, looking for horses,' Deck said. 'But if he sends me a batch like the last, he might just as well be down here whittling shavings. Them jug-heads was all broke to the saddle instead of a collar. They won't pack a neck yoke, much less pull a binder.'

Zack guessed if it was binder teams the 101 needed, he had them. He and Deck went down to Bliss and brought up enough mules to drag off every binder in the country.

And that's what the mules just about did. Most of them had been broken to drive with a jerk-line and what they didn't know about reins, they weren't eager to learn. Hooked three to a binder, they snorted and hit out across the field in a high-headed run, cutting wheat the fastest it was ever cut on the 101. The teamsters finally put in one old horse with each two mules, snapping the mules up short to the old horses' hames so they couldn't get enough slack to run. The mules fell into their collars then, cutting wheat as if they'd been trained for the job.

Zack left out again before his father showed up at the ranch. And in the next ten or eleven months, he kept dodging G. W. They had said some pretty hard things to each other that morning when they'd locked horns over Zack's mule-buying. They'd built up a fence between them, and Zack was too young and hot-headed yet to make the first move to climb over it.

He kept buying and shipping mules out of California, taking a good profit on every shipment. He guessed, if he had to, he could make it on his own from here on out.

On one of these trips, Zack went to look at some mules belonging to one Don Marcus ———, a typical Spanish grandee, whose *ranchero* lay along the coast. The don, with true California hospitality, insisted that Zack visit him at his *hacienda* in the village of San Juan Capistrano, some ten miles from the mule pens.

The two rode out to the palatial home in grand style. They rode in an elaborate coach, hooked to four fast little mules, with outriders flanking them on both sides.

And there, Zack met Inez.

The Spanish girl was the daughter of Don Marcus, about seventeen, with pale olive skin, flashing black eyes, and hair the color and sheen of a raven's wing. Grace was in her every movement. Laughter lurked in her eyes and played about the corners of full red lips. The first sight of her lit a fire in the young bushwhacker that never died.

Zack entered the lavish home, awkward and uncertain among strange conventions and customs. It flustered him, having a Jap servant to come running at him with a lighted taper every time he started rolling a cigarette. He sensed that his way of talking was too blunt, too direct, too much the language of the range. And when at mealtimes the family came down to the dining-room in formal dress, he felt like a lumbering mule hitched to a sulky. He'd never owned 'soup and fish' clothes; they didn't belong with the life he'd led, where a man ate his meals from a split-board table under the sod roof of a Salt Fork dugout.

But Zack stayed on. Because he'd found in this laughing-eyed Inez a thing he wanted, even if he hadn't known before that he was looking for her. He wanted her more than anything he'd ever wanted in his life. And he meant to stay on till he'd paved the way for getting her.

That first night, he lay awake for hours, knowing a warm feeling of excitement that kept mounting. It was a strange experience for Zack. He'd known women before. But up to now, his chances for romance had been limited. Back there on the Strip country, a cowhand had his choice of two kinds of women — Indian girls and dollar whores.

Zack had tampered with the Indian girls a little. There'd been the four sisters, for instance, who'd gone to the government schools and learned to like white man's ways. But that had soon wound up in a big hair-pulling between the girls, each wanting to keep Zack for herself. So Zack had had to step aside there, to keep his feet dry.

Then there'd been the daughter of old No Knife. She'd been a pretty thing, in a wild sort of way. Of a night, when Zack would ride up to the spring in a grove of trees and whistle like a plover, she'd slip out of the shack where she lived with her daddy and come to him. But that soon ended, too. Zack made the mistake of letting the reservation dogs get wind of him one night and raise the alarm and old No Knife cut down on young Zack with both barrels of a muzzle-loading shotgun. All the old warrior hit was a couple of dogs, but Zack hadn't liked the way they'd died. He'd given up riding to the spring and whistling like a plover.

Such experiments were a part of a reckless young cowhand's life. But this Inez now — she was something else again. She was no Indian girl for a man to bed down with in the tall grass. She was a lady, a little queen, a live, proud thing, all fire and laughter and beauty. She was something for a man to cherish and take pride in calling his own.

And before Zack went to sleep that first night, he'd made himself a promise. He'd take this Spanish beauty back to Oklahoma with him.

There were complications from the start, however. Don Marcus was proud of his *ranchero* and that next day kept Zack in the saddle from early morning to almost dark, showing him his holdings. At the evening meal, Zack got to see Inez and speak a few formal words. And that was all.

Or was it? Zack couldn't be sure, but it seemed to him that during that evening meal, there'd been a light of excitement in her eyes to match his own feelings.

Evidently, Don Marcus had seen the same thing. And while the Spanish grandee was willing to deal in livestock with this youngster from east of the Rocky Mountains, at the same time he couldn't see taking a *Yanqui* son-in-law into the family. During the following days he gave no sign that Zack wasn't welcome. His Old Country code of hospitality couldn't allow that. But from that second day on, he kept a sharp-eyed and disapproving duenna following his daughter like a cold, black shadow.

The forbidding presence of that governess was a thing Zack didn't know how to fight. Nothing in his background or training had prepared him to handle a situation of the sort. Polite parlor talk had never been a part of Zack's life, and with this duenna around, every word he said made him feel like a blundering fool. And the duenna was always there, every moment, watching Zack with suspicion, and weighing every word he managed to say. It made Zack's blood boil; it made him want to double up his fist and drive the old woman's teeth back into her head. But he held a tight rein on his temper, trying not to let it show, hoping to get a break.

Likely, the break would never have come if it hadn't been that Inez had resources of her own. One morning, the Jap brought coffee to Zack's room earlier than usual.

'The *Señorita*,' the Jap said, 'will breakfast this morning at seven-thirty!'

Zack's heart flounced like a fish out of water. He was up and dressed and down at the breakfast table by seven-twenty. He found Inez at the table waiting for him. She smiled a welcome that put Zack's pulse hammering in his ears. He knew then that all the hours had been wasted that he'd spent thinking up pretty speeches to say when he got the chance. There was no need for talking. Not when the promise is plain in a woman's eyes!

The next morning again they met early at breakfast. But on the third, the duenna had caught on and had given up her last beauty nap to come down and throw a wrench into the party. But not before the two had promised to meet in the plaza just at moonrise.

Zack stayed four more nights before Don Marcus's *vaqueros* brought word that the mules were ready. Four nights when Zack was closer to heaven than he's ever hoped to get since. Those were nights that Zack still keeps locked in his memory. He knew them; they were his; and even today, he'd just as soon not talk about them.

Zack loaded out his mules in the corrals so close to the pounding surf that the salt spray turned all the colors of the mules into gray. He billed them to Bliss for a Guyton and Herrington buyer to take over. Then he headed for the Kern River Valley, where he'd learned there were more good mules for sale.

He wrote to his brother Joe, telling him what he'd found. He told Joe to try to square things for him with his father; that he'd found something besides mules that he wanted to bring home; that the way he felt now, this was no time for him and his father to be at outs with each other.

Joe wrote back, telling Zack he'd better stick to mules. Joe said he'd talked to G. W. and G. W. had his own ideas about mixing up races like that. Joe said Zack had better come home and do his own talking, that maybe he'd have better luck that way.

But Zack didn't go home. Things were moving too fast. He was writing to Inez every day, through the Jap servant, and they were making plans to meet and marry in Los Angeles. He wished G. W. could see things different, but the way his father felt toward him and this Spanish girl he aimed to marry wasn't stopping him. He wished, for Inez's sake, that Don Marcus would come through with his consent. But if the old don couldn't, then that was all right, too. Zack was riding too high a cloud in those days to worry himself about the opinions of others.

Then the cloud he rode went out from under him. The next letter he got was from the Jap servant. Old Don Marcus had got wind of what was taking place under his aristocratic nose. He'd got hold of Zack's last letter somehow, and two days later he'd shipped Inez and her mother off to Spain. The girl never did see Zack's last letter, the Jap wrote.

Zack knew some of the blackest days of his life then. He wrote the Jap servant, trying to learn where he could locate Inez in Spain. The Jap didn't know. She was gone, that's all he could tell Zack.

Zack tried other sources. He sent out tracers all over California, trying to get a lead on the whereabouts of his first love. But it was like trying to catch a small whisper in a loud wind. Don Marcus, who'd have no *Yanqui* son-in-law in his family, had managed to blot out all traces of his laughing-eyed daughter.

Heartsick and lonesome, Zack finally gave it up and caught a train back to the 101.

There his father handed him a pretty cold shoulder. G. W. didn't bother to ask how Zack had made out in the mule business. G. W. hadn't forgotten how Zack had run out on him the day he'd needed somebody to go to West Texas for those steers. And he hadn't forgotten how that same son had lost his head over what G. W. called a 'greaser woman,' and had wanted to bring her home to the 101 as a bride. That high fence was still between the two of them; higher, if anything, than it had been at first.

Zack let the fence stand. He wasn't being stubborn now. He just didn't know how to go about climbing over it. He piddled around home in Winfield a little, then went out to the ranch where he spent long hours in the saddle, trying to shake the hurt and lonesomeness that dogged his heels day and night.

Then one day he heard his father mention that he'd have to go see his banker about borrowing some more money.

Zack spoke up then. 'I've got seventy-five thousand dollars I made off Boer War mules,' he said. 'Use that if you need it.'

Deck Chase was there when Zack told G. W. that, and the 101 hand claimed you could have roped Miller's eyeballs with a grapevine.

'Goddamn!' G. W. whispered. Then he got his voice back and roared: 'Why'n the hell didn't you let the rest of us in on it? We could have used some profit like that!'

Zack knew right then that the fence was down. His father couldn't help having some real respect for a son who could run seventeen hundred dollars into seventy-five thousand in less than a year's time. Not to mention the four hundred good mules Zack still had on hand.

Six months ago, Zack would have felt like a young Indian buck who'd come in off the warpath with a belt full of fresh scalps. But now the flavor was all gone out of it. Proving to his father that he was a man now didn't seem to matter much.

Inez was gone. And a part of Zack was gone with her.

Zack told himself he'd find her yet someday, but he never did.

In 1904, Zack married a girl named Mabel Pettijohn from Red Rock, Oklahoma. They lived together six years and had one daughter named Virginia before the marriage went on the rocks. In 1919, Zack married again, a Marguerite Blevins, of Shreveport, Louisiana. To them were born two children, Zack, Jr., and Blevins, another daughter. But that marriage didn't take, either.

Here and there, Zack tried another woman or two. It never worked; always, there was something missing. The chances are, it was a black-eyed beauty from old California.

Among cowhands, it's generally understood that when the love bug bites a young man deep, the place is liable never to heal.

12

FROM RANCH TO EMPIRE

IT WAS ONLY FIVE MILES from Bliss to the 101 headquarters on the Salt Fork. So when G. W. got off the train there one day in the spring of 1903, and found none of the hands at the station with a rig to ride him out, he headed toward the ranch afoot.

On the way a rain blew in from the north, a cold, drenching spring rain that soaked the cowman to the skin and chilled him to the bone.

G. W. thought nothing of it. In his time he'd taken a hundred worse wettings. And all any of them had ever amounted to was to give him more relish for dry clothes and a drink of good whiskey when he got to them.

It didn't turn out that way this time, however. He made it to the ranch, changed to dry clothes, and thawed himself with a long pull at the whiskey jug he kept under his bunk. But an hour later he was sniffling at the nose and the ache was still in his bones. He tapped his whiskey jug a second time; seemed like the strength was gone out of the liquor. By morning, he was laid up in bed with a bad cold. Three days later, he had pneumonia in both lungs.

His wife Molly came down to the dugout, bringing a doctor with her. They did all they could. His boys and his daughter Alma and a lot of his friends — they all came down and stood around and wished there was something they could do.

But there wasn't. There wasn't anything anybody could do. G. W. was a big, tough, double-fisted sort of man who'd never been sick a day in his life. But by Friday, April 24, G. W. knew he was bound for the far side of the river.

He took it calmly enough, and he did his best to keep it from preying on the minds of the others. The way he looked at it, he'd made out pretty well in this world and he was willing to gamble that he'd do all right in the next one. He didn't bother about making a will, but called his folks to his bed and told them what he wanted done. He said he was leaving the 101 to all of them; that he hadn't built up his outfit from nothing to a fifty-thousand-acre holding for it to be cut up into little pieces that would likely dribble away. He said he wanted them to hang together and keep the 101 together and build it right on up to fit the plans he'd had for it at the beginning.

He died the next day, a couple or three hours after he'd invited his visiting friends to eat a hearty dinner and made his apologies for not being able to sit at the table with them.

They made plans to ship the cowman's body back to his old home at Crab Orchard Springs, Kentucky, to be buried beside the grave of his father. That's where he'd asked to be buried. The Ponca chief White Eagle and a select few of the tribe's head men came down to the dugout to pay their respects and take a last look at the remains of the friend they called Tescanudahunga, 'the biggest cow boss.' None of the Indians would join the funeral procession, however. With deep sorrow showing in the broad flat planes of his face, old White Eagle explained.

'I would not weep,' he said with dignity, 'where men and women may see me. I must retire alone.'

An escort of G. W.'s favorite cowhands rode beside the hearse as it rolled from the ranch headquarters toward the Bliss railroad station, traveling through the domain Zack's father had built up, past great wheat fields, past cattle grazing on the prairies — cattle wearing the 101 iron. They were dressed in their best hats and boots, these cowhands, and they rode silent and awed in the presence of death.

That night the Ponca mourners wailed in camp and the next morning the Indians set about butchering beeves and preparing a big feast in honor of their departed friend.

Mother Miller and Joe went to Crab Orchard Springs to attend the burial; Zack stayed at the Salt Fork, numbed by the great emptiness the loss of his father had left. Up to now, everything in Zack's life had hinged upon his father. Everybody on the 101 had looked to G. W.; his word had been the law. In fact, G. W. had been the 101. And now that he was gone, nothing was the same; there was no mainspring, no one to look to in time of trouble, no one to make final and lasting decisions.

That terrible numbness was a long time in leaving Zack.

It was a big outfit that Zack's father left to his family. On the 101 payroll were some two hundred men — farmhands, cowhands, blacksmiths, mechanics. It took over a hundred head of good cow-horses to handle the cattle on the range. Tools and machinery to the value of thirty thousand dollars were used to make crops on the ten thousand acres of land under cultivation. Annual expenses amounted to something like seventy-five thousand dollars. But the income often totaled four to five hundred thousand.

It was big, all right, but nothing compared to what his family set out to make it after they recovered from G. W.'s death. With the thirty thousand dollars insurance money left to her, Molly Miller bought the first land ever owned by the 101; up to this time everything had been leased. As G. W. had advised before his death, she bought the six sections that were to become the site of the 101 Ranch headquarters. She bought it from the Ponca Indians. It lay on the north side of the Salt Fork River, opposite the old ranch headquarters dugout that G. W. had built back in 1893, after going broke.

On this land, the same year of Miller's death, Molly Miller and her sons built the first 101 Ranch home. It was a pretentious affair, built of lumber, and on the lines of the old southern plantation homes. That was the type house G. W.'s plans had called for, and that's what they built. By October of that year, the house was nearly enough finished that Zack's sister Alma and William Henry England married there. It was completely done by Christmas and the Millers ate their first meal inside it on Christmas Day.

Alma was given her share in the 101 estate at the time of her marriage — later she sold it back to the others. Molly and her three sons were left then to carry out the plans G. W. Miller had made. And they were equal to the job. The boys were all grown and had enough experience and their father's training behind them to go right on without a hitch. Joe took over the actual supervision of the farm and ranch; Zack did the big part of the buying, selling, and trading; George did the more and more complicated bookkeeping for the outfit, gradually becoming the financial backbone of the 101 and eventually stepping into the big middle of the oil business when the sign got right.

Molly Miller made her sons a home, leaving the management of the outfit pretty much to them unless they called upon her to help make a decision. Her tastes were simple and she was kept well occupied by the household demands of the growing 101. Most of her time was taken up in caring for some sick Indian or doctoring any reckless cowhand who'd maybe piled up with his horse and come out with a broken arm or leg. But simply being hostess at the great ranch was no small matter and took up a good deal of Molly Miller's attention.

One for all and all for one — that's the way the Miller brothers operated most of the time from then on. They pitched in together and in a little while had the ranch built up so that at one time there was a turnover of more than a million dollars a year. They bought and leased more land, checker-boarding the deeded land with land they'd leased.

A lot of big ranch outfits did that in those days. That way, it took less fencing to hold their livestock, but mainly it discouraged little outfits from crowding in on their holdings and getting underfoot.

Before the Miller brothers were done, they had around a hundred and seventy-two sections of land under control, with about three hundred miles of wire fence built around it. These fences killed off the old-time way of making spring and fall roundups, with the chuck wagon's being a cowhand's only home. So after the Millers got their Salt Fork home built, they started the construction of line-camps out on the range and bunkhouses at headquarters. One big mess hall, built there at the ranch house, fed all ranch employees and their families, from field hands to bronc-busters.

Year by year, the outfit grew bigger. Industrial buildings mushroomed around the ranch house. For cowhorses and work teams, there was a blacksmith shop that needed two full-time blacksmiths to keep the horses and mules shod and the plow tools in repair. There were machine shops. Out of the field crops grew the granary, the silos, and the warehouses. For the fruit there was a cannery, putting up several thousand pounds of apple butter and jelly each year and manufacturing some two hundred barrels of cider. When Joe began to develop his own breed of milk cows, along with them he developed a dairy capable of handling the milk of five hundred cows.

A packing plant was built, the meat coming right off the grass of the 101. The plant had a daily capacity of a hundred hogs and fifty head of cattle. The meat was sold to butcher shops within a radius of a hundred miles of the ranch and delivered in refrigerated trucks. The plant cured its own hams and made quite a reputation of it. And from the packing plant, it was natural for the outfit to build up a tannery, then to hire saddle- and harness-makers to handle the leather.

There was a poultry department, where chickens, geese, guineas, peafowls, and pigeons had the run of the place. The poultry houses, like all the other livestock shelters, were large and modern. There were incubators and brooders, everything right up to the last word in scientific methods.

The oil wells, the first being brought in a couple of miles northeast of the Miller home in 1911, produced enough so that the Millers operated their own refinery, which turned out a hundred barrels of gasoline daily.

It was in 1909 that the ranch house burned to the ground; but the Millers immediately set about building an even more elaborate home. They built the basement, foundation, and first floor this time of reinforced concrete; they didn't mean to risk another fire. This building they called the White House. It stood three stories high and there weren't any pennies pinched when it was furnished.

And still the 101 grew. A general merchandise store was built for the convenience of the ranch employees. This store grew into a mercantile center of northern Oklahoma. Out of this store developed a novelty shop, with Indians making and selling to tourists rugs, beaded belts, clothing, drums, bows and arrows, hand-wrought silver — all the trinkets and plunder that Indians like to make and tourists like to buy.

There was an ice plant, a laundry, a café. There was a private telephone system from the business office at the White House that needed thirty-five miles of wire to reach every foreman in buildings scattered about the ranch. The outfit grew so big and became so famous that motion-picture companies came out to film stories of pioneer ways of life. *Trail Dust* was filmed completely on the ranch. *North of 36* was partially filmed there, and scenes for many other movies were shot on the ranch and then incorporated into the main body of the pictures.

Eventually, the Wheel Club was organized, a club composed of the heads of each ranch enterprise in order that the ranch as a whole could be run more smoothly, with co-operation from each of its separate departments. There were twenty-six members in the organization.

With the start G. W. had given it, the 101 had grown

from a cow herd, with men housed in a hillside dugout, to what now amounted to a corporation. Not even the ambitious G. W. had ever dreamed up anything to match what his sons managed to build.

By a sort of mutual understanding between the brothers, Joe took his father's place as boss of the 101. Zack was gone a good part of the time, buying and selling, earning his title of 'bushwhacker'; and George grew into the financial wizard of the family. But Joe it was that the Indians turned to as children turn to a father, and Joe it was to whom the 101 employees went to settle their disputes and for help in making decisions.

For an older brother or for a boss, Zack couldn't have found a better one than Joe Miller if he'd been doing the picking. Joe was a tall, slender, soft-spoken man who'd go a long way around to keep from hurting anybody's feelings. He couldn't even call a man a son-of-a-bitch without doing it in a nice, friendly way. This saved him a lot of the bloody noses and black eyes that the hot-tempered Zack picked up as he went along.

But anybody who set out to rub Joe's steel found there was plenty of edge to it. Like the 101 Ranch blacksmith Joe had sharpening some plow discs one time. Even after Joe had pointed out that he was sharpening the discs on the wrong side, the blacksmith kept right at it. He was a blustery, bullheaded man who didn't want to be told anything.

Joe kept talking nice to the blacksmith, trying to get him to do the job right. The man wouldn't listen. Finally, Joe's patience ran out. He picked up a hammer handle and quietly knocked the man completely over his anvil, put the handle back in its proper place, and walked out of the shop.

When the blacksmith came to, Joe wasn't there to tell him how to sharpen the discs; but the blacksmith didn't need to be told now.

Joe was a cowman by training, but a farmer by nature. After G. W. died, he turned the big end of the cattle- and horse-trading over to Zack and went in for diversified farming. Joe liked to see things grow. He knew, and sometimes was the man to speak the last word in plant- and hog-breeding. He'd spend the hottest kind of day in the fields, marking ears of corn he wanted to save for seed.

Even back in the days before there was a foot of the 101 sod broken, Joe was tampering with growing things. A missionary by the name of Hammond knew that, and one time brought Joe five bushels of hard-kernel drought-resisting corn from Brazil. Joe had nowhere to plant that much corn; so he got old man Holmes, a Kansas farmer, to plant it for him. That year, Kansas had a bad drought and all the corn Holmes harvested was from his Brazilian crop. Joe made a trade with Holmes then to keep planting the seed every year, but not to sell any of it. Then, when the 101 went in for farming, Joe started planting the corn and crossing it with spotted, soft-grained Indian corn. Within five years he had developed a drought-resisting corn with a fairly soft grain that he called 'White Wonder,' and started selling the seed to corn-growers all over Kansas, Texas, and Oklahoma. It proved so hardy that in no time Joe could get two dollars and fifty cents a bushel for all the seed corn he could grow.

Joe was always experimenting with something like that.

Luther Burbank took notice of what he was doing and helped him a lot. And to return the favor, Joe would make a try at growing any new type plant Burbank was experimenting with, and keep records on it for the plant genius. A year or so before Joe died, Burbank sent him an entire orchard of improved fruit trees, some four hundred in all.

But while Burbank limited his experiments pretty well to plants, Joe barred nothing. One year, it was frogs!

That year big rains started falling right in the middle of wheat-harvesting time. And along with the rains appeared one of nature's wonders — millions upon millions of toad frogs, ranging in size from a dime to that of a big man's hand. They were so thick upon the ground that a horse couldn't take a step without flattening one to a dozen. Where all these frogs come from so quickly during a rainy spell and where they all go when it's over, nobody's ever explained to Zack's satisfaction.

That wasn't all that came with the rains, either. The chinch bugs came, too. The chinch bugs jumped on a fifteen-hundred-acre field of corn Joe had planted south of the Salt Fork and had every stalk covered till it was black.

Sight of those chinch bugs in his corn made Joe pretty sick; time they were done with the crop, there wouldn't be enough grain produced on that whole field to fatten a scrawny shoat.

While Joe sat on his horse looking at his corn and swearing at the chinch bugs, he noticed a peculiar thing. The toad frogs were as thick in the field as anywhere else and right before him was a big old warty-backed toad licking his tongue up the side of a cornstalk, catching chinch bugs, it looked like to Joe.

Joe got down and caught the toad and sliced him open with his pocketknife, just to be sure. He was right; the toad had about a tablespoonful of chinch bugs inside him.

Squatted there on his bootheels, Joe had a big inspiration. If toads liked chinch bugs, what was to keep him from using them to save a corn crop? He damned well had plenty of toads!

He rode back to headquarters where about a hundred harvest hands were wearing out good bunkhouse blankets, waiting for the rains to let up so they could go back to harvesting the wheat crop. Joe put the whole crew to work catching toads out of the wheat fields and loading them into five wagons with the sideboards on. They caught them in mosquito-bar nets built on the plan of those Zack had seen bug-catching scientists use.

That was slimy, worrisome, back-breaking work, catching frogs out of those muddy fields and pitching them into the wagons. The field hands were real disgusted; they felt like fools, slopping around out there in the rain, and some didn't mind letting Joe know they thought him the biggest fool in the crowd.

Zack was one of these. Zack belly-ached louder than anybody else. He told Joe it looked to him like things had come to a hell of a pass when grown men took to frog-catching like a bunch of river coons. He admitted to pulling some fool stunts in his time, but he'd be damned if this didn't take the cake.

Joe let them suffer. 'Hell,' he said to Zack, 'while it's too wet to work, you and them hands just as well be out here frog-catching as rubbing sores on your tail-ends around a poker table. Keep after them frogs; you're doing fine!'

When the wagons began to fill, some of the toads started hopping out over the sideboards and Joe had the hands to throw shocks of wheat on top of the loads to hold the toads in.

Zack started raising another fuss at that. 'Dammit,' he declared, 'you'll kill the things that way. Quit wasting good wheat till we find out if this'll work.'

'Now, Zack,' Joe soothed, 'if a frog can stay buried in the dirt all winter and not smother, he surely can last out a wagon ride from here to across the river.'

'Who in the hell says they stay in the ground all winter?' Zack argued. 'I've heard tell that it rains frogs sometimes — same as it does water.'

'Did you ever see it raining frogs?' Joe wanted to know.

Zack had to admit he hadn't. He was also willing to admit that he didn't give a continental damn where the frogs came from; he still didn't like to catch the slimy things. He assured Joe that it wouldn't hurt his feelings a bit if every one of them smothered to death on the ride across the river.

But they didn't. When the wagons pulled into the corn-field and Joe lifted off the wheat-shock covering, there wasn't a dead frog in the load. Not even a crippled one, best Zack could tell.

They scattered the frogs in the corn like fertilizer, then went back for more. It was after dark before Joe was satisfied to call it a day. He turned the grumbling hands loose and went to supper, proud of the day's work. To-morrow, they'd gather more.

Tomorrow, however, the rains had let up and the sun was shining and the frogs soon became scarce in the wheat fields. Joe hauled a couple of loads and let it go at that. He believed he had enough frogs on that cornfield now to clean up the chinch bugs.

A neighbor by the name of Bill Vancellus came by the second morning. Joe told him what he'd done and took Bill out to the cornfield. He wanted to show the old man how the toads were saving his corn crop.

'Look,' said Joe, 'I'll catch one and cut him open. That'll show you how many chinch bugs he's eaten during the night.'

Joe caught a big toad and sliced him open. The toad had three crickets inside him!

Joe was sure hacked about that, but a little farther down a corn row, he cut open another. It was full of chinch bugs.

He and Bill Vancellus stood and watched the toads at work. Some of the creatures would circle a cornstalk, licking their tongues up the sides of the plants as far as they could reach, raking in the chinch bugs.

And the 101 made corn that year. Not a bumper crop, but a lot more than anybody else around them. And Joe always swore it was his toads that saved his crop. Ever after that, when it rained and the frogs came out, Joe hated to go anywhere in an automobile and listen to those little frogs popping under his tires.

'I recollect how the little boogers worked for me one year,' he'd always say. 'It hurts me to kill them.'

On the 101 farm, Joe experimented with the breeding and raising of horses, cattle, chickens, watermelons, kaffir corn, anything that came to mind. But hogs were his big weakness. Joe could spend hours in a pen, scratching a hog's belly. To his ears, the cracking of good sound corn between a fine hog's teeth was greater music than some men could hear in a big symphony orchestra. Joe did like his hogs.

Long before there was a serum for hog cholera, Joe was working on the idea. He had heard how people made the diphtheria serum and he tried the same thing with cholera. Where he made his mistake was in taking blood from a hog with cholera to inject into his horses, instead of from a hog that had recovered from the disease and built up anti-bodies.

Like his father and his brothers, Joe didn't like to do things in a small way; so when he decided to get into the hog business, he plunged in up to the hilt. He went up into Indiana and bought one boar and forty gilts, the best Duroc-Jerseys he could find, paying five hundred dollars apiece for the gilts and five thousand dollars for the boar, which was not yet a year old.

Zack and George thought their elder brother had lost his mind. 'My god!' Zack exclaimed, 'you're throwing money around like you'd picked it up in the road!'

But Joe let them talk while he went to work getting the proper quarters fixed up for his boar, which he called 'The Great I Am.' No Turkish sultan ever lived in more lavish swank. The Great I Am had a tile bath built in his shed, with two electric fans going day and night to keep his quarters cooled. An Oklahoma A & M hog specialist exercised him daily, fed him scientifically, and brought him a sow from his harem as often as was good for his health.

When the first crop of gilts reached the breeding age, Joe told Zack and George he was now ready for the payoff.

'I aim,' he said, 'to get enough out of sixty gilts to pay for all the hogs I bought.'

He put ads in all the hog papers and magazines, blowing up the merit of The Great I Am till it sounded as if a hog man was ready to go out of business if he didn't buy one of these gilts out of The Great I Am strain. The auction was held at the ranch and the gilts brought eight hundred dollars apiece! The total was almost double what Joe had paid for the original breeding stock.

Zack and George came alive then, ready to go into the hog business with Joe. They bought more fine boars. Within a few years they had over five thousand registered Duroc-Jersey sows. From a distance those red hogs made the hog pasture look like a big red sandy bottom.

As happens to any man if he fools around long enough, one of Joe's experiments in hog-breeding got out of hand and came close to boomeranging. That was the time he bought the big wild Russian boar off Scout Younger, who'd kept the hog with a little two-bit show and circus till the animal got too tough to handle.

The boar was a big gray, spindle-rumped creature, long as a fence rail and standing better than three feet high at the shoulders. He was all head, bristles, and tushes, and when he was angry looked like a bad dream come to life. And he was mostly always angry. He didn't know a booger from a cottontail rabbit; let him sight a man or horse and his bristles would rise along the high ridge of his backbone. His tail would come up, his long ears shoot forward, and somebody'd better start climbing a tree. There was no bluff to that Russian boar. He meant business when he charged.

Younger was doing his best to keep the boar in a big cage at Tulsa when Joe saw him first and got the idea of buying him and crossing him with his belted sows, just to see what would come of it. Joe thought he could sell the pigs to men in the South who were running hogs on the range. Joe figured hogs with a daddy like that could stand their ground against any wolf pack or two-legged hog thief.

Joe shipped the hog to the 101 Ranch and put him in a pen stout enough to hold a bull elephant — he thought. And it did hold the boar for about six weeks. Long enough for Joe to breed him to a good part of the sows he wanted to experiment with. Then one night the boar got tired of his close quarters and dug out from under the pen, moving more dirt than a badger in making his escape.

Joe put men and dogs on the boar's trail, but had no luck. One whiff of that old boar's rank trail scent, and the best hog dog on the ranch tucked his tail and came back to travel under the bellies of the horses. And the cowhands were no more anxious to ride up on that long-tushed nightmare than the trail dogs. So it got to where it was easier to trail the boar by the wild tales of nesters that had sighted him down the Salt Fork than it was with dogs and riders.

The story came in that the big boar had killed a couple of dogs and crippled a horse for one nester and had almost got the man himself. Another story got out that he'd run a woman and three children into a shack and kept them holed up there all day before he decided he couldn't get to them and wandered off.

Joe got scared. 'Jesus Christ!' he said. 'That devil might run into a bunch of school kids and kill two or three of them.'

After that, the men he sent out for the boar were packing rifles, with orders to shoot the hog on sight. Joe was the last man on earth to want a dangerous animal like that left on the loose.

But none of the hog hunters ever managed to cut the big boar's sign. All they picked up were wilder and wilder tales of the boar's depredations. Here, he'd killed somebody's blooded boar; there, he'd stampeded a herd of nester milk cows, scaring them into running through barbwire fences and cutting their udders all to pieces.

Then one day in the dead of winter, a squirrel hunter was crossing the Arkansas River on the ice forty miles below the 101. He heard the rattle of hard hoofs on the ice behind him. Glancing back over his shoulder, he sighted the worst thing he could imagine charging him from behind.

The man wheeled to run, slipped on the ice, and went down. He tried to get up, saw he didn't have time, and swung his squirrel gun around. He was scared half blind, but he managed to line his sights on a spot between two red, hate-filled eyes.

The animal was barely three feet from the muzzle of his gun when the squirrel hunter pulled the trigger.

Even after the wild animal quit pitching and wallowing in its death throes, and the squirrel hunter had got over his scare, he still didn't know what he'd shot. In fact, he didn't find out till the next Saturday when he carried his kill into Ralston, Oklahoma, and displayed it for the curiosity of his neighbors. There, somebody suggested that maybe this was Joe Miller's Russian boar that had been on the loose for so long.

Joe heard about what the man had killed and went down

to Ralston to identify the boar. The squirrel hunter got scared all over again when he found out what he'd shot.

'Damnation!' he exclaimed. 'If I'd recognized the sound of that old hog's teeth popping, I'd never be alive today. I'd a-been too scared to a-squoze the trigger on my gun!'

The old boar was dead, but he'd left his sign on the Salt Fork. All up and down the river that next year sows littered red, gray, and striped pigs. The pigs didn't show much of their Russian heritage till they were about six months old; then their heads began to outgrow the rest of their bodies and they lost the placid nature of tame hogs and began going out of their way, hunting trouble.

Joe killed off every one of the wild breed that cropped out on the 101; he was through with Russian wild boars. But that old boar was a good begetter, considering his opportunities. Zack is willing to bet some of his wild blood is still roaming the brakes and bottomlands of the Salt Fork River.

Joe laid claim to owning the costliest saddle in the world. Like all riders, he'd always keep good saddle gear, but he'd never thought much one way or another about owning a fancy saddle till he made a trip to Europe in 1912. While prowling around over there, he visited Napoleon's tomb along with some other American tourists in charge of a guide and lecturer.

In a case outside the tomb was the conqueror's saddle. 'Here,' said the guide, 'is the most expensive saddle in the world.' And he told what the saddle had cost.

Joe looked the saddle over and didn't think much of it. It didn't look to him like it'd hold the scrawniest kind of a little old Texas steer.

'How much,' he asked the guide, 'would Napoleon's saddle have cost in American money?'

'About seventy-five hundred dollars.'

'And how long,' Joe persisted, 'have you been singing your tune about this being the most expensive saddle in the world?'

'About six years,' the guide told him.

'Well,' said Joe, 'I aim to make you change your story. I'm going home in about a month and send you a picture of a saddle. And after that, you'll have to say that Napoleon's saddle is the most expensive in the world — with the exception of the one owned by Joe Miller of Oklahoma, U.S.A.'

Back in the States, Joe got in touch with S. D. Myers, a saddle-maker who then lived at Sweetwater, Texas. He outlined the general plan of the saddle he wanted and had Myers give him an estimate of the cost of the leather, decoration, and labor. Then Joe went to George F. Jordan, one of the biggest diamond importers of New York, and got this outfit ready to do the jewel work.

Myers did a real job of saddle-making. And Jordan set sapphires and rubies in the silver steer-heads in the tooling of the leather. On top of the saddlehorn was one big diamond with the circle of little blue shiners around it. Back of the saddle was a silver plate with 'Joseph C. Miller' engraved upon it.

Finally done, the saddle cost a little over eight thousand dollars and was the wonder of the cowboy world. When the Miller Brothers 101 Wild West Show went on the road, Joe rode it in the show.

Joe was always getting in fatherly moods and getting taken in by somebody on the make. When he was on the road with the show, nobody liked to give away passes better than Joe. The show managers were always agreeing on just how many passes they'd give out, then winding up in the end having given away some extras because Joe got big-hearted and overdid the good thing.

Once up in Michigan, a man came up to Joe and told him he'd once worked on the 101 Ranch, that he'd come thirty miles to see the show.

Joe didn't remember the man, but anybody who'd ever worked on the 101 got passes from Joe.

'How many in your party?' he demanded.

'Five,' said the man, 'but there's six in the family that we rode with.'

Joe handed out eleven passes. The man took them, but couldn't let good enough alone. 'How are your brothers Tom and Jim?' he wanted to know.

Joe snatched the passes out of the man's hands. 'Get going,' he said. 'A lot of people have talked me into giving them passes to this show, but you're the first damned feller who ever talked me into the notion, then talked me plumb back out of it!'

One day after the highway was built through the ranch, a one-legged man with a crutch came up to the White House. He wore about enough clothes to wad a shotgun and told Joe he knew he wouldn't make much of a hand.

'But haven't you got something a man in my condition could do?'

'Why, sure,' said Joe. 'You're just the man I've been looking for. We've been needing a ranch fisherman here for a long time, but couldn't find anybody to handle the job. Do you chew tobacco?'

The tramp's eyes widened. 'N-no,' he stammered, 'but I smoke.'

'Cigarettes or a pipe?'

'A pipe,' the man said.

Joe called the ranch storekeeper in and told him to fix his new hand up with the things he'd need for fishing.

A little shaken, the tramp came back to Joe's office a while later, fully equipped. He had a new shirt, new overalls, a straw hat, and a new shoe for his one foot. He was packing a cane pole, with plenty of line, hooks, and bait.

Joe led him out on the front gallery of the White House. 'Right west of the highway bridge yonder,' he said, pointing, 'is a big flat rock. Go down there and fish till the dinner bell rings, come up and eat your dinner, then go back. This evening when the supper bell rings you come in and tell me how you're getting along. We'll have a bed for you here.'

The old man hobbled off down to the flat rock extending into the water of the Salt Fork River and fished till supper time. Then he reported to Joe.

'Mr. Miller, I never had one bite all day,' he confessed. 'What do you want me to do in the morning?'

'Why, fish,' said Joe. 'That's what I hired you for and that's what I want you to keep right on doing. I'll tell you when to quit.'

The cripple fished the next morning, then hunted Joe up at noon. 'Mr. Miller,' he complained, 'I still haven't had a bite.'

'Well, go on back and keep your hook baited,' Joe told him.

About three o'clock in the afternoon, the fisherman was back in Joe's office. 'I guess I'll have to quit that job, Mr. Miller,' he said nervously. 'I can't stand sitting down there on that rock all day and watching people drive by and never getting a bite. I feel like a fool. If you've got anything else I can do, I'll be glad to do it.'

'All right,' Joe said, 'I guess I can fix you up with another job. You go tell Weldon, the farm boss, to put a bale of hay out on the gallery here and you sit on it. And I don't want you to say a word to anybody or answer any question of anybody who comes along. If I catch you talking, you're fired!'

The ex-fisherman swallowed. 'I don't see how that'll do any good,' he said.

'That don't make any difference,' Joe told him. 'I'm paying you and I want you to do what I tell you. We've got no room on this ranch for a man who can't take orders.'

The cripple sat on the bale of hay all afternoon. People came by and spoke to him. He pretended not to hear. When a cowboy stopped and asked him what he was doing, just sitting out there on that bale of hay, the color came to the old man's face, but he looked away and didn't answer.

A little later that same cowhand came past with another man. 'That old son-of-a-bitch,' he said to his partner, 'is either deef or crazy. You can't git him to say a word.'

After breakfast the next morning, the hay-sitter came into Joe's office, more nervous than ever.

'Mr. Miller,' he said sheepishly, 'I can't stand the abuse. I'm thanking you for the jobs, but I believe I'll drift on down the road.'

Joe turned to his bookkeeper. 'Give this man three dollars for the three days he's been working,' he said.

'But — but,' stammered the cripple, 'what about these clothes? I haven't worked them out yet.'

'That's all right about the clothes,' Joe told him. 'I figure you've earned 'em . . . If you'll wait around a little bit, we can get you a ride into town with the mailman.'

When the mailman came, the cripple got into the car beside him, handed Joe one of the queerest looks Zack ever saw on a man's face, then rode off. He never did show up at the 101 again.

Joe never forgot a friend of the Miller family. Before he'd ever thought about going into the chicken business on the 101, old George Van Hook came to him one day.

'Joe,' Van Hook said, 'my wife's dead and all my children are married off and I'm tired of trying to live alone. I want a job with the 101 where I'll have somebody to bet windies with in my old age. I'm too stove-up to handle a riding job, but I figure I can be worth my wages feeding chickens or puttering around in a garden.'

Joe's mind jumped back to stories of the time forty years ago when his father had had his only brush with Indians. G. W. had just crossed Red River with a trail herd out of Texas when a party of fifteen Cheyennes rode up, demanding 'wohaw.'

G. W. cut them out three or four cull steers; but these were young bucks, insolent, and on the hunt for trouble. They weren't satisfied; they wanted more cattle. G. W. refused.

The Indians rode up to the point of the herd then and started hazing out several lead steers. This angered one of the point riders and the cowhand dragged out his six-shooter and shot one of the bucks between the eyes.

There was hell to pay then and no water hot. The warriors turned on the trail crew with guns and bows and arrows. The cowhands scattered, taking to the brush, leaving the herd to G. W. and George Van Hook. These two crawled into the chuck wagon and made a fight of it, killing seven warriors before the rest of the young bucks decided this attack was a mistake.

And in gratitude for the way George Van Hook had stood hitched through the thick of the fight, G. W. had told him: 'George, from now on, anything I've got is half yours — any time you want it!'

Joe had been told plenty of times about how old George Van Hook had stayed with his father in that Indian scrape. Now he exclaimed: 'Hell, George, I've been wanting to go into the chicken business. Just couldn't find the right man to take over the management. Go get your stuff and move out here. I'll build you a house and then build a house for the chickens!'

Up to that time, Joe had had no more idea of going into the chicken business than he had of starting a trained flea circus. But when he started, he didn't skimp. He built George Van Hook a house to live in. He built a chicken house and run and bought chickens by the thousands. He hired a poultry specialist out of Oklahoma A & M to supervise the job, but gave him specific orders not to ever let old George Van Hook get the idea that George wasn't the dog with the big brass collar around the chicken outfit.

The thing paid out, all right. They sold eggs by the millions. And the day he died, old George Van Hook didn't know but what it was his personal judgment and care that made the 101 so much money out of chickens.

13

TENDERFEET

As the new 101 outfit grew and prospered, its western hospitality got noised about, and before long, visitors were drifting to it like wild animals to a new water-hole. Some came for a free meal, some for their health, and some on business. Zack says the politicians came for one of two reasons: to get drunk or to sober up. Many visitors came out of pure and simple curiosity.

Among these last were many Easterners attracted by what they considered the raw, frontier atmosphere of the place. They became so numerous that finally, in an attempt to get them out from underfoot, the Miller brothers built a number of cabins down on the river to house them, thereby establishing what was probably the first dude ranch in Oklahoma.

On the guest lists of these cabins were to appear soon the names of such personages as William Jennings Bryan, Randolph Hearst, Walter Teagle, Mary Roberts Rinehart, and Luther Burbank, not to mention a herd of others who were unknowns then and still are today.

For instance, there was the little Eastern tenderfoot remembered only as Nick Carter. All the hands agreed that Nick Carter was a peculiar bird. He'd never mix and mingle with other men when he could avoid it. All he'd do was sit around and read Nick Carter detective magazines and then try to act out the hero parts. There at the ranch, he packed a six-shooter and a dirk knife on a belt around him all the time. He wore these weapons about as natural as a cowhand would wear a powdered wig; and George Miller offered to bet he could take a corncob and a lightning bug and run Nick out of the country. But Nick Carter was such a fiercely shy little man that nobody ever bothered him.

Now and then, some of the boys would trail him when he went off down to the creek to read his Nick Carter detectives and they'd get a big kick out of watching him suddenly jerk out his knife and make a savage stab at the sand upon which he sat. Or, back at the bunkhouse, they'd hear him cut down on some story-book villain with his six-shooter and they'd say: 'Well, another redskin bit the dust. Old Nick Carter's battling the heathen again!'

The boys sort of liked Nick Carter and his play-acting, especially after the night he rode down to Ponca City and matched himself a scrap with some cowhand and got beaten all to hell. When he showed up at daylight with two blue-green eyes and his face hammered to a pulp, he sure was a sorry sight. Zack met him at the corral and could just barely tell him from a fresh hide.

'Jesus Christ! What did you run into, Nick?' Zack asked.

'Sir,' Nick Carter said stiffly, 'I ran second in the altercation; but I upheld the reputation of the ranch. I fought him till everything turned black and I could see no more.'

The boys thought that over and decided that when a man's done his best, that's all anybody's got a right to expect of him.

'By god, he tried!' exclaimed Spot Maxwell. 'That's all a steer can do!'

'The only trouble with Nick Carter,' observed Bert Colby, 'is that he's like all the rest of these raw tenderfoot birds. He talks so goddamned nasty-nice!'

There were the Cudahay boys, too, Young Jack, and his cousin Big Jack. They came from Boston.

Young Jack right away fell in love with an Irish girl at Ponca City. But he made the mistake of writing his mother about his new love before he did much about it, and his mother wired Zack that under no circumstances was he to let her son marry this girl. Zack wired back that he wasn't in a position to interfere; so Mama Cudahay came down and rescued her boy before nature could have its way.

Later, Young Jack was aboard the *Lusitania* when that ship sank. He was talking about that Irish girl to a man named Clote, manager of Vickers-of-England in Mexico, at the very moment the ship went down. Young Jack swam and floated twenty miles and escaped death, only to commit suicide afterward. Still thinking about that Irish girl, Zack always figured.

The case of Big Jack Cudahay was just as bad, or maybe worse. Big Jack stayed out at the ranch awhile, fascinated by the manner in which cowboys worked cattle. He told it around that if his luck held, he was liable to go into the cow business himself.

But his luck didn't hold. A few days after Big Jack left the ranch, Zack found a piece in the paper about him. Big Jack had gone home and found in bed with his wife a Catholic priest, Father Jerrillis. Big Jack had thrown a gun down on the Man of God, tied him up and done as clean a job of castrating him as any of the 101 boys could have done on a bull calf. Then he kicked his wife out.

Later, he took his wife back for a time, but it was no good. The next thing anybody knew, Big Jack had committed suicide, same as his cousin. Seemed like, the boys at the ranch said, it just wasn't in the cards for those tenderfoot Cudahays to come out on the long end of a deal.

Of all the dude visitors to make sign on the 101 outfit, Doctor George Ramsey, of Pittsburgh, Pennsylvania, will likely be the longest remembered. It was his misfortune to hit the 101 with the stage all set for the sort of rough horseplay that no cow outfit can seem to thrive without.

The first anybody heard of Doctor Ramsey was when Zack got a telegram from Fort Riley, signed by Army Lieutenants King and Kenny, whose acquaintance Zack had made recently in connection with selling some army mules. The telegram read:

MEET EVENING TRAIN WITH TEN HEAVILY ARMED MEN AND STAGE-COACH STOP WE'RE BRINGING A LIVE ONE

Knowing King and Kenny, Zack wasn't sure what to expect. The captive those two were showing up with might be anything from a cinnamon bear to a blonde with a tattooed bottom. But he rounded up some of the boys anyhow and had them bring along their hardware. Zack took the stage-coach, and all met the train at Bliss.

Together, they made a tough-looking bunch, riding up to the depot with six-shooters on their hips and Winchester rifles lying across their saddle bows. When the train pulled in, everything from the engineer to the passengers ducked for cover; they thought it was a hold-up.

Then off the train stepped Lieutenants King and Kenny

with a big, tall tenderfoot between them. From head to
toe, the tenderfoot was rigged out in garments for a formal
dinner, even to a black silk hat.

'This here,' Lieutenant King said to Zack, 'is Doctor
Ramsey. Doctor George Ramsey. A personal friend of
ours from Pittsburgh, Pennsylvania. He's come West in the
hopes of seeing cowboys in action and maybe a little Indian-
fighting.'

'Which reminds me,' put in Lieutenant Kenny, 'how is
the Indian situation now?'

Zack pulled a long face. 'Tough,' he said, shaking his
head. 'Plenty tough. They've killed might' nigh every
white settler west of here!'

'We told Doctor Ramsey,' King said, 'that you Millers
were right face to face with the hostiles every day!'

Excitement glinted in the doctor's gray eyes. 'Do you
suppose,' he said, 'that we may encounter any of the savages
on the way to the ranch?'

Zack allowed there was a good possibility. He put the
doctor into the coach and laid a rifle across his lap, in case
trouble started.

They made it safely to the ranch; but Zack, who drove
the stage-coach, loaded his passenger plenty heavy with
blood-dripping accounts of Indian raids he and his brothers
had fought off in recent weeks. The doctor had his ears
standing out wide for just such stuff and the yarns ran into
them like rainwater filling a dry buffalo wallow.

That night after supper, they pulled the old snipe-hunting
gag on the new visitor. They took him over to Cow Skin
Creek about a mile from the house and helped him to prop
open the mouth of his snipe sack and light the candles that

were to stand on either side. The candles, they explained, were to attract the snipes and finally to blind them till he could run the creatures into the sack. They told him to keep whistling all the time so that the men rounding up the snipes could keep him located. They said that if anything happened and he got lost, all he had to do was head for the big light on the front gallery of the 101 ranch house that he could see yonder across that big cornfield. Then they rode off into the hazy moonlight and left the doctor out there alone with his whistling.

Up at the store there were a number of old Indian costumes. Zack and George and three of the hands went over to the store and put them on; they even painted their faces. They still hadn't made any really good plans about what to do with the doctor. All they'd thought of was how funny it would be to give him a big scare and see how fast he could make it across that cornfield to the house. With that in mind, they rode back down to the creek, chanting a weird war song as they went.

In the moonlight, the doctor saw them coming. His whistling faltered. A slight breeze drifted past and snuffed out his candles. The chanting rose higher and broke into savage war-whoops. The Indians had spotted their victim.

Doctor Ramsey's feet got the best of them then. He dropped the snipe sack and took out down the creek. One of the yelling Indians spurred around to head him off. The doctor darted into a patch of brush with the rest hard on his heels. They found him lying inside the thicket, clawing up dry leaves like a dog scratching out a holed-up cottontail. The doctor was working hard to dig in for cover.

Zack ran up and shot twice into the ground beside him.

The doctor squalled in holy terror and quit his leaf bed like a wild shoat jumped by wolves. He burst out of the thicket. A catchrope snaked out and the loop jerked shut around his neck, throwing him flat on his face.

A cruel savage grasped him by the hair and yanked him to his feet, at the same time drawing a long scalping knife.

'Miller! Miller!' the doctor gasped. 'Me friend Miller.'

Some of the boys had told the doctor that if the Indians ever got hold of him, to tell them he was a friend of the Millers. They said the Millers had some friends among the tribes and that other Indians were so afraid of the Miller brothers that they would be slow to harm one of the ranchmen's friends. The doctor was now calling on his last desperate hope.

Most of the 101 hands knew the Ponca tongue; so Zack used it now, ordering them to turn the doctor loose. The Indians withdrew for a muttered conference, giving the doctor his chance to escape. He wasn't slow to take it. He hit for the house, streaking out across the field and making the dead cornstalks pop like firing muskets.

When the Indians had ridden to the store and dumped their paraphernalia, they went on up to the house. They found King and Kenny down in the wine-cellar, along with John Newton, the 101 bookkeeper. The white-faced, trembling doctor was relating his narrow escape. King and Kenny were aghast at the doctor's experience and kept urging more tall drinks upon him to steady his nerves.

'I'll have to make a report of this,' King said gravely. 'Will you support it by an affidavit, Doctor?'

The doctor gulped another long drink and nodded. King turned to George. 'John Newton, here, is a notary public, isn't he?'

George said he was and John Newton didn't deny the charge. They called on Kenny to write out the report. Kenny started writing, reading as he went:

'I, Doctor George Ramsey, of Pittsburgh, Pennsylvania, after having been duly sworn, make the following statement for the Army and the Department of Indian Affairs: that I was peacefully engaged in snipe-hunting on this 7th day of November when, without provocation, I was attacked by a band of fifteen Caw Indians ——'

The doctor interrupted Kenny. 'I don't know exactly how many Indians there were,' he said. 'There might have been only thirteen. And let's say "supposedly" Caw Indians, I'm not certain they were Caws.'

Kenny made the necessary changes, then continued making out the report, describing the attack. 'And after a short parley,' he wrote, 'and after the chief had threatened to take my hair off with a knife, I took my elbows and knocked down the two Indians holding me and calmly but firmly walked away.'

'Now wait,' the doctor protested. 'There's no use in going into those minor details. Just say that I left the Indians and came on down to the 101 Ranch headquarters.' But it was evident that he was mighty pleased about how the report read of his knocking down two Indians and escaping with dignity.

The next morning, George used the telephone to call a few friends in town, and that afternoon they got ready to take Doctor Ramsey into Ponca City.

Lieutenant King argued with George. He said they ought not to risk this trip to town without a military guard. Those Caws might still be hanging around. But George

said he thought he could talk any of the Caws out of causing
trouble, that the Millers had always been friends to them.
So they hitched up some fast horses to a buckboard and
rode in, hitting town about sundown.

The saloonkeepers and bartenders were primed. In the
first saloon, owned by John Nieman, whose son is now a
leading doctor of Ponca City, the saloonman said: 'My
god! You men come to town with all these Indians killing
people!'

Zack admitted it was a hell of a risk, but said that they
were low on whiskey at the ranch and that a cowhand can't
live without whiskey, Indians or no Indians.

It was drill night for the militia stationed there and a
group of young soldiers came marching down Main Street.

John Nieman looked sad. 'Now ain't it a shame,' he
mourned. 'To send them young boys out like that. There's
not over fifty or sixty of them and likely two thousand
Indians. There'll never be a one of them boys come back.'

Others came into the saloon and related how this and
that nester had been murdered and scalped, how wives
and children had been stolen, houses burned. They told
it plenty scary. They had the doctor fighting his whiskey
like a cowhand just in off a long trail drive. He wasn't at
all sure they ought to risk going back home that night.

While this was going on, George Miller made a telephone
call back to the ranch and told the boys what he wanted
them to do and what to bring for the job. Then he rounded
up the doctor and hands and lit out home. Lieutenant
King, the doctor, and Zack went ahead in the Studebaker
buckboard; Lieutenant Kenny and George came behind
in a lighter rig.

Just ahead of them rode a drunk Indian on a stove-up pony. He wasn't bothering anybody; he was just happy-drunk and yelling. But it sure made the doctor nervous, hearing that red man let out a whoop every now and then.

It was at Bois d'Arc Creek that they ran into the ambush. Zack and George suspected that's about where they'd run into trouble; so just as they reached the ford, Zack and King let Doc hold the horses while they got down and went ahead on foot a piece to have a look-see. They walked out of sight up the road and Zack fired off a Winchester a couple of times as a signal to the boys in ambush. All hell broke loose then. The cowhands opened up with a ring of shooting and yelling.

The doctor didn't wait to see what his soldier friend Lieutenant King meant to do. The doctor had ideas of his own. He jumped out of the buckboard and took off up the road. He passed George and Lieutenant Kenny in their rig without ever turning his head.

Some of the ambushers came running up with the live chicken George had ordered brought along. They wrung its neck and flung some of the blood in Lieutenant King's face. Then Zack got into the rig with him and they swung it around and whipped up the team into a run, chasing that light-footed doctor. It took the horses a half-mile to run him down.

When they finally caught him, Lieutenant King ordered the doctor to get into the buckboard. 'We've routed them,' he told the doctor, 'and we think we've killed one.'

Zack lit a match and touched it to a cigarette, giving the doctor a chance to discover the blood on King's face.

'Oh, my god, King!' the doctor yelped. 'You're cut all to pieces!'

'No,' said King, 'I was gripped in a death-lock with one when Zack shot him through the neck. He bled all over me, but I'm not hurt.'

On the way back, King said to Zack: 'I think we ought to get the doctor a souvenir of this Indian battle. You think you can find where that dead Indian fell?'

Zack allowed he could, but the doctor protested; he didn't think it safe to waste the time.

'They're gone!' insisted King. 'I heard their horses running west as they pulled out. I'll just pick up those head-feathers I saw fall. You can keep them to show your grandchildren some day — the feathers of a savage Indian you helped to kill.'

Zack and King got out of the buckboard and went to pick up the old musket and Indian war-bonnet the boys were due to leave on the creek bank. About the time they found them, Zack stumbled over a log.

'What'll we do with this red devil's body?' he asked King, loud enough for the doctor to hear.

'Throw him in the creek!' King said harshly. 'He'll make good catfish bait.'

Zack picked up the log and pitched it into the water with a big splash. Then he and King went back to the buckboard with the musket and war-bonnet.

The doctor felt squeamish about having the tools and garments of a freshly dead Indian in the same buckboard with him. When he thought nobody was looking, he pitched them out into the road.

But George and Kenny were right behind and they picked the stuff up again.

In the safety of the house, George hauled out the dead

Indian's effects and examined them carefully in the light.

'Well, we've played hell now!' he said.

'What is it?' Zack wanted to know.

'Look at the bead-work on this headdress,' George said. 'Only a chief has bead-work on each side of the forehead like that. You've killed a chief and they'll never stop till they get us now!'

George's glance fell upon the doctor's big feet. 'You know,' he said slowly, 'they'd never guess who'd done the killing if the doctor hadn't left the tracks of his big feet back yonder in the road. But come daylight, they'll see those tracks and they'll be on the lookout for the man with the big feet!'

'But I didn't kill him!' protested the doctor.

'That won't make any difference,' Lieutenant King said. 'They'll think the man with the biggest tracks was the chief among us and that's who they'll be out to get.'

They let the doctor sweat over that all night, and the next morning George came in with a pair of the Negro houseboy's shoes. He told the doctor that he'd better put them on. That way, he could hide his own shoes and might be able to escape detection. The shoes were too little for Doctor Ramsey's feet, but George made him cram them on anyhow. Then he sent the crippling doctor outside to hide his big shoes under a fig bush.

About ten o'clock that morning the Reservation Indians began bunching into the 101 store, buying grub and calico cloth for a big funeral feast they were fixing to pull off. Some of them came toward the 101 office.

'Get out of here!' George said sharply to the doctor. 'If those red devils catch scent of you, you're a gone gosling. They've got noses on them like bloodhounds.'

The doctor dashed up to his room and shut the door.

A big buck Indian, Hairy-Back, came into the office. Speaking the Ponca tongue, George gave Hairy-Back the lowdown on the horseplay and told him to start sniffing around the foot of the stairway, then to smell out the doctor's shoes under the fig bush.

Hairy-Back did a good job. He smelled over each step on the way up the stairs, growled at the doctor's door, then came on back down and smelled his way out to the doctor's shoes under the fig. The doctor stood peeping out the window and died three deaths as old Hairy-Back picked up the shoes and carried them out and put them in his spring wagon.

George hurried up to the stricken doctor. 'They've got us up a tree now, Doc,' he said. 'But don't you worry. They'll never get your scalp while the rest of us are alive!'

Zack was up in the doctor's room when the telephone rang. Zack told the doctor to listen in on the extension. It was the government clerk named Lewis calling George from the Agency building. Lewis sounded excited.

'George,' he said, 'you boys are in a hell of a jam. The Indian police are here now. You've got a man in your house they want for killing their chief. They know he's in your house and they aim to get him.'

George stood his ground. 'If he's here, he'll stay here,' he said. 'We don't aim to give him up. We'll fight you to the last man.'

'Now, George,' argued Lewis, 'be reasonable. You know what that'll lead to. There are better than two hundred Indians here at the Agency and they're all putting on their war-paint. If you boys don't give up that big-footed man who killed their chief, they'll massacre every one of you.'

'Cut the damned wolves loose!' George snapped at Lewis. 'We're not giving our man up.'

The doctor dropped the receiver, his face the color of flour-and-water paste.

All morning and into the afternoon, more Indians came and gathered around the 101 ranch store. The doctor wandered around the house, suffering from cramped feet and trying not to appear nervous. The two lieutenants rode in off a hunt about four o'clock and reported seeing Indians coming in from every direction, all of them wearing their war-paint.

King said: 'There's not much we can do. The best place we have to stand them off is right here in the house. I hope we've got enough ammunition to last.'

'If we play out,' George said, 'we'll just have to take to the third floor of the house and fight them off with clubs.'

'That's an idea,' said Kenny. He turned to the doctor. 'Doc,' he said, 'you could be carrying the sticks of wood up to the third floor, just in case we have to use it.'

While the rest loaded guns and made plans about where each should be stationed during the raid, the doctor labored and sweated, packing wood up the stairs and piling the sticks near the door where they would be handy to grab up as clubs. When he thought he had enough piled up, King came up and had him move it.

'We're all right-handed,' he pointed out, 'and only a left-handed man could get that wood where you've piled it without exposing himself!'

By supper, the house was ready for the siege. Every man

knew his job and place. The doctor's job was to supply guns and ammunition to anybody who called for it — and tend the wounded!

Just at dark, they heard the whoops and pan-rattlings of the 101 hired hands who'd gathered down by the river and started advancing on the house.

'Get to your stations!' George called and grabbed up a Winchester.

'Don't shoot yet!' Zack called. 'That's old John de Lodge stirring up all this trouble. I'm going to ride down to the river and hold a pow-wow with that old booger. If he won't talk to a friend, I'll shoot him down right there.'

King thought that was a good idea. He said that in the army, he'd noticed that if a leader was killed, it always demoralized the warriors.

Zack slipped out and got on his horse. He rode around the house to face the whooping cowboys and farmhands. He shot into the air a couple of times, then wheeled and spurred back to the house.

'Head for the peach orchard!' he shouted. 'They're too many for us. We'll never stop 'em!'

Doctor Ramsey led the retreat, running in his sock-feet; the Negro's tight-fitting shoes had been hurting him so long that he'd taken them off.

Nobody followed the doctor. Some of the boys fired a few rounds toward the river, then, when they could get their breath for laughing at the way that tenderfoot doctor had left out, they put out the lights and all went down to the wine-cellar to catch up on their drinking.

About half an hour later, George thought maybe they ought to go after the doctor. He said the weather was too cold for the poor devil to lie out in the open all night. Kenny said they'd find him behind the first brushpile, but they didn't. The whole bunch went out and combed the orchard and hollered for the doctor. They couldn't stir him out anywhere.

Zack got bothered. The doctor might have run head-on into something and hurt himself, or fallen off a creek bank maybe into deep water. Zack got his horse and rode a wider circle.

There was a corncrib standing about half a mile from the house. It was filled half full of shelled corn. At the back was a little window about eight feet from the ground with a ladder leading up to it from the outside.

Zack rode up to this corncrib and shouted for the doctor again. He heard the corn rattle inside and a scared voice called out: 'Is that you, Zack?'

'It's me,' whispered Zack. 'Come out, but be quiet about it.'

The doctor climbed through the window and down the ladder. 'What happened?' he wanted to know.

'We made it a hell of a slaughter,' Zack said. 'Then the Indians called for a truce till daylight so they could bury their dead. They just a minute ago dragged off the last one of the thirty that we laid out.'

The doctor's feet were all cut up from his hard run across the peach orchard. Zack's horse wouldn't pack double; so he got down and let the doctor ride back to the house.

They took him down into the wine-room for a drink. George explained that every one of them there would die at sunup unless they got help. By sunup, George said, they'd be ringed by thousands of Indians.

Zack thought that the doctor really ought to write his wife a last letter. He said Harry Kendall, the houseman, would get it through. He said Harry had been of service to one of the Caw chiefs one time and was held sort of sacred by the tribe. He said they were sending Harry out in a desperate hope that he could get help from the militia and he'd be glad to take the letter and mail it.

Faced with sure death, the doctor bravely composed his letter, with plenty of assistance. He told his wife his predicament, how he was surrounded by thousands of blood-thirsty Indians, accused of a crime of which he was innocent, but that he had no way of proving his innocence. He told her how to handle the property, that he still loved her, and that these were his last words to her unless a miracle occurred.

When he addressed and sealed the envelope, there were tears in his eyes. George handed him a tall glass of whiskey as a brave-maker.

The doctor took the whiskey and looked around him. 'How can you men drink and joke in the very face of death?' he demanded.

'If there ever was a time for a man to eat, drink and be merry,' Zack said, 'it's right in the face of death. Drink your whiskey, Doctor!'

The doctor drank it.

Harry Kendall went out and actually mailed the doctor's letter.

With plenty of drinks making the rounds, the bunch was able to keep up the death watch till about four o'clock in the morning, when George suddenly had an idea.

'I just thought,' he told them. 'Why don't we hitch up

the coach and make a run for it with the doctor. We just might manage to make it through while it's still dark.'

Everybody thought that was a good idea. Zack said they'd better send three good men to the south side of the river to locate and kill off any Indian scouts hanging around. If these men could do that, there was a pretty good chance of their getting through.

The three men rode off to stalk down and cut the throats of the Indian scouts while the rest hitched four fast horses to the coach. Then they poured the barefooted doctor into the coach, gave him a quart of whiskey to work on, and pulled out.

Bert Klein handled the ribbons. He put the horses into the river ford at a hard run, knocking the water high and nearly drowning those inside the coach. The boys they'd sent ahead to kill off the Indian scouts heard the commotion and rode down to ambush the stage as Bert loose-herded the wild-running team up the far bank. The ambush bunch whooped and yelled. They took fine beads on the stars and burnt up a lot of good ammunition. But they couldn't stop that stage. Not with Bert Klein up there in the driver's seat, shouting at the lunging team and bathing their rumps with the loose end of a rein. Bert Klein brought those four coach horses up out of the river with every one of them running like scared jackrabbits.

He kept them at that pace for the next couple of miles. And if he missed a rock or log or deep rut anywhere along the road, nobody ever knew when. The doctor came close to knocking his front teeth out with his whiskey bottle, just trying to take a brave-making drink.

They barely escaped with their lives, but they made it.

They put the doctor on a train and told him to keep out of sight till the train pulled out. George got on a telephone and called Fred Bard, an Associated Press man at Guthrie, giving him all the particulars of the Indian raid; then they all hit for the ranch. They'd worked so hard and stayed up so much at night keeping the doctor scared out of his pants that the whole bunch was worn out and dead for sleep.

Fred Bard caught the train at Guthrie and hunted up Doctor Ramsey to get his version of the big Indian raid on the 101. The doctor gave him plenty of colorful side-lights. Bard went to work, and by the time he stepped off the train at Oklahoma City, he had a story that made all the leading papers in Kansas and Oklahoma before the doctor could get out of the country. Some friend of the doctor's read the story in the *Kansas City Star* and put the tenderfoot wise to the whizzer the 101 outfit had run on him. So when he reached Pittsburgh, Doctor Ramsey sent a wire to Zack:

HOPE SOME DAY YOU COME TO PITTSBURGH STOP WILL TRY TO HAVE YOU THROWN UNDER A STREET-CAR

But the doctor held no grudges. He shipped to the 101 a couple of barrels of sauerkraut. Packed in each barrel was a case of good whiskey. He'd packed it that way because he knew it was against the law to send whiskey to an Indian Reservation.

14

RODEO

In 1900, 'rodeo' was still a Spanish word and little known among cowhands. But here and yonder about the country, cowboy roping and riding contests were cropping up. These were the forerunners of present-day rodeos and were strictly amateur. However, barring a few rules and regulations that have come along as the sport grew into big business, the general idea was the same. It was a get-together for cowhands wanting a chance to demonstrate their roping and riding skill. They'd pool their entrance fees and make up purses that went to the winning contestants. Any man was welcome to try his luck.

The 101 got into the habit of entering men in these contests. Like all other cow outfits, they felt it was a feather in their caps to have top-notch ropers and riders on their payroll. Will Rogers and Tom Mix were only two of them.

There was Kurt Reynolds, whom old White Deer had saved from ptomaine poisoning. Kurt was an all-round cowhand, able to keep a hot seat on a salty bronc or pick up a running steer's heel with less effort than it'd take most men to rope a fencepost.

There was Johnny Brewer. Johnny was a bronc-buster. The 101 had hired him off a little wild west show called 'Buckskin Bill' that showed in Ponca City in 1900. It was common knowledge that Johnny Brewer couldn't wad up a rope and throw it into a well; but when it came to staying with a bad horse, Johnny had a lot in common with a cockleburr — he stuck.

Jim Hopkins was the Number One rope hand. There were men who swore Jim Hopkins could do anything with a rope except picture-drawing. Dog-drunk one day at Wichita, Kansas, Jim Hopkins won a five-hundred-dollar steer-roping bet for the 101, using a 'Johnny Blocker loop,' a small loop that a man swung up over his head and gave a quick wrist-twist before he pitched it out. Johnny never had tried that cast before, but he laid it around that steer's horns like he was an old hand at it. And with Zack threatening to shoot him out of the saddle for taking such a risk.

In his day, Zack's seen Ellison Carroll and all the other big-time ropers perform; but he still puts Jim Hopkins — drunk or sober — at the top of the heap.

And then there was Bill Pickett. Bill was a Negro, a big-handed, wild-riding South Texas brush-popper that the 101 hired on at Fort Worth one time. Bill could ride and he could rope, but bulldogging was his specialty. Bill laid claim to originating the idea of bulldogging 'bite-'em-lip' fashion, and nobody ever disputed his claim. Mighty few men ever had the nerve to try such a feat.

The way Bill went at it, he piled out of his saddle onto the head of a running steer, sometimes jumping five or six feet to tie on. He'd grab a horn in each hand and twist them till the steer's nose came up. Then he'd reach in and grab the steer's upper lip with his strong white teeth, throw up his hands to show he wasn't holding any more, and fall to one side of the steer, dragging along beside him till the animal went down.

Sometimes Bill would miss getting that tooth-hold.

When he did, he'd just peg his steer by shoving the left horn into the ground, letting him roll, rump-over-head. 'Fair-grounding,' they call it today.

Either way, it made a show to take a man's breath; and either way, it took guts, bull strength, and the same peculiar sense of timing that makes art out of dancing.

Zack never in his life saw a steer try to hook Bill after the Negro let him up. Sometimes Bill would get out in front of the old steer, bellowing and pawing up sand, a cow-brute's way of talking fight. Maybe the steer would talk back at him a little, might even run at him. But all Bill had to do was stand his ground. No steer ever got up the nerve to hit him. At the last minute, the animal would turn aside.

Lon Sealy was with the 101 and he was a good bulldogger. But he never offered to set himself up as a match for Bill Pickett. Zack says that that black-skinned Bill Pickett was the greatest sweat-and-dirt cowhand that ever lived — bar none. He says that when they turned Bill Pickett out, they broke the mold.

There were a lot of good ropers, riders, and bulldoggers on the 101 payroll, and with this hand-picked crew, the 101 got to packing off more purses and honors than is a good idea when an outfit wants to keep the good will of its neighbors. By 1904, places like Wichita, Kansas, and Enid, Oklahoma, were barring the 101 bunch, claiming they were professionals.

They had some grounds on which to base their complaints, all right; Zack knew a good money-making thing when he saw it and he'd been paying all expenses for the hands on these trips and splitting fifty-fifty with them on the take.

That was the year that Frank Greer, publisher of the *Guthrie Leader* at Guthrie, Oklahoma, took Joe Miller to Atlantic City to attend the National Editors' Association convention there.

On the train-ride up, Frank got to thinking. 'You know, Joe,' he said, 'it would be a great thing for Oklahoma if we could get the editors' convention here next year. But I don't see how it could be done. We've got nothing to offer in the way of entertainment.'

'The hell we haven't!' contradicted Joe, and he started telling Greer about the 101 ropers and riders who'd won all contests till they'd just about worn out their welcome. 'Let me get a hundred good cowhands together, and I'll put you on a show the like of which your editors never saw. I'll give them something to write about.'

It was an idea, and Frank Greer carried it with him to the convention. And when the time came for locating the 1905 convention, Frank Greer made a bid for it. He called on Joe to tell them why Guthrie was the place.

Joe wasn't backward; he told them. He told them about Jim Hopkins's roping. He told them about Johnny Brewer's riding and Bill Pickett's bulldogging. He told them they'd all been to cities in the past, but here was a chance to see what it was like out on the prairie country. Something new.

'Out at the ranch,' he said, 'we won't have hotel accommodations; but if you can make out with sleepers on the trains from Guthrie, we'll manage to give you one full day's entertainment on the 101.'

Guthrie got the 1905 convention of the National Editors' Association.

The editors did a good job of publicizing that convention and the railroad outfit offered special rates. And for the 101's day of entertainment, sixty-four thousand people showed up on the Salt Fork. How many more made it to Guthrie and never got to the ranch, nobody ever knew. Thirty-five special trains couldn't haul the crowds, with passengers riding the tops of the coaches. People overran the 101. There were camps strung out up and down the Salt Fork for four miles. The Millers had wagons hauling water from a seep-spring pond to water the crowd, and before the day was over, that pond was dry and the wagons were having to haul from a second one. The 101 had built a grandstand a mile and a quarter long, but it wouldn't hold the crowd.

Main feature for the morning entertainment was the shooting of a buffalo by old Geronimo.

Geronimo was the bandy-legged little Apache Indian chief who for years had outwitted armies of both the United States and Mexico in a last-stand fight against civilization, murdering and pillaging on both sides of the border. He was old and wrinkled now and a prisoner of war at Fort Sill, and it was Joe Miller's idea to let people see him kill his one last buffalo before he died. The meat, Joe planned to feed to the newspaper editors.

It had taken some finagling to get old Geronimo off the Fort Sill Reservation. And by the time Lute Stover, a Kansas friend of Joe's, had pulled the right political strings to get permission from the Secretary of State, the humane societies had reared up on their hind legs, pawing the air and howling.

News of the buffalo killing had reached back East, and

the story had grown some with telling. The Millers had bought three buffalo from Colonel Charles Goodnight and they'd meant to kill only one of them. But the newspapers had it that the 101 was butchering a hundred head, aiming to turn loose a band of savage Indians who would kill off the herd in one last grand bow-and-arrow hunt. They made a big bloody slaughter out of it, and the humane societies were crying to the skies.

Dan Beard, a big writer and outdoor man, got hold of the yarn in that form and wired Joe, wanting to know if he really meant to let the Indians kill off all the buffalo in Oklahoma.

Joe started to write Beard and tell him the straight of it, then held off. He'd been trying to get the Adjutant General of Oklahoma to send out a couple of soldier companies to handle the crowds, at the expense of the 101; but he'd been refused. He thought he saw now how to get the militia a lot cheaper. He let Beard's telegram ride; and the deal worked out as he'd hoped.

Getting no reply to his wire, Beard telegraphed Teddy Roosevelt, asking him to stop the slaughter. The President had already been hounded by the humane societies; now he wired the Governor of Oklahoma, ordering him to send out three companies of the state militia to the 101.

So, without its costing him a cent, Joe got his troops to handle the crowd. They stayed to help the spectators drink up a full carload of soda-pop and then watch old Geronimo shoot his last buffalo.

The grim old Geronimo made his last kill with a .30–.30 Winchester, shooting from the high seat of a White Steamer automobile that belonged to Doctor Harold E. Thomas, of

Chicago. Maybe the eyes of the old Apache warrior had
grown dim with age or maybe he was bothered by the
plug hat that Lute Stover put on his head for a picture he
took and labeled 'East Meets West.' It might even have
been the sun glitter on the hundred or so pounds of brass
the White Steamer sported along with its monstrous car-
riage lamps. Anyhow, when they drove the old Apache
out into the pasture where the buffalo grazed, he botched a
standing shot. His bullet took the bull too high in the
neck and a cowhand by the name of Stack Lee had to
finish the job.

Twenty years before, it would have been no stunt at all
for that old Apache to have killed a white man at twice the
distance, hanging to the off-side of a running horse and
shooting from under the animal's neck.

The newspaper editors ate the buffalo for dinner and that
afternoon witnessed the hair-curling stunts performed by
dare-devil cowhands showing off just for the hell of the
thing.

The last act of the show was unannounced and plenty
dramatic. It came just at sundown. Ten covered wagons
drove in from the west as if they were coming late to the
show. The leader pulled them into a circle on a slope about
half a mile from the show grounds; the drivers unhooked
their teams and pitched camp.

They had their mules tied up and campfires going when
here came three hundred whooping Indians in full war-
paint — riding wild. Screeching and yelling for the kill,
they piled off down a long slant with their horses' feet hammering out a low thunder on the sod. They fell on the
encampment, circled it, shooting off guns loaded with

blanks, some of them quitting their horses to lock in a death struggle with the wagon men.

The crowd watching the massacre didn't know whether to faint or go blind. This might just be a part of the show, and then again, it might not. Nobody had said.

Up at the wagons, the mules had broken loose and were stampeding toward the show ground. One wagon started burning, then another.

The audience stared, wild-eyed, mouths hanging open. A woman broke under the strain. She stood up and screamed. Her shrill voice cut the silence like a sharp knife, and before she was through, she was getting help from all around.

Just before a general stampede started, the murdering Indians mounted and left out. And from behind the same hill, six hundred mounted cowboys and Indians came riding into the arena for the Grand Finale.

The newspaper editors had plenty to write about when they left the 101. Joe claimed that from the looks on the faces of some of that crowd, he'd bet the laundry business was good for the next few days.

In February, before the 101 put on the big show for the editors' convention, Zack ran into a man named Gue in a Pullman coach out of Kansas City. Gue was manager of the horse fair staged at Madison Square Garden every year. He said he wanted to know where he could get hold of some cowhands to put on some exhibition roping and riding. He thought a little such entertainment on the side might draw crowds enough to make the horse fair a paying proposition. It hadn't been for years.

Zack guessed the 101 had what Gue was looking for. He told about some of the outfit's ropers and riders and what they could do. When he got to talking about Bill Pickett and the way he bulldogged a steer, Gue said that was a lie. He said there wasn't a man alive could throw a steer with his teeth.

Zack told Gue that he was just talking through his hat, that there wasn't a steer alive that Bill Pickett couldn't throw with his teeth. He offered to back his talk with good money, in case Gue had a little cash he wanted to slough off. Gue didn't, but right away he got interested in having the 101 outfit exhibit their wild west skill at the horse fair. He wanted to know what it'd take to get them.

Zack didn't know. He thought about it a little. 'Tell you what,' he said, 'we'll come — for a good time and our expenses.'

That looked like a good offer to Gue; he agreed.

Will Rogers was one of the 101 bunch that went to Madison Square Garden that year. Will wasn't a regular 101 hand; he never was on the payroll. But for the last four or five years, he'd been coming down to prowl the Salt Fork range. He'd put up with the 101 outfit awhile, doing more cow work in a week than some riders would in a month, and never take a cent of pay for it. Then he'd maybe drift over to the Mulhall range or throw in with some other cow outfit for a while. Just prowling, for the sake of prowling, like he kept right on doing till the time of the plane smash-up in Alaska that killed him and Wiley Post.

Back in 1901, Will and Zack had taken in the Buffalo Bill road show at Guthrie, Oklahoma, together, and Will had sure got excited at a rope-twirling act put on by a Mexican trick roper called Oro Paso. Will had to stay and see a second performance before he was satisfied. On the ride back to the ranch he said to Zack: 'In a year from now I'll be doing anything that Mexican did — or wear out every well-rope them Ponca Indians have on the Reservation.'

He went right to work, too, and kept his word. He tried out every kind of rope made — rawhide, maguey, hemp — learning which one worked best for the rope trick he wanted to pull off. There on the 101, he used the little Negro Henry Clay to help him with his practice. He'd have Henry come past him riding hell-bent on a fast horse, and Will would set his loops to whirling and try to pick up whatever foot Henry called out.

By the time he went to Madison Square Garden, Will could make his spinning trick ropes do just about anything but talk.

Tom Mix was in that bunch, too. Tom was shoving drinks across the mahogany in an Oklahoma City bar when Zack blew into town for a cowman's convention in 1902 and ran onto him. They got into a conversation and Tom let it be known that he would admire to be a cowhand.

Zack sized him up. The 101 was on the lookout for some handsome, easy-talking gent to wrangle tenderfeet on the 101 dude ranch. Tom just about filled the bill. A mixture of French-Canadian and Italian blood had given him a fine tall figure and good looks; he wasn't shy around a stranger. All he needed was to learn how to ride and rope a little.

Zack kept him in mind and in 1904 the 101 signed him

on. Tom had been saving up bar tips and wages, and he landed at the ranch with a hundred dollars in his pockets. With this, he had Zack order him a good saddle and a bed-roll. Some of the hands had to saddle for Tom the first time or two, but after that, he was fast to catch on. In a little while, he could handle a horse or rope well enough to fool any dude.

And that was Tom's main job, anyhow, peddling loads to the pilgrims, betting them windies about the ranch, its wild and bloody history, and that sort of thing. And at that, Tom was an artist. To hear Tom tell it, he had won the Boer War single-handed after serving for years as a Texas Ranger. Zack says Tom could color a story redder than a Navajo blanket. He told his scary tales so often that he finally got to believing them himself, Zack says. Especially the one about his being half Indian.

At Madison Square Garden, Tom was prettied up in fancy cowboy garments and saddle rigging, mostly just to be looked at. Zack says Tom never did get to be much of a cowhand, as good cowhands go; but when it came to looking the part, Tom was all there.

When the cowhands pulled into New York, Gue tried to do right by them. He quartered the outfit in a big swank Fifth Avenue hotel. But they didn't stay there long. They hit town early one morning and had breakfast sent up to their rooms; but when dinner time came and they headed for the dining-room to put on the feed bags, everybody was in his shirt-sleeves. A waiter in a claw-hammer coat stopped them at the door. He told them they'd have to be rigged out in coats to get in.

That made Zack as mad as it did the rest of the boys.

He got the hotel manager on the telephone and really rode him bug-hunting. 'Why,' he told the man, 'me'n' the boys had rather eat in a stable than dress up like show monkeys for a chance to eat in that damned dining-room of yours.'

The manager called Gue. Gue came rushing down to straighten out the trouble. Zack and the boys voted to change quarters. They wanted a place where a man ate because he was hungry, and not just because he wanted to put on the dog. Gue moved them down to the Putnam House nearer the Garden. The management turned the hotel over to the 101.

This was more to the cowhands' liking. Here, they could holler if they felt like hollering; and some did after a few rounds of champagne. The boys worked out a system with the bellhops so that all they had to do to get the brand of drink they wanted was to buzz a bell so many times.

There wasn't much of a crowd on the opening night. But the few that did come saw a show there's never been a repeat on. It wasn't a scheduled show, but that didn't keep it from being a top-notch thriller.

Bill Pickett had his horse backed up on one side of the chute, fixing to do his bulldogging act. Will Rogers was on the other side; he was to do Pickett's hazing. Inside the chute was a big old cactus boomer steer with the map of Texas written all over him.

Bill Pickett quieted down the horse he rode and gave the chute man the nod. The gates jerked apart, and out into the arena lunged Bill's steer.

Best anybody could tell, there was just one thing on that old steer's mind when he quit the chute. That was to head back for the Lone Star State. If he had to climb out over the grandstand, that was all right, too — he'd likely climbed steeper ridges in his time. That old steer had him a big bellyful of New York's bright lights; he was gone to Texas!

He had the jump on Bill Pickett's horse from the time he quit the chute. He set a straight course across the arena and held it, running like a scared wolf. Bill Pickett's horse wasn't able to catch him.

They tore across the arena, fogging the dust. The steer came to the arena gate and never checked. From where Zack sat on his horse, it looked like that old longhorn just sprouted wings and flew. His hind feet knocked the top boards off the high gate, but that didn't slow him. Before him was an aisle of steps leading up into the first balcony of the grandstand, a trail that was a lot more open than the *senderos* he was used to following through the huisache thickets along the Nueces River. He took out up it, making four steps at a jump, wringing his tail and roaring as he went.

But he hadn't made his get-away yet. Right behind him, Bill had jumped his horse through the hole in the gate and was feeding the spurs to him up that row of steps. Bill had set out to bulldog that steer for the crowd and he aimed to do it if that old *ladino* climbed to the moon first. The big Negro was yelling like a man gone mad.

And popping the boards right on the heels of Bill Pickett's horse rode Will Rogers. Will was a little far behind for good hazing, but he wasn't one to quit a man in a tight. He'd reached down his catch-rope and was shaking out a loop.

The crowd was on its feet now, screaming and falling

away from both sides of that wild uphill chase. The climbing steer blared like a trumpet. And down at the arena, the announcer, fearing a human stampede, lied like a dirty dog.

'Keep your seats, folks!' he bawled at the top of his voice. 'Keep your seats! Don't get panicky! There's not the slightest danger!'

They caught the runaway steer on the third balcony of the grandstand. Will Rogers crowded his scrambling horse up beside Bill Pickett's, reached down and picked up the steer's heels with his loop. At the same instant the big Negro quit his saddle, piling off onto the steer's head.

The crowd watched Bill Pickett hang to that steer's horns while Will Rogers dragged him, bumping and scrambling and bawling, down out of the stands into the arena where he belonged. And not a one of the spectators had the slightest idea then that what they'd just witnessed was the ruination of a promising young lawyer's career.

But, according to Zack, that's just what it was. Zack said Will Rogers came to him after the show that night and confessed. Will claimed he'd always planned to make a lawyer out of himself; but after that stunt, he was ruined. He'd be damned, he said, if he could stand around arguing a case in court when there was excitement like that bulldogging to be had in this world.

The show ran the rest of the week. No more steers were bulldogged up in the grandstand, but that didn't matter. The newspapers had got hold of that first night's performance and played it up big. From then on, every night, they packed the crowd in like sardines. That Bill Pickett bulldogging act was a scalp-shifting sight.

Every night the same girls came to Box 23. They were a handsome bunch and talkative, and Zack and Tom Mix took to shining up to them between acts. One night the girls got to hurrahing Zack about not riding any of the bad horses. Up to now, all Zack had been doing was snub up, for saddling and mounting, the pitching horses that the busters rode. But the girls, they said they wanted to see Zack ride. They said they didn't think he had the nerve to ride the bad ones, especially that old Bawling Mare.

Zack took it as long as he could, then told Tom Mix to snub up Bawling Mare; that he'd show these girls what real bronc-twisting was like.

Mix snubbed for Zack, all right. But he knew Zack could scratch out Bawling Mare without much trouble; so to keep him from looking too good to the girls, Tom turned old Bawling Mare loose before Zack got his right stirrup.

Bawling Mare swallowed her head and went after it, grunting and groaning and bawling. Zack stayed for five jumps, then went straight up without even leaving a spur track in the saddle to show he'd been there. He took a buster when he hit the ground and, according to the story Tom Mix told the girls, Zack had been thrown so high that a couple of bluebirds built a nest in his pocket before he landed.

This tickled the girls and they rode Zack pretty hard about the brags he'd made before mounting Bawling Mare. Then one of the girls called Tom Mix over and lifted one eyebrow. 'Can you ride that mare, Mr. Mix?'

Mix wasn't much of a rider yet, but bad as old Bawling Mare looked and sounded, anybody on to the mare's tricks could ride her if he got set in the saddle first. Mix agreed to show them how it was done.

Tom didn't trust Zack to snub for him. He called on a breed trick-rider, George Hooker. But Zack gave George the wink and George cut Tom's latigo strap nearly in two so that Tom didn't last two jumps before Bawling Mare made a windmill out of him and his saddle.

Zack says that in trying to outshine each other before those girls that night, he and Tom Mix took some mighty hard falls for nothing ever to come of it.

Between exhibitions, the 101 bunch took in the town. Nights, after the shows, they'd all booze up and get Gue to hire them an automobile and they'd ride it up and down the streets, whooping and yelling like prairie wolves at a kill. If it was a wet night and the pavement slick, they'd come helling it down a street till they found a broad place and then, without checking speed, they'd whip the car around just to see how long it would spin on the pavement before lining out again. They took in all the leg shows, drank everything in sight, and prized up hell in general whenever the notion struck them. New Yorkers thought they were the wildest and wooliest outfit ever to hit the Big City, and the chances are the New Yorkers were right.

It was while they were showing in New York that time that Zack loaded up his first and last time on Scotch whiskey. He blacked out on it a little before the start of the morning parade through town and when he finally came to, he found himself horseback, but he didn't know why nor where.

He managed to recognize Will Rogers riding beside him. 'Where in the hell are we, Will?' he roared.

'Shut up, you damned fool!' Will told him. 'We're right out in the big middle of the show!'

Before that performance was over, Zack was green around the gills and hanging to his saddlehorn with both hands to stay on. That Scotch had him sick as a poisoned pup. He swore right there he'd never take another drink of the stuff and he hasn't. Not Scotch.

Out at the Garden, the management had a rule that none of the boys were to take liquor into their dressing-rooms. Will Rogers may not have been the only cowhand to break this rule, but he was the only one to get caught. Will thought how nice it'd be to have a drink of beer on hand when he came up to his room to dress; so he pulled off his leather chaps and Zack helped him tie one leg shut with a string.

They sacked up five quart bottles of beer and Will slung the chaps over his shoulder and started to his room. On the way up the stairs, he met one of the Garden managers. About the same time the string broke, letting all five quarts fall out. They bounced and clattered to the bottom of the stairs, dropped on the concrete floor, and broke.

The manager turned a hard look on Will, but the re-formed lawyer was equal to the occasion. He scratched his head, stared at the beer with a puzzled look on his face, then grinned the sheepish grin that later was to be known all over the world.

'Now, wasn't that a hell of a dirty trick somebody pulled?' he said. 'Putting all that beer in my chaps?'

And he got by with it, of course. Jim Hopkins was willing to bet Will could have grinned his way out of a murder if he'd been the kind to commit one.

Will did some of his trick-roping acts in the Garden and they attracted attention. One night a Doctor Woodend took Will and Zack to Shanley's on Sixty-Sixth Street. The doctor made them acquainted with the manager and told him that Will was the greatest rope manipulator in the world. He talked Shanley into letting Will put on his act there that night. Shanley was willing to give the cowboy a try; he told Will to call up the boys and have them bring his ropes.

The boys brought them. Shanley left Will backstage and went to announce him. The orchestra gave him the come-on. Will picked up his ropes, and for the first time in his life stepped out alone to face an audience.

He was sure a scared cowhand that night. But shaky as he was, his ropes came alive in his hands, spinning and rolling, licking out this way and darting that. He did the double-barrel roll with his whirling loop. He started a big one and brought it up over his head and let it spin down around him, then brought it over his head again. He jumped in and out of his spinning loops, danced around them, all the time gnawing savagely at a nickel's worth of chewing gum bulging his jaw.

A few times he got too shaky and fouled his loops around his spurs or ears. That'd nearly kill his soul. But the shamefaced grin he'd use as a cover-up was as good a show to the crowd as the rope tricks he pulled. They ate up his act. They kept him at it till he'd gone through his entire routine. And when he finally staggered off the stage, cold sweat running clear down into his boots, he got a bigger hand than the twenty-six dancing girls that had just finished kicking up bare legs to show what kind of lace was sewed to their drawers.

When the show closed and the 101 outfit pulled out for

home, they left Will Rogers in New York. He was still spinning his ropes and working hard to keep his teeth from rattling out of his head every time he stepped out on the stage.

Gue came to Zack while the outfit was loading the 101 livestock for the return trip. Gue said he wasn't satisfied to hold the 101 to their first agreement, to show for expenses and entertainment. He said they'd made money out of the horse fair for the first time in years. Big money, he said. And he thought the boys ought to get a cut out of it.

'Let it ride,' Zack told him. 'The boys have all had their money's worth. They're satisfied.'

But Gue wasn't. As a farewell gesture, he ordered a special car to Chicago for the bunch to ride in and made arrangements for them to have anything they wanted in the way of food and drink.

Zack said there were some big whiskey heads in the outfit by the time those cowhands landed back in Oklahoma.

15

BIG TIME

IT WAS Lewis Schauss, manager of Convention Hall in Kansas City, who started the 101 bunch to commercializing on their dare-devil show. Up to now, all the ropers and riders had been after was a rip-roaring time and a chance at a contest purse now and then. Nobody had thought anything about putting the thing on a money-making basis.

But in 1906, Zack and some of the boys put on a bronc-busting exhibition at Enid, Oklahoma, and when they came back to the ranch, there was Schauss, waiting for them. Schauss said he'd come down for a quail hunt and to see if he couldn't get them to put on a show at Convention Hall following the coming November horse show. He said he thought he could make it worth their time.

The hands were agreeable. If they could keep right on having a big high-heeled time at a sport they loved and make money, to boot, they had no row to raise. So that fall they pulled out for Kansas City with about seventy-five riders and ropers and several carloads of livestock.

They landed there with no billboards or newspaper advertising. Zack had never heard of a press agent. But the show clicked from the start and the *Kansas City Journal* gave them more publicity than they could have bought with good money. The show was a natural, the *Journal* said, because there was no attempt at a grandstand showmanship made. The ropers and riders just went through their paces the way they would have done if they'd been out on the open range.

A front-page story or two like that had the show selling out every day before opening time.

During the third night's performance, a boy found Zack backstage and handed him a note. The note read: 'Will you kindly call on us at the Midland Hotel at your convenience tonight after the show?' It was signed 'Rex and Cathgart.'

Zack was new in the show business; he didn't know Rex and Cathgart from a couple of dry land terrapins. He sent the boy back to the Midland to see what these birds had on their minds. They might be trying to peddle the Brooklyn Bridge, for all Zack knew.

In a little bit the messenger came back. 'They want to make a trade with you to put on this show in Virginia,' the boy said. 'At some kind of exposition.'

Zack caught a cab to the Midland. Rex and Cathgart, he learned, were big-time show promoters. They had charge of the show billing at the Jamestown Exposition the next year. They said they had a Pocahontas pageant scheduled for that show and they weren't satisfied with it; they wondered if the Millers would be interested in showing in its place.

'We'll want it for a hundred days,' Rex said. 'What will you take per day to put your show on, two shows a day and no Sunday show?'

This was new stuff to Zack and coming a little fast. But he was G. W. Miller's son; win, lose, or draw, he'd try to make a deal any time it had a money smell to it. He made some quick calculations. Best he could figure, it would take something like nine hundred dollars a day to handle the performers, the horses, and the feed.

'If you'll furnish everything — bedding, corrals, sleeping quarters under the grandstand for the performers — I'll put it on for seventeen hundred and fifty a day.'

The promoters talked over the proposition a little, then said they were ready to sign a contract. Zack held off. He thought he had a good deal made, but this show business was 'way off his home range and he'd just as soon his brother Joe looked into it first.

'We Millers,' he said, 'do business together — one for all and all for one. My brother Joe'll be in town tomorrow. I'll wait on him.'

Joe came to Kansas City the next day. He studied the proposition a little and agreed to sign.

When Schauss heard about the contract, he hunted Joe up. 'Look, Joe,' he said, 'I'll get in touch with Spaulding, manager of the Chicago Coliseum. Before you take on the Jamestown Exposition next spring, you just as well go by the Coliseum and show there.'

Spaulding wrote that the 101 could get the Coliseum for four hundred dollars a day or twenty per cent of the gross intake. The Coliseum, he said, would furnish lights and prepare the building.

Joe and Zack made a grab for the twenty per cent deal. They weren't right sure yet what they were getting into and they figured it best to play the thing safe till they got their feet on the ground.

The next spring they shipped out without rehearsing any of the show. They pulled into Chicago on a Saturday morning and unloaded at eleven o'clock. It took them till nearly night, then, putting their buffalo and wild cattle inside the Coliseum Building. Those old cattle fought it every step of the way; they'd come off an open country, and entering a building was a boogery proposition to them.

When the job was finally completed, Zack said to Joe: 'Now, we better put this outfit through its paces and get everybody lined up on what to do at such things as the Grand Entry and the horseback quadrille.'

It looked simple, but it wasn't. Since their showing in Kansas City, the Millers had hired on some show hands out of the old Buffalo Bill show. Among them were California Frank Hefley, Mamie Frances, Winona and George Hooker. These all had more ideas than a pet pup has fleas about how things ought to go in the show. They kept interrupting the rehearsal, running up to tell Zack that such-and-such wasn't done the way they'd done it on the Buffalo Bill show.

Zack's sand began to warm up, then Frank Hefley came up. 'Let me take charge,' Frank said. 'I'll take it from start to finish and show you how it was done on the Buffalo Bill show!'

Zack's temper stood him up in his stirrups. 'The next goddamned man, woman, or child that mentions the Buffalo Bill show,' he bawled, 'is going to get throwed out the back gate!'

That stopped the sluice of free advice, but it didn't help to keep the rehearsal going. The Buffalo Bill bunch sulked and didn't try to help and the rest of the hands were greeners and didn't know what to do. Again and again, Zack lined the performers up and put them through the drill. The Grand Entry looked like a sloppy funeral march. The quadrille got some of the performers so confused and tangled up that Zack looked to have to cut them free with a knife. He called the rehearsal off for supper.

'But we're trying it again right after we eat,' he warned.

Spaulding and Joe had watched the procedure. The two of them took supper together. Spaulding was looking down a long nose.

'Joe,' he said, 'it'll never click.'

Joe felt the same way about it. But Zack was still mad and he claimed he'd put the thing across if he had to drill the outfit all night.

He just about did it, too. But when he finally called it off, the performers still acted like all their folks had died. Zack felt like he ought to cut the throats of the whole outfit and head back for Oklahoma afoot.

Just what happened when they opened for the first afternoon performance, nobody but a showman could understand. Maybe it was due to the fact that the performers were all rigged out in their best bibs and tuckers. Maybe the sight of the audience waiting to see what they could do had some bearing on it. Maybe that wild, ripping yell that George Hooker cut loose with put the right spirit into it. That big yellow-skinned half Negro, half Mexican had a holler that could split an eardrum two city blocks away; and Hooker was always plenty willing to give it out.

Maybe all these things together or none of them was responsible. The thing is, from somewhere, the outfit got a big load of the spirit that sets a show off on the right foot and keeps it moving.

At top speed, they went through their acts without a falter. Johnny Stewart mounted a bad pitching horse without the help of a snubber. He just made a run, went up in the saddle, raked the bucker from shoulder to flank for a piece, then hopped off to run in front of him, waving his hat and hollering.

The Indian riders, stripped to breech-clouts, were all over and under their racing ponies, sometimes clinging to nothing but the flank hairs, it looked like.

The ropers were on, heeling and heading, throwing down and tying tough old outlaw steers with all the speed and grace of a dancer whirling on her toes.

And when old Bill Pickett tied onto a runaway steer's nose with his teeth and busted him against the ground, the crowd reared up on its hind legs screaming. Right down to the last puff of dust kicked up in the arena, that show was wilder than a wolf. Zack thought the spectators would yell the roof off.

Spaulding came running up to slap Zack on the back when it was over. 'My god!' he boomed. 'The world never saw anything like that before. Half a dozen times if I'd shut my mouth, I'd have bitten off the end of my heart!'

The crowd for that first afternoon showing hadn't been a big one. But by the time of the night performance, the news had got around, and every seat was taken. Next morning, the newspapers were playing the show up. Joe got the idea of putting on a special show for newspapermen. It went over with the press men. From then on till the show was closed, the Millers had close to a full house at every performance without ever bothering to advertise.

When the show left Chicago at the end of a week's showing, the Millers had thirty thousand dollars to the good, after paying expenses. But Zack, the bushwhacker, wasn't satisfied.

'Where we played hell,' Zack told Joe, 'was in agreeing to pay the Coliseum bunch twenty per cent of the take when we could have got it for four hundred a day.'

The show's main drawing card for little kids on this trip was Teddy, a pet bear cub Zack had raised on condensed milk. Zack had Teddy trained to sit up on the radiator of his car in parades, where he'd wave his paws in the air and grin at the youngsters. During show times, Teddy was tied outside the building where kids without the money to see the main show could come watch him. He'd sit around and grin at them there and drink his milk out of a pop bottle. If a dog got curious and came up to sniff at him, Teddy would set his bottle of milk down, slap the dog clear into tomorrow, then go back to drinking his milk. The little ones got a big kick out of Teddy.

Women had fashion fads in those days, same as now, and this was the year that every self-respecting young lady went around packing a stuffed teddy bear under one arm. One of these was an actress. Zack's forgotten her name, but she was quality stuff on Chicago's stages in those days. She got a look at Teddy and told herself that here was a chance to be different. She'd just buy Teddy from Zack and pack around a real live bear.

There was a lot of high-chinned pride about this actress. She couldn't afford to come see Zack herself; that was beneath her. She sent around her agent to do the buying. The man felt Zack out about the bear and made an offer — twenty-five or thirty dollars. Zack handed him the laugh.

'I wouldn't sell that bear for five hundred,' he said.

So the man offered Zack five hundred just to see if he was lying. Zack wasn't. But when the buyer went up to a thousand dollars, Zack got to studying. Evidently, this dame was hell-bent to own Teddy; and a thousand dollars isn't chicken feed in anybody's language. When the actress herself came and offered fifteen hundred, Zack couldn't stand the pressure; he went to see Joe.

Joe said hell, no, don't sell that bear! Joe said the little kids got too much fun out of him. He said let that actress dame find her another live bear or be satisfied with a stuffed one. Joe had a soft heart when it came to little kids.

So Zack turned the actress down; but a couple of nights later he'd have sold Teddy to her for four-bits and thrown in the lead chain to sweeten the deal.

On the show were a few Indian children. Somewhere they picked up a whooping-cough germ and it wasn't long till the whole bunch was down with it, whooping and sucking for air like a cow choked on a bone. And Teddy, not to be left out, took it, too. Teddy was sure a sick bear. When it came to whimpering and fretting, he had the baby-world skinned a city block and his whooping was a sound to stop a man in his tracks. During the worst of Teddy's sickness, Zack kept him in his hotel room. Usually, when things got too rough, he could feed Teddy another bottle of Star Brand milk and the cub would quiet down and go off to sleep.

One night Zack played out of Star Brand. He sent for more. But when the bellboy came back, he brought a couple of cans of Borden's. He said he couldn't find any Star Brand.

To Teddy's way of thinking, Borden's milk wasn't worth a damn. He took one taste and then slapped the bottle out of Zack's hand. Zack tried mixing a little water and sugar with it. No go. Teddy fell back on the bed whimpering and fussing like a spoiled kid. In a little while he'd fretted and cried around till he was whooping every breath.

The hotel manager came up, hammering on Zack's door. 'That baby of yours,' he called to Zack, 'is keeping everybody on this floor awake.'

He left before Zack had time to explain that this was a bear cub instead of a baby.

Teddy kept coughing and grunting and whining. The man in the room across the hall from Zack came to kick on the door. 'Why don't you take that baby to a doctor?' he hollered.

Zack didn't bother to explain. He just slung a boot at the door and the man went away.

Zack sent the boy out after more milk. When he came back this time, he was loaded down with Eagle Brand, thick and sweet. But that wasn't what Teddy wanted, either. He'd been raised on Star Brand milk and that's what he wanted and what he aimed to get. He took a taste of Eagle Brand and slapped it away, then fell over in a worse spoiled-brat fit than before. Zack tried a mixture of the two. The way Teddy took on after a taste of that mixture, you'd have thought Zack had tried to poison him.

Zack was just about in the notion of doing it, too, when another knock sounded at the door. He was getting a big bellyful of being told what to do with his baby. With the bear in his arms, he made a run for the door and yanked it open, all set to drive somebody's teeth back down his throat.

It was a motherly looking little old woman, lost in a man's bathrobe and holding a big box of patented salve in her hand.

Likely, she'd brought that salve to rub on the baby's chest; Zack never did know. One look at Zack's face and the bear in his arms satisfied this little old woman that she'd just met a madman. She wheeled with a squawk, caught up the robe and everything under it. Bared to the waist, she took out down the hall at a pace that would have made a fast-running horse look like he was standing still.

Zack didn't know whether to laugh or cry. He went back to the fretting bear, then called the bellboy again.

'Boy,' he told him, 'go get me a can of Star Brand milk if you have to steal it.'

It took the boy about an hour. If he stole the milk, he didn't say. Anyhow, he got it. Zack fixed Teddy up another bottle. The bear drank it down and went right off to sleep and so did everybody else.

While the 101 showed at the Jamestown Exposition, the Ringling Brothers circus outfit bought out Barnum and Bailey, and in merging the two shows, cut loose a lot of good circus men. One of these was Eddie Arlington, general agent for Barnum. Eddie came down to Norfolk and watched the 101 cowhands go through their paces. He thought he saw the makings of a top-notch wild west show in this bunch. He found Joe in his hotel room.

'This is better than the Buffalo Bill show ever hoped to be,' he said. 'Couldn't we get together and put it on the rails?'

Joe didn't know. They had been making good. But the performers still just looked on themselves as Oklahoma cowhands out on a big spree; there was plenty of cow work waiting for them back on the Oklahoma prairies when the fun was done.

'Look,' Arlington said. 'The Lemon Brothers circus is on the rocks and ready to sell out. We can buy their equipment right. I know how to run a show business; you've got a show. Why don't we take a whirl at this on a fifty-fifty basis?'

Joe talked it over with his brothers George and Zack. It looked like a good thing to them. So the Miller Brothers teamed up with Eddie Arlington and became full-feathered show people.

When they wound up at the Exposition, they took their show and circus men and equipment back to the 101 ranch on the Salt Fork to get the program lined out and in motion. Joe had some ideas of his own about what sort of show they should put on.

'There's boys ten years old,' he said, 'who've never seen a genuine wild west show. We're going to make it possible for them to see one.'

With this in mind, Joe planned the program to present as much actual old-time ranch and frontier life as he could pack into it. He filled the big tent with Indians. He had them stage buffalo hunts. He had them put on some of their Indian dances, kill a whiskey peddler, and act out all over again the Pat Hennessy massacre that took place in 1876 at Hennessy, Oklahoma, looting and burning the wagons.

The only man to get away from that Pat Hennessy massacre had been Billy Malaley and they had Billy on hand as lead character. Chief Bull Bear of the Cheyennes was generally given credit for pulling off that big slaughter. Old Chief Bull Bear wasn't admitting anything, but he was willing to lead the Indians in the make-believe kill.

Joe put a bunch of noted Indians on the show. There was old Crooked Nose, a Comanche buck who was an artist when it came to shooting a bow and arrow. There was old Flatiron, a chief of the Ogallala tribe of the Sioux Nation. Flatiron was a big orator among his people; it'd been his war talk that helped to sell the tribes on ganging Custer and his men.

Charlie-Owns-The-Dog, Standing Cloud, and Long Bull — they'd all helped to make 'Custer's Last Stand' a popular piece of art. Charlie-Owns-The-Dog was shirt-tail kin to old Geronimo. Standing Cloud was an old warrior, but one of the fastest foot-runners that ever kicked up the dust.

There were plenty of others, along with their squaws and offspring, not to mention old Swift Deer, who went along as the medicine man for the show Indians.

Among the famous white performers on the show was George Elser, of Hunnewell, Kansas, one of the first trick riders in rodeo history. And Chet Byers, who'd learned trick roping from Will Rogers and is today a champion in his line. Sammy Garret, a California trick roper, came to hold the world championship title for seven different times in his life.

Every act had its champion and there were plenty of acts: roping, riding, bulldogging, stage-coach hold-ups, Mexican raids, and forty-niners whipping up ox teams on the long trail to California. There were over two hundred performers taking part in that first exhibition put on at Ponca City, Oklahoma, April 14, 1908, by the Miller Brothers 101 Wild West Show. The big tent went up at the show lots on Grand Avenue, and Mayor Hutchison declared a legal holiday to give it a running start.

And the show needed it.

There was nothing wrong with the show itself; the Millers were turning it off in grand style. It was the weather that went bad. They were fixing to learn quick that the weather plays a big part in the show business, same as with corn-growing or cow-raising. They hit Holdenville, Oklahoma, next, putting up their canvas and trying to show in mud butt-deep to a giraffe. A good-sized wagon sheet would have covered the crowd that came to see it.

It was the same in the next town and the next. It looked like when they moved, they took the rains along with them. They left Oklahoma and went into Missouri. The story was the same in that state. They landed in Joplin, Missouri, thirty days from that first showing in Ponca City, and they hadn't loaded a dry canvas in the whole round. Thirty days out and thirty thousand dollars in the hole. That's the way they stood with the world when Eddie Arlington hunted up Joe. Eddie was looking plenty sick.

'We're out of cash, Joe,' he said. 'Do we close — or what do you think? I can't raise any more money myself; I'm clean as a whistle.'

Joe said: 'Eddie, all our neighbors prophesied we'd go broke at this show business. Maybe they're right. But I figure this loss is just like a drought at home with cattle. I'm willing to put twenty thousand more into it. Take the show where you think it's best to go, but don't get farther than this twenty thousand will bring it back. Then, if we go under, we'll just mark it off as a bad deal, like maybe two thousand steers had starved out and died. And we'll forget it.'

Eddie looked relieved. 'I believe,' he said, 'that we can

take this show into western Canada and clean up. I'll contract us up through St. Paul, through Wisconsin, and into Canada at Winnipeg.'

They made long jumps and landed in St. Paul in four days. But it was a gloomy bunch of green show people who landed there. More than a month of showing in ankle-deep mud and knowing they were going in the hole had taken the heart out of them. They thought their luck had run out.

Just seeing their horses kick up dust in an arena again helped their feelings some. But that wasn't enough. They needed to make money. And they didn't make it in St. Paul. That is, nothing to brag about. They made expenses and a little better, but what they needed was to make a killing.

Their next billing was at Fergus Falls, Minnesota. They landed there on a Monday morning. When Zack went downtown for breakfast and saw the size of this place, he wanted to go back and kick Eddie Arlington's tail. How come he'd contracted to show in a little one-horse town like this? A man could throw a rock across the business district; Zack couldn't see enough people in town to put out a fire in a shoe box.

A stiff west wind was whooping in off the prairies, kicking up street dust and whirling loose newspapers along the streets. Zack found a hotel restaurant and turned in to eat, but he was too disgusted to do more than piddle around with his bacon and eggs.

Thirty minutes later, he stepped out on the street again and the sight that greeted him was enough to stop a man's heart ticks. As far down each road of the intersection as he could look, Zack could see wagonloads of whites and Indians coming in off the prairies, wagon tongues to end-gates. And siding them on either hand were long strings of horsebackers, traveling in the same direction.

A show had come to town and these prairie farmers aimed to see it!

The sight looked so good that Zack turned right around and went back into the restaurant and ordered a whole new breakfast.

Arlington's father, general lot superintendent, knew the sound of Old Opportunity's knock. Zack claims old man Arlington knew more about the show business than any other man Zack ever knew. Arlington took one look at the crowd jamming the streets of this little prairie town and jumped admission prices from fifty cents to a dollar, adding on another dollar for reserved seats. Side-shows went up from ten cents to two-bits. But even at that, they couldn't possibly seat the crowd that lined up for tickets. Every reserved seat sold. They cleared out the band platform and sold out every chair as a reserved seat. They piled hay in the aisles, and between the seats and the arena net, and stacked people in those places. They had the show laid out with an Indian camp in the background, with five teepees. They pulled down the teepees and let Indian customers come in the back gate. Zack handled that gate and took blankets and furs in place of money when the Indians wanted it that way. He got fifty of the best Indian blankets that day he ever laid hands on, and from then on made a practice of taking furs, hides, and blankets for ad-mission when the Millers showed in Indian country. The show was so jammed they had to pull some of the meanest horses out of the show to keep from tramping the spectators to death.

They took in seven thousand five hundred dollars at the afternoon showing at Fergus Falls, and had a turn-away crowd that night. This was more like it. This way, a man could get his mind off financial worries and keep it on putting out a good show. This way, there was a grin on the face of every performer. The yelling spirit was back inside the cowhands again.

They showed at Calgary on Dominion Day. At Winnipeg, the crowds were so big they had to get the bobbies to straighten out the lines to the ticket windows and keep down trouble. At the end of a four-day performance there, they were out of their thirty-thousand-dollar hole and had twenty thousand to the good. They had the world by the tail and on a downhill pull. Every cowhand in the 101 was convinced of that.

Before the last night's showing, Zack found his brother Joe and Eddie Arlington straightening up the account books in the Miller brothers' private car. Joe was beaming all over; Eddie looked like the cat that had caught the canary.

'We're riding high, Joe,' Eddie crowed. 'Where do we go now?'

'Go?' said Joe. 'Why, hell! Go where you please. Take the thing to Mexico if you feel like it.'

So that's what they did; they took the show to Mexico.

16

VIVA EL TORO

IT WAS DURING THE TIME of trouble between Madero and Porfirio Diaz that the Miller Brothers took their 101 Wild West Show to Mexico City. At the port of entry, an Indian squaw hunting lice off her buck's scalp couldn't have given it a more thorough combing than the customs officers gave the show wagons and equipment. In Nueva Laredo, on the Mexican side of the Rio Grande opposite Laredo, Texas, the officials held up the train a day and a night to see that the Millers weren't hauling in guns and ammunition for the revolution. They prized up the floor boards of the show wagons and looked under them. They opened the ten-gallon lard cans on the cook's wagon and stabbed bayonets into the lard, just to make sure. They all but stripped the eight blonde-haired hootchy-kootchy dancers in their search for implements of war. It was a shakedown that didn't leave a tent fold unexplored.

Agua Caliente was their first watering stand. There, they showed for an afternoon performance and, for the first and only time in the history of the 101 Wild West Show, took in more money at a side-show than they did at the big top.

It was the hootchy-kootchy dance that made the killing. Zack had always been willing to let anything short of stealing go into the show as long as it made money. But Joe was different. Up to now, he'd drawn the line at hootchy-kootchy dances, and the girls wouldn't have been with the outfit this time if the side-show boss hadn't kept pestering till Joe finally gave in for the Mexico trip. But the girls were to get no billing; Joe had put his foot down on that.

In Agua Caliente, however, the girls needed no billing. Whatever it is about a blonde woman that fascinates a Mexican man, those eight girls had. The price was fifty *centavos* to enter the tent and watch the dance and fifty more to see the strip act; but when the rest of the show was over, the tents down and loaded on the cars, there was still a solid stream of Mexicans pouring through the kootchy tent.

The girls had long since been forced to stagger their act, two dancing at a time while the others rested. But at that, they were danced completely off their feet, some crying, they were so tired, when their tent was pulled down at the last minute before the train rolled.

But they had cleaned up. The rest of the show barely made expenses. The take of the hootchy-kootchy girls ran into the thousands.

They unloaded in Mexico City the night before Guadalupe Day and found the city jammed. Tomorrow there was to be a big to-do in honor of Mexico's favorite saint, La Virgen de la Guadalupe. Thousands of worshipers would march up the slant of a high mountain to pay respects to the dead virgin in her last resting-place. Then they would be free to see what excitement the Americans had to offer.

The 101 show made its parade through the city next morning, moving down the Paseo de la Reforma, a parade ground if Zack ever saw one.

It came close to turning into a battle ground that morning, however. The show Indians paraded in their warpaint and stripped down to their breech-clouts, just as they were in the habit of going on the stage. Sight of them was too much for the Mexican *peones*, who even this far down had heard of the bloody deeds of old Geronimo and his Apache warriors along the northern border of Mexico. The *peones* thought the Indians were Apaches and set out to kill them. They attacked with sticks and rocks, screaming in Spanish: 'Down with the Apaches! Kill the murderers! The dogs of dogs! Lizards' bellies!'

They made it too hot for the Indians. The red warriors finally had to quit the parade and high-tail it to the show lot.

Robbed of the Indians for targets, the Mexicans went to work on the rest of the parade. They broke every mirror on the tableau wagons as they rolled past. And by the time the parade was over, the *peones* had found the Indians back on the show lot and it took a regular army of Mexican policemen to keep them from mobbing the red men.

The big tent went up that night — and immediately fell down. Every stake rope had been cut and many of them were gone completely. They got more rope, raised the tent again and put guards on. Zack went to his tent to prepare for his shooting act and discovered that both his Colts' pump rifles were gone. He had given up his hunt when in came the boss hostler.

'My god, the sons-of-bitches are stealing us blind!' the hostler raved. 'There's not a hub tap left on a third of the wagons. How'n the hell can we move a wagon with the taps gone? And where can we get more? There won't be a tap to fit these wagons this side of the States!'

The big man stamped around inside Zack's tent, pawing up sand. A Mexican interpreter the show had hired back at the border came in and listened a while.

'It is nothing,' the interpreter said. 'Tomorrow, we go down to the Laguna and buy them back out of the Thieves' Market.'

And that's where they found them, early the next morning, the wagon taps tied up in three bunches and laid out for sale in a stall of the Thieves' Market. Zack bought them all back for ten or twelve *pesos*. The hostler then hired guards to be put at every wagon and then, when the guards started stealing the taps, he had to hire more guards to watch the first.

Zack's guns he found in a government pawn-shop, held for twenty *pesos*. On top of that, he had to pay a bribe of ten *pesos* because he couldn't furnish the serial numbers to the guns. Zack argued, swore, threatened a killing, but finally paid off and left, mad enough to bite himself.

The President of Mexico came down to the second night performance, bringing along a group of his brother's grandchildren. The grandchildren liked to play with the show clowns. They liked to put the show dogs after the clowns and chase them up tent poles to keep from getting bitten. So the President gave the show his nod of approval and that helped to put it over. At the same time, his approval didn't keep the show out of hot water every time a breach of strange law was committed.

The Millers found, for instance, that a man billed to perform at a certain show must perform, else the show owed the Government fifty *pesos*. There was another fine of fifty *pesos* if the show didn't open the very minute it was scheduled for opening. And if the ticket agent let in one man for whom there was no seat, the show was liable for another fifty *pesos*.

At mealtimes on the show lot, the tents would be ringed by hundreds of hungry Mexican children and old people who waited around for the scraps to be thrown out. The Millers never had to clean off a lot as long as they were in Mexico. Always, there was a mob of these hungry ones who would fall upon anything that resembled food, fighting for it, as savage and desperate as winter-starved wolves.

For a while, the showmen could get no hay for their horses. There was none to be bought. Then they put out the word that they would pay fifty *centavos* for a hundred pounds and were suddenly swamped with hay. For that price, the *peones* would trot all day toward the surrounding mountains where they'd cut wild grass, bundle sixty or seventy pounds of it on their backs, then trot all next day getting back to town with it.

When the *peones* had finally brought more hay than the show outfit could use, they fought each other all over the lot for the chance to sell.

Zack weighed out the hay and paid for it by the pound and it was Muchacho who discovered how some of the *peones* were wrapping their hay around five- and ten-pound boulders to up the weight. Muchacho was a little Mexican stray Zack had picked up in Monterrey and brought to Mexico City in search of his parents. When the parents couldn't be located, Muchacho had come to Zack and said: 'We not find my papa and mama. From now, you my papa.'

Having adopted Zack, Muchacho was proud for a chance

to serve him. From the time he found the first boulder in the hay, the little Mexican stood about, as important as a young rooster in a new hen-yard, making each *peon* open and scatter his bale of hay before it went on the scales.

It was Muchacho, too, who saved Zack's guns for him the second time. One day the lot supervisor heard a loud scream and commotion in Zack's tent and ran inside to investigate. Near the back wall of the tent squatted the ten-year-old Muchacho with a murderous knife clutched in his hand. The long blade of the knife was run through a hand, pinning it to the ground, while the pilfering *peon*, who had sneaked up to the back of the tent and reached under for Zack's guns, lay on the ground outside, wallowing and pitching and screaming.

The grinning boy continued to squat there inside the tent till he was sure that the lot supervisor and some of the Mexican police had a good hold on the thief. Then he pulled his blade from the hand and wiped it across his pants leg to clean off the blood.

After that, Muchacho stayed with Zack and the show. Zack hid the little waif in his own private car when they came out of Mexico and safely smuggled him across the Rio Grande into the United States.

There were two leading newspapers in Mexico City in 1908 — *El Heraldo*, printed in Spanish, and *The Herald*, published for residents of the English and American colonies. The two papers fought like cats and dogs.

The Miller Brothers' press agent worked on *The Herald* for publicity. One day *The Herald* made the statement that Bill Pickett's bulldogging act was a greater show than any Mexican bull-fight. This raised a big howl from the

Mexicans, and the next morning *El Heraldo* came out with a statement that any bull-fighter could do Bill Pickett's act, do it as well and in less time. The fight was on.

Joe knew good publicity when he saw it. He also knew what that Negro bulldogger, Bill Pickett, could do. He went straight to *The Herald* offices and ran an advertisement, challenging any two bull-fighters of Mexico to come into the 101 show ring and throw one steer in the same time Bill Pickett was throwing two.

No bull-fighters took the challenge, but the newspapers had a good fight started now and they couldn't stop. They continued to throw insults back and forth. The fight built up interest in the show till the Millers were showing to a turn-away crowd at each performance. Finally, through *The Herald*, Joe challenged any bull-fighter to do Bill Pickett's act; he'd give a thousand *pesos* to the charity hospital of Mexico City if some bull-fighter could do it.

One bull-fighter accepted the challenge. But he wouldn't perform in public. He claimed it would be unethical, a disgrace to the art of bull-fighting. He said he'd fight only in a private ring, but would allow representatives from each newspaper to witness the feat.

The time was to be nine o'clock the next morning. The stage was set and the newspapermen arrived. But the bull-fighter didn't show up. He sent a note explaining his absence. He said that the bull-fighters' union had served notice on him not to stoop to doing Bill Pickett's act, that they'd throw him out of the union if he did. But they'd offered a counter-proposition. They'd put up five thousand *pesos* which said Bill Pickett couldn't keep his black hands on one of their bulls five minutes.

Joe called in the Negro bulldogger. 'You think you can handle one of them fighting bulls, Bill?'

Bill Pickett looked at his big black hands then grinned up at Joe. 'Boss,' he said, 'they ain't never growed a bull Bill Pickett can't hold with these old hands.'

Joe put up his money. The performance was to be held in the Plaza del Toro. Under the terms of the agreement, the Millers were to pick the bull. They took Bill Pickett along to size up the animals, held in the corrals beside the bull-ring.

One look at these bulls convinced the Millers that Bill Pickett had a job on his hands. These weren't old Texas longhorn cattle, brush-wild and proddy only when cornered. These were fighting animals, bred and reared for the bull-ring and from a long line of fighting blood that had its remote beginning in early Spanish history. These bulls held their heads high and proud and they had long horns, set for hooking.

Joe looked the bulls over and felt uneasy. 'You still want to go ahead, Bill?' he asked.

Bill Pickett rolled his eyes and grinned. 'Mistah Joe,' he said, 'Ise done picked the bull. That little specklety booger yonder with the long neck. He's got horns built just to fit old Bill's hands.'

The bull Bill Pickett had picked out was a fierce, waspy little animal called Chiquito Frijole, or 'Little Bean,' because of the bean-sized speckles all over his body. Frijole had been in the Plaza del Toro ring only the week before, where he'd fought so hard and made such a showing against a fumbling matador that the crowd forced the bull-fighters to spare him, in spite of the ruling that no bull was to leave the ring alive.

'But look at them sharp horns,' Ves Pegg pointed out. 'For Bill's protection, we ought to tip them horns off.'

'Nossah, now,' argued Bill. 'Evah inch long them horns is, is just that much in old Bill's favor. We'll let them horns be!'

That night Bill showed up at Zack's tent, twisting his hat in his big hands.

'Mistah Zack,' he said, 'Ise wanting to ask a favor. If my luck was to maybeso happen to run out, does I git to be buried back on the 101?'

Zack's eyes searched the Negro bulldogger's face. 'You scared of it, Bill?' he demanded. 'You want out of it?'

The bulldogger was offended. 'Now, Mistah Zack,' he protested, 'you's got this nigger wrong. I ain't a-feared of that little old specklety bull. I'll wrassle that booger, jist like Ise done the others. But you know how it is. Nigger or white, man's time's bound to come. And when he hears the call, he's got to go, be he dogging a bull or busting a bronc hoss. Maybe this is my time; maybe it ain't. All I wants to know, is I going to be put away amongst friends when it happens?'

'You can bank on that, Bill,' Zack promised.

'In the ha'd ground, Mistah Zack? Whar the coyotes can't scratch out old Bill's bones?'

'In the hard ground, Bill,' Zack promised.

The bulldogger's face split in a wide grin. 'That's all, Mistah Zack,' he said, plainly satisfied. 'Ise ready for that little old specklety bull now.' He was still grinning when he left the tent.

Joining the 101 show parade on the day of the performance was a group of strutting bull-fighters, carrying between them an elaborate coffin upon which was written in bold letters: '*El Pincharino.*' That's what the bull-fighters called Bill Pickett, meaning one who's already been horned to pieces by a bull. And the coffin was for the black bull-dogger, when Chiquito Frijole was done with him.

At the arena, the seats of *El Sombre* and *El Sol* had been jammed for an hour before the performance was to begin. The gate receipts netted twenty-two thousand *pesos*, after the rental on the bull-ring was paid. The Miller Brothers turned Mexicans away in droves.

Zack and Joe had fixed to run off a few preliminary acts before the main feature, wanting to give the crowd its money's worth. But the crowd wasn't interested. The Mexicans had come to see their favorite bull Frijole rip the guts out of a black bulldogger and they had no time nor patience for anything else. Bronc-busting was nothing; the crowd booed the performers. Trick riding and roping were worse. The Mexicans called, over and over again: '*El Pincharino! El Pincharino!*' The stands rocked with the thunder of sound. And then they started calling for the bull.

'*Chiquito Frijole! Viva el toro! Viva el Chiquito Frijole!*'

Zack and Joe sat their horses at the main gate, listening to them. Zack turned to his brother.

'We just as well call this all off and let them have it, Joe,' he said. 'That's what they've come to see and they don't give a whoop in hell for the rest. Let's call old Bill in.'

Joe nodded and ordered the arena cleared. A vast silence fell upon the stands. Joe announced the main event. The silence still held. Up in the stands a Pathé cameraman started grinding, taking moving pictures of the show. Then out into the ring rode Bill Pickett on his little bulldogging horse Spraddly.

Bill's show garb wasn't much, compared to the fancy rigs sported by the Mexican bull-fighters. Bill had on a good pair of bench-made boots. All cowhands wore good boots. And he had on a good white Stetson hat. In the cow country he'd come from, that's all a cowhand needed to be considered dressed up — good boots and a Five-X Beaver Stetson. What he wore in between didn't much matter. Bill was in the habit of wearing ducking overalls and a coarse blue shirt, and that's what he wore today.

The crowd booed Bill Pickett. The bull-fighters led the booing.

Timbers popped and rattled in a chute at the far side of the ring. There was a nasty cracking of firecrackers, then the chute gate was thrown open and out into the arena charged the speckled Chiquito Frijole, jumping high and long, tossing his horns, looking for trouble.

The crowd roared and roared again. Here was their favorite. Here was the bull to put those braggy *Americanos* in their places!

There was no bluff to Frijole. He had more than just paw and beller. He didn't wait for the fight to be brought to him. His sharp eyes lit on Bill Pickett astride his little bay horse Spraddly and the bull came on the run, horns lowered for the kill.

Spraddly knew about bad bulls. He'd put Bill Pickett up alongside too many of them not to know. He stood his ground to the last possible instant, then leaped to one side and out of reach of those wicked horns.

The bull shot past. Spraddly whirled and was after him

in as fast a get-away as any roping horse on the show. But before the horse could put Bill up close enough to pile off onto Frijole's head, the little bull had wheeled and was charging back on them. Spraddly dodged again.

In three tries, Bill Pickett still hadn't got into position to quit his saddle and drop down upon the Mexican bull. The bull wouldn't run and give Spraddly a chance. Bill tried a fourth time, missed, and with the jeers and cat-calls of the crowd hammering his eardrums, he spurred toward the main gate. Joe and Zack and Ves Pegg sat their horses at the gate with cocked loops, ready to spur in and pick up the bull's heels if anything went wrong.

There was a worried look on Bill Pickett's face when he slid Spraddly to a halt in front of the three. 'Ise got to have me another hoss, Mistah Zack,' he said. 'Ise got to let that bull kill a hoss befo' I kin git my hands on him. They ain't no other way!'

Zack and Joe both knew what had Bill Pickett so bothered. It wasn't that speckled bull and it wasn't that screaming, yelping mob up in the stands. It was Spraddly. Bill Pickett loved that little Spraddly; he didn't want to put the horse in danger.

Back at the ranch, when Spraddly was a colt, he'd jumped a corral fence and run a pine splinter into his brisket. A tumor had formed, growing to be as big as a bushel basket. But even with that, Spraddly had been able to outrun any colt in the pasture.

Zack and Bill had cut out that tumor, cured up the colt, and Pickett had taken him over. He'd trained him till Spraddly was the best bulldogging horse in his string. And now he couldn't stand the thought of letting that killer bull get to the little horse.

But right now wasn't a time for switching horses. The crowd was on its feet and growing wild. The Mexicans thought Bill Pickett had weakened. They thought he was fixing to turn tail and throw the fight to the speckled bull. They thought they were going to miss seeing a gory kill and they were ready to mob Bill Pickett and all the rest of the showmen.

Zack handed Bill Pickett a drink of whiskey and told him: 'Go back in there, Bill, and get that bull. If you don't, they're going to get all of us!'

Bill downed his whiskey and dragged a shirt-sleeve across his thick lips, but still hesitated. It looked for a minute as if he didn't aim to carry out Zack's orders. Then he turned his head to keep the white men from seeing the tears in his eyes and rode his little horse out to meet the charging bull.

The bull came on and Spraddly wheeled to dodge him and no man will ever know what it took for Bill Pickett to haul back on the reins and stop his beloved Spraddly horse square in the path of that charging killer.

The bull hit the little horse from behind, driving those vicious horns up to his head in the thick leg muscles of the horse's rump. Spraddly screamed and gave down in the rear. The bull hauled back for another lunge and Bill Pickett went out of the saddle backward, slid down over the root of Spraddly's tail and tied onto those blood-smeared horns.

For the next two minutes, the bull made a whip-cracker out of Bill Pickett. He slammed the Negro's body against the arena wall. He threw up his head to sling the clinging man creature right and left, trying to dislodge him. He whipped him against another wall. He reached with his forefeet and tried to paw him loose. Finally he got down on his knees and drove his sharp horns into the ground, time and again, trying to run Bill through.

But Bill Pickett was working close in. This wasn't the time or the place for a fancy, show-off job of bulldogging with his teeth. This was a fight to the finish and nobody knew it better than the big black bulldogger. So he clung to the bull's head, one arm over each horn, his hands clamped like a vice around the bull's throat and his bent knees squeezing against the bull's nostrils.

He clung there and took what punishment the mad bull handed out and breathed in the rank, hot scent of the angry animal. The sweetish smell of fresh blood was there, too. Spraddly's blood. And the smell of boiling dust. And over it all rolled the high-pitched clamor of the mob, screaming for Bill's death.

'*Viva! Viva el toro!*'

The shouts and screams of the crowd beat around Bill Pickett's ears and the Negro's lips peeled back from his white teeth in a grin that had no mirth in it. He started twisting the bull's head, rocking the animal on its feet.

For a little while, it looked as if Bill Pickett would throw the bull right there in the middle of the ring. Just like throwing a rodeo steer. He could rock Frijole till one forefoot came off the ground at each swing. That clinging weight on his head was too much for the speckled bull. He was tiring.

Gradually, this fact seeped into the minds of the spectators. They'd thought Frijole was killing the black man there on the ground. They'd been reared up on their dewclaws for the sight of the mangled remains of Bill's body when the bull was finished with him. And now they knew they'd been fooled. Bill Pickett was tiring the bull fast. The black man was about to throw him.

That was a keen disappointment to the Mexicans. They couldn't bear the sight of the black foreigner downing one of their favorite bulls. The bull-fighters would be shamed. The national sport would be disgraced. Mexico and bull-fighting would be the laughing-stock of the world.

That's when they started throwing things at the bull-dogger. Beer bottles, seat covers, planks, oranges, bricks, anything they could get their hands on.

A quart beer bottle came whistling down out of the stands. It caught Bill Pickett in the side, breaking a rib.

Pain shot through the Negro bulldogger and for the space of a breath, his grip loosened. The bull sensed this weakness and was quick to take advantage. He reared back. He lunged sideways. He lifted Bill Pickett high in the air and headed around the arena again, slinging the bulldogger back and forth and slamming his body into the walls when he could.

They circled past Zack, where he watched with Joe and Ves Pegg. Zack could see the sweat popping out on Bill's forehead. He could see the whites of the Negro's eyes rolling up. He could tell by the set of Bill's mouth that sheer guts was all that kept him hanging to that bull's head now.

Zack looked at his watch. Four minutes had passed. 'It's not long, Bill!' he hollered. 'Hang and rattle, you black rascal!'

When a man's life hangs by one slim thread, as Bill Pickett's was hanging then, the minutes can drag out into an eternity of time. They dragged now. Around and around the bull-ring the two went, the bull bellowing and waving Bill in the air. Zack had seen lots of wild crowds, but he'd never seen anything to match the hysteria of this bunch. The Mexicans were screaming at every breath and chunking the black man with whatever they thought might knock him loose from his hold on the bull. When everything else was gone, some of them tied up big batches of silver money in handkerchiefs and threw them.

But Bill kept hanging to that fighting bull's head. And still the time stretched on, out and out.

Five minutes came at last. The second hand on Zack's stop watch completed its fifth circle and went on past. Zack listened for the bell. It didn't sound. He looked at Joe and at Ves Pegg. They looked back at him. Nobody said a word.

Five and a half minutes came. Six minutes. The bull passed them again, and it looked to Zack as if Bill Pickett's black face was turning gray under the strain. Zack could see the muscles of Bill's back bulged and trembling under his sweaty shirt.

Zack felt his gorge rise. He snapped shut his watch and growled at Joe. 'They're not going to ring that bell, Joe. The sons-of-bitches aim to let that bull kill Bill Pickett!'

Joe bawled at the gateman 'Abre la puerta, hombre!'

The man swung the gate open. Zack and Ves Pegg spurred into the arena, loops ready-made for the catch. They picked up Frijole's heels with their ropes, spread his legs and threw him.

Bill Pickett fell away from the bull. He came to his feet and headed across the ring in a staggering run, never looking back once. He was headed for his little bay horse Spraddly, who stood humped with pain under his saddle next to the wall. Streams of blood still ran down both hind legs of the little horse.

'*Muerte el Pincharino!*' came the cry from the stands. Others took it up. 'Kill the black man! Kill all the American dogs! Mexico for the Mexicans!'

Bricks, bottles, even swords and *machete* knives came whizzing down into the arena. Most of the missiles were thrown at Bill Pickett. But Bill didn't hurry. He'd seen the terrible wounds in Spraddly's hind legs and he would have taken his time leading the crippled horse to safety if they'd been shooting at him with guns.

It began to look as if the howling mob would go crazy and rip up the stands to get at the showmen who'd brought such shame and dishonor to them. Zack ordered all hands to load their six-shooters; but in the face of five thousand aroused Mexicans, Joe knew better than to start shooting.

'Hold your fire!' he shouted. 'Shoot one, and we'll have the whole goddamned outfit to kill!'

A troop of *rurales* came galloping up. The captain ordered Joe to get his show bunch together and line them up between the lines of Mexican soldiers.

In spite of the excitement and confusion, Zack took time for a look at Spraddly's wounds. The bull had run his horns almost full length into the big muscles of the horse's legs. How could you doctor wounds like that? Zack turned away to keep from meeting Bill Pickett's eyes.

At that moment, one of the show Mexicans shouted: 'Get me some bananas! Quick! I cure him.'

Zack sent a boy running for bananas. The boy came

back with yellow ones. The Mexican cursed him and sent him back for red bananas. When they came, he peeled the fruit and shoved one big long banana into each of the gaping holes in the horse's rump.

'That feex him,' he said.

It must have. Spraddly never even swelled from the wounds that should have killed him. The wounds healed perfectly — and Spraddly was apparently as good a horse as ever.

Under guard of the *rurales*, the 101 performers moved toward the show lots, with the mob raging alongside, still screaming and throwing things.

One little man in a brown derby ran up close and threw a fist-sized rock at Zack's head. Zack dodged, and the rock struck a Mexican captain riding beside him, almost knocking him off his horse. Zack pointed out the culprit, who had wheeled to run, and the army captain broke ranks to spur after him. With an expert thrust the captain ran his sword through one of the little man's big ears and came leading him back on tiptoe. The captain held him half-hanging by one ear to that sword till his men tied up the man's hands behind his back and led him off.

Joe, white-faced with anger, collected his five thousand *pesos*. And the time-keepers told him again and again, talking with their hands to make it strong, how sorry they were that something had gone wrong with their watches.

From then on till the sixteen-day engagement in Mexico City was wound up, the Mexican Government had to keep a steady guard around the 101 show lots to keep the *peon* mob from slaughtering them to the last man.

Nobody was bothered with regrets the day that the show outfit crossed to the north side of the Rio Grande again.

17

RED FRIENDS

THE RENT MONEY which the 101 paid for farming and grazing leases was turned over to the Indians through the Office of Indian Affairs. By white man's law and custom, this was as far as the Millers' dealings with the Indians had to go. But Indian ways are not the ways of a white man. The Indians were friends of the Millers, and, to an Indian, friendship works both ways and is on a lot higher level than mere dollars and cents. And to whom but a friend should a man go when he is broke and hungry?

So when a Ponca was hungry, he went to the 101 for food. When he was broke, he went to the 101 for money. When he needed advice on the strange laws shoved upon him by the white man, the 101 was the first place he headed.

When the railroads first built on Indian lands, they were forced to sign a contract to pay the Indians a hundred dollars each for every horse killed by a train.

Harry King, a Ponca declared noncompetent by the Government, got an order from the Agency, giving him the right to buy a work team. Zack sold him a matched pair of duns, one of them the first clipped horse ever to be seen on the Salt Fork. The duns were broken to harness and Harry King was well satisfied.

A couple of nights after Harry had bought the duns, a south-bound train ran into them, killing both horses. Harry King was at the 101 next day, looking for Zack.

'My friend,' Harry said, 'I come to you with a sad heart. Last night, old Clippy, he kill the train. Old Dun, he kill the train, too. Maybeso, Harry King, he need money for more horses.'

Zack went to the railroad agent and got Harry reimbursed so that he could buy another team.

In any group of Indians, you can find as many honest ones as you could find in the same number of white men. But saving for a rainy day isn't an Indian's way of doing and plenty of times the lease money the Poncas received from the Millers failed to cover the debts they'd made. When this happened, none of them hesitated to hit up the 101 for a loan, promising to pay when the lease money came again.

One Indian borrowed two hundred dollars from Joe Miller, promising to pay on a certain day. The same Indian also owed another man the same amount. On the day he had promised to pay, he got three hundred dollars from the agent. He had immediate use for one hundred of it; so he kept that. With the two hundred left, he paid the second debt, leaving Joe holding the bag.

Joe jumped him out about it. 'Where's my two hundred?' he wanted to know.

The Indian caught Joe by the sleeve and led him to one side. 'Me no like other man,' he said confidentially. 'He bad man. Pay him; he go away. You friend. You stay here. You good man. Me pay you some other time!'

Most of the Poncas felt that way about their debts to the Millers. The way they figured it, the Millers held their land as security; so there was no hurry. At one time the

Poncas alone owed the 101 twenty-two thousand dollars for money borrowed on word of honor, debts that were never entered on the 101 books. And those word-of-honor debts were eventually paid.

Now and then there was an Indian, however, who never got around to paying. These, the Millers finally refused to lend money. And in these cases, Zack was always the goat; he had to be the one to tell them no. Joe couldn't say no; George couldn't, either. So when one of these spongers hit them up, they'd tell him to go see Zack. And Zack, knowing his brothers never refused an Indian they trusted, knew what it meant when they sent one to him. He said no. That system worked even with white men. When George and Joe hated to turn a man down on a proposition, they always sent him to Zack. Zack was the 101 'no' man.

White man's ways never ceased to be a puzzle to the Indians. There was the time when Zack took about forty-five of his red-skinned friends to the Alabama State Fair in Birmingham, exhibiting them along with the 101 rodeo. Among them was Harry King, whose horses had 'killed the train.' Harry had never been off the reservation before; never seen a streetcar or an electric light. Harry was about twenty-five years old; he stood six feet-four in his moccasins and was much of a man.

One night some of the Indians missed Harry and reported to Zack. Zack hunted the town over, but found no trace of Harry till the next morning when he heard that an Indian had been arrested the night before and thrown into jail.

Zack went down to the police station to get Harry out

and found him standing on the courthouse steps, looking as if all his folks had died. Zack could tell that Harry was lost, that he didn't know where to go or what to do.

'I think,' Harry said to Zack when they met, 'that I ought not come here. Too many kinds of people in this place. Strange people. Not same here, like Oklahoma.'

'What's the matter, Harry?' Zack asked. 'What happened?'

The big Indian took a long breath and told his story. 'Last night,' he said, 'four men, they come to camp. One say to me, "John, you like go see town? We bring you back pretty soon."

'I never see men like that. Front of her coat cut off at belly. Coat got tail, all same crow. Big white thing around neck; hard, not like Indian clothes.

'These men, they take me out. We ride buggy with glass all around. That horse and buggy make no noise on street. The man say, "John, you want eat?"

'I tell no. Already I eat. Plenty beef. Plenty coffee. Belly full.

'He take me down here to house. Twenty girls. Not got many clothes. Plenty paint, all same Indian. He bring out soda-pop in big bottle with white cap on it. That girl, he push cork. It go all same pistol, up to ceiling. I drink soda-pop. Strange thing, that pop, she go up my nose, big bubbles.

'The women, he come over and put arm around Harry's neck. That woman, he got good smell. One woman, he say: "You wanta go bed, John?"

'I tell him no, me not sleepy. Maybeso them man, she go off leave me. We stay and drink more soda-pop. Men say, "Let's go some other place."

'We go some other place. More same women. More same soda-pop. Then we go three place. Find yellow women in place. Man, she say, "Maybe John, he like yellow women!"

'Harry, he no like yellow women. Drink more soda-pop. Lights go this way, lights go that way. Ground, she move under Harry's feet.

'Man say, "John, you make loud holler."

'Long time, I been wanting do this. I make loud holler. Women, he scare. 'Nother man, she say, "John, make dance!"

'Harry make dance and make loud holler.

'Here come soldier. But woman go to door, tell him all right; they go off.

'All time drink more soda-pop out of big bottles. Pretty soon, these man, she help me in buggy. We come back to camp. Harry feel fine. Makum big holler. Hairy-Back, he come out where I makum holler. I say to Hairy-Back: "Hairy-Back, I makum fight!"

'We makum fight.

'Three soldier come. One get one side, one get other side. One makum loud whistle. Wagon come, all same wagon put circus lions in. Got iron all around. Buggy, he makum big noise, all time ring bell. Take me down to big house. Put me in and lockum door so nobody get in.

'This morning, man open door. Soldier man. Take me down long stairs to big room. Big white chief, she sittum way high. I think she boss this house.

'Soldier, she tell big chief things. Big chief, she tell me things. I think maybeso I not say right thing; I no tell nothing. Big chief, she tell soldier. Soldier take me to door. "Go to fairground," soldier say.

'And for my bed and my breakfast, he no take money!'

Harry King was a little awed by the fact that they didn't want any money for his bed and board in the Birmingham jail. But he was convinced he never wanted to come back. The soda-pop that the man with the crow-tailed coat had fed him was good, but it made the drums beat too loud in a poor Indian's head.

The Indian, however, wasn't always the one to appear foolish in the constant conflict between white and red man in their laws, customs, and religion. A missionary once sneered at old Chief White Eagle for putting food on the grave of his son.

'You ought to know better than to think your dead son can come back and eat that food,' the missionary said scornfully. 'Why do you Poncas do that?'

The old Ponca chief drew himself up proudly, tightened his blanket around him and answered:

'I'll tell you that thing when you tell me something. When that banker died at Ponca City, Joe Sherburn, he say: "White Eagle, banker big man. You big man. When one big man die, all big men to go funeral."

'We go. I get in Joe's buggy. We go up there and go to big house. Lots of people. Medicine man make long-time talk. Then we go out and put that man in hole in ground and cover him all up. Then on top of him, put wagonload of flowers.

'Now, you tell me. Don't you think my boy come back and eat when banker come back and smell flowers?'

Zack once heard White Eagle make a speech to the

Dawes Commission which had been sent down to the Ponca Agency to see whether or not the Indians were competent to manage property before they gave out allotments of land.

Grave with concern over the outcome of the issue, which he well understood, the Ponca Chief faced the white leaders and told them what he thought of the matter in a manner befitting a man of his dignity and position.

'Now again our Great Father in Washington sends men to make trade with Indians on something new,' White Eagle told them. 'Five times we have made trade with Great Father. Five times we make marks on paper with red, white, and blue ribbons upon it. And they read this paper to us and our children tell us what it says. And all of those paper say that Indian has this land as long as the water runs and the grasses grow.

'But every time Indian mark on these papers, Great Father's man come with soldiers and move Indian to different place, then make other papers.'

White Eagle's deep voice held a great weariness. 'We think the Great Father in Washington not make two kinds of talk. But some of his chiefs make the papers read one way and then talk another. Every paper the Ponca Indian sign says he is to have this land for his own so long as the waters run and the grasses grow. My friends, the waters run and the grasses grow in the land of our forefathers. But we have not that land.

'And now you come to tell us that we must make another paper. We must each take small piece of land. And we must live on this land. And the Great Father will make houses for us, all same as white man's houses. But, my friends, many Indians like to live as his father and his fathers and his fathers lived.

'I must have time to think and counsel well with my people. And I must tell them that every paper we have made has taken the size of our holdings down and down and down. Three days I'll come back, after I hold council with all my wise men. When I come back, we'll talk more.'

But more talk was useless, as old White Eagle probably knew. The allotments were made; the Indian's land was cut into little pieces and he was forced to live upon those little pieces because there was nowhere else for him to go.

But while White Eagle and his Ponca tribe had deep and bitter griefs against the white man's Government, nevertheless, they showed a strangely vital concern for the Government inasmuch as it affected their immediate white friends.

Once on the ranch, over in Joe Sherburn's store, White Eagle saw a newspaper with the picture of Prince Henry of Sweden on the front page. He asked Sherburn who this man was.

Sherburn told him that this was a chief from across the big waters, that the Great Fathers in Washington were celebrating his coming and giving great feasts in his honor.

White Eagle studied the picture and shook his head. 'This make me think,' he said slowly. 'My grandson, he have white teacher in school. Teacher tell grandson about when first white man come. He come in boat like this chief. Indian run down and meet him with glad hand. Give him corn and meat. Treat him good.

'Pretty soon that man, he get on boat and go away. Next time, many boats come. White man bring guns.

Indian never before see guns. White man make Indian go 'way back. Give Indian whiskey; Indian never before have whiskey. And more white men come along coast of the big waters. Indian fight some white men, help other white men fight against some more white men.

'But all the time, white man move Indian farther back, farther back. My people had big country, ten days' horse-back ride across. Now, he can go this way and that way before sun sets.'

White Eagle paused dramatically and pointed at the picture of Prince Henry.

'Maybe this man,' he said, 'he come to look same as first white man. They show him this country and he like it pretty good. He not tell this white man what he going to do. But he go away. Maybeso he come back. Maybeso he bring gun that shootum today and killum tomorrow. And he make all these white men move back, little at a time. Pretty soon, maybe he get agent tell white man what to do, like white man have agent for Indian now.

'More better, Joe,' he advised, 'that the Great White Father in Washington not treat this man too good. Then he won't come back. They make White Father eat what they eat, make you talk what he talk, make you work like he work. Yes, more better, you not treat this man so good.'

White Eagle was tolerant of white man's religion, but clung steadfastly to his own. And his friends, the Millers, never tried to interfere. In fact, Joe Miller was about half-converted to White Eagle's belief about the hereafter.

Before White Eagle died, the old Ponca Chief sent a messenger to Joe asking him to come. Joe went to White Eagle's teepee.

'Friend Joe,' White Eagle said, 'tomorrow at sundown I die, and I have no horse worthy of carrying a Ponca chief into the land beyond. We are good friends; so I ask you for a good horse to take with me.'

He described the horse he wanted, a big roan the 101 had bought off the Buffalo Bill show.

Joe promised him the horse. They shook hands; Joe came back and gave orders to get the big roan ready.

Zack raised a row the minute he learned which horse Joe had promised old White Eagle.

'Hell, Joe!' he said, 'that's too good a horse. He'd bring a thousand dollars in New York right now. Get another one. Old White Eagle will be dead; he'll never know the difference.'

Joe stopped him. 'Now, hold on, Zack,' he said. 'I promised White Eagle that roan horse and he's going to get it. Some day I might wind up in the same place he does, and I'll be damned if I'll have him accusing me of cheating on him at the last minute. We're going to kill that horse over White Eagle's grave, just like he asked me to.'

Joe had the horse caught up, fed and groomed. And the next day White Eagle, one of the greatest chiefs the Ponca tribe ever had, died at the very moment the sun sank below the western rim of the prairies.

Zack saw he couldn't get anywhere arguing with Joe; so he hunted up a cowhand called Big Boy and told him what was up. Big Boy got mad as hell. Old Roany was in his string, the best horse he had.

'Why, goddamn it!' Big Boy declared, 'I'd druther quit punching cows and go to shucking corn than kill that roan horse. Has Joe gone and lost his mind?'

He went with Zack and together they put the proposition up to the rest of the hands. Would any of them want the job of choking to death a fine horse like that big roan over White Eagle's grave?

They didn't. They thought a man was a damned fool to pay that much attention to a heathenish religion. One of the hands said that if he had to, he might be able to shoot a horse over White Eagle's grave; but he'd be god-damned if he'd choke one to death.

'Tell you what,' said Big Boy, 'let's slip old Roany out at the last minute and take him over to the Bar L and get another one. Joe can't tell one roan horse from another by the time it's laid there a couple of days and got ripe.'

'The hell he can't,' said Zack. 'We'll never put nothing like that over on Joe. Our only chance is to balk on him, to get every man on the ranch ready to quit before he'll take the job. That might stop him.'

They buried White Eagle the next day on a limestone ridge that held the graves of many Ponca braves. They buried him in a white-man coffin, but with a little air-hole bored in the top of it, in case the air got stuffy inside.

The white missionary to the Ponca Agency thought the old chief was buried in a shroud. According to the missionary's lights, a shroud was the only decent and Christian garment a man could wear to meet his Maker, and he'd raised a row from the start to see that that's what White Eagle wore. Best Zack could tell, the missionary had it figured that if he could get this red chief into white-man burying garments, then that'd prove to the Almighty that he'd saved another heathen from hell. And that'd be a big shiny star in the missionary's crown when he stood knocking at the Pearly Gates.

But while old White Eagle had never fought white man's religion, at the same time he'd never got around to pitching his own beliefs out to the dogs. The Ponca leaned to the opinion that his gods matched anything the white man ever set up beside them, and before he died, he'd ordered his squaws to put him away in the pick of Indian garments.

So the squaws, to keep peace, let the missionary wrap their chief's body in a shroud and lay it out in the coffin; and then, after dark, they took the shroud off and put it away to make dresses out of and rigged White Eagle out in the finest of beaded and fringed doeskin, as is fitting and proper for a big chief bound for the Happy Hunting Grounds.

Since the coffin wasn't opened after that, the missionary likely never did know what a whizzer the squaws had run on him till the time came when Saint Peter tapped him on the shoulder and asked him to ante up that heathen soul he'd bragged so much about saving.

In the meantime, Zack and Big Boy had done a prime job of selling the 101 cowhands on the idea that old Roany was too good a horse to be wasted on a dead Indian. When night came and it was time to take the horse to White Eagle's grave, there wasn't a hand on the ranch that would agree to do the job. To a man, they swore they'd sack their saddles and quit first.

Zack sat around the bunkhouse, feeling pretty smug about it, till Joe turned the thing around and pitched it right back into his own lap.

'All right, Zack,' Joe said. 'You've got them all ribbed up till they won't do it. So that don't leave anybody but you.'

'Me!' yelped Zack. 'I'll pay hell killing that horse ——'

'You'll kill him,' Joe cut in. 'Because there's one thing a Miller won't do. He won't lie to his friends! And White Eagle was our friend.'

Something about the way Joe said that made Zack feel guilty. It hit him so hard that he'd led the roan almost to White Eagle's grave before it ever occurred to him to wonder why in the hell Joe couldn't have done his own horse-killing if he had to be so damned honorable about keeping his word.

Zack took the Negro Henry Clay along to help him get the job done. The Negro didn't like it. It was a black, cold, misty night with the rain blowing in from the north, not the sort of time Henry Clay would choose to fool around the graves of the departed. By the time they'd reached the burial ground, leading the roan between them, the little Negro was shivering like a dog in the wet.

'Just take it easy, Henry,' Zack said. 'You don't have to do a damned thing but hold your horse. I'll do the choking.'

They found White Eagle's grave and led the roan up till he straddled the mound of fresh dirt.

Using the middle of his catch-rope, Zack tied a slip-knot around the roan's throat. One loose end he tied hard and fast to the horn of Henry Clay's saddle. The other, he wrapped around his own horn, then touched spurs to his horse. Between them, the slip-knot tightened, shutting off the big roan's wind.

Frightened, the roan reared, grunting and straining, pawing the black night in front of him. And at the same moment, from down under the hill arose an unearthly wail, the first cry of the squaws who'd come to mourn the death of their chief.

'God-d-d-amighty!' moaned Henry Clay. 'Oh, my god-d-d-amighty!'

'Hold what you've got, Henry!' Zack called. 'It won't take long now.'

Zack knew something of what the scared Negro was feeling. The grunting and heaving of the big roan fighting to get a breath was enough to make the hair crawl on the back of his own neck. And when the second screaming wail of the mourners tore through the darkness, Zack felt his scalp shift under his hat.

Henry Clay held what he had. And in one last lunging effort, the big roan reared high and went down, where he pawed and threw fresh dirt high in his death throes.

That's when panic gripped Henry Clay. The little Negro cut loose with one wild choking scream and quit his saddle. He hit the ground running and faded into the night.

Before Zack could get loose from the roan and overtake the Negro, Henry Clay was halfway back to the ranch, still running. Zack stopped him, got him back into the saddle, and started trying to talk him out of his scare.

Henry was whimpering like a pup. 'But, Mistah Zack,' he said, 'didn't you see what I see?'

'I don't know, Henry. What did you see?'

'It was right when that hoss went down, Mistah Zack,' Henry Clay cried. 'I see White Eagle. I see him come right up out of that groun' and put his hand on old Roany's neck to lead him away. Come up in a great blue light, he did!'

Zack rode silent for a while, letting the little Negro talk himself back into a better frame of mind. Zack hadn't seen White Eagle come up out of that grave. At the same time, he knew the little Negro wasn't lying about what he'd seen. Henry'd thought he'd seen White Eagle come up in a blue light to lead old Roany away and maybe he had. Like an Indian, a Negro's more primitive, closer to the earth, closer to life and death. Zack told himself he'd be the last one to call Henry Clay a liar about what he claimed to have seen.

'Mistah Zack,' Henry begged before they reached the ranch, 'you won't tell the hands nothing about what I see tonight? You make me a promise not to do that, Mistah Zack. You tell 'em, and they won't believe me. They'd rawhide this niggah to a frazzle.'

Zack promised and kept his word. And the time came in his life when he was glad he hadn't been able to talk Joe out of his promise to White Eagle. Like his brother, Zack isn't right sure now but what he'll meet up with old White Eagle. And there's always a chance that a friend in the hereafter might come in as handy there as he does in this life.

18

ON THE ROAD

Jackson, Kentucky —— Now, that was a town with the hair on!

The 101 show outfit's advance agent, Eddie Arlington, tried to warn the Millers about Jackson. He said it was a bad town.

'It's feuding country,' he wrote back. 'And when they feud up here in these mountains, they play for keeps. But the take ought to be good if you're not afraid to try it. There hasn't been a show here in twenty years.'

Joe wired Eddie to use his own judgment.

The booking was short and Eddie was desperate for a place to show; he took a chance and booked the Miller Brothers 101 Wild West Show for Jackson.

When the show pulled in, Zack and Joe soon learned that Eddie hadn't half-told how tough Jackson was. The mountaineers trooped in out of the hills by the thousands, some muleback, some afoot, but all of them packing a squirrel rifle in one hand and a gallon jug of fighting moonshine in the other. They drank and they fought all over town. One killing took place down in front of the courthouse while the show paraded the streets.

At the first showing, Zack took up tickets at the front door for the afternoon performance. A little sawed-off mountaineer lugging a rifle longer than he was came up without a ticket and started in. Zack blocked his way.

'Where's your ticket?' he demanded.

The little man stabbed a thumb at a wisp of white ribbon pinned to his shirt-front. 'I'm deputy sheriff in these here parts,' he said.

'We can't let you in on that kind of a badge,' Zack told him.

'Well, I'm a-gonna go in,' the mountaineer blustered.

'I'll be damned if you are!' Zack said. 'You'll go buy you a ticket, like the rest.'

The little mountaineer stood his ground a moment with a look in his eyes that made Zack wonder if he'd be fast enough to step in past that rifle muzzle before the little man could get set to shoot. Then the mountaineer backed off.

'I'm going to get the other boys,' he threatened the showman, 'and we're going in on ribbons just like this.'

'You'll play hell doing it while I'm on the door,' Zack told him.

But Zack already had it figured that he wouldn't be on the door when the man came back. As soon as the deputy was out of sight, Zack turned the ticket-taking over to one of the other boys and stepped out back. He felt satisfied the man and his pards would go in; and, from the number of six-shooters and rifles showing up around this place, Zack had an idea the Millers weren't looking for any trouble.

On the circus ground behind the tents, Zack found seven mountaineers perched in a row on top of a wagon where they could look in on the show free of charge. Their jugs sat just behind them, handy to reach, and they held their squirrel guns in the crooks of their arms.

'Get down from there!' Zack ordered.

A lean, hungry-looking mountain man cackled down at him. 'Come up and git us down from hyar!'

Zack looked them over and guessed he'd talked out of turn. He hated to tuck his tail and back down now, but he didn't know what else to do. The last thing the Millers wanted was to mix in a fracas with these gun-toting mountaineers.

A boy selling seat cushions came by. Zack flagged him down. 'Here, boy,' he said, 'give them gentlemen up there on top of the wagon some cushions to sit on.'

The mountaineers settled their bony rumps into the soft comfort of the cushions and grinned down at Zack. 'Come up and have a drink?' one of them invited.

'Much obliged,' said Zack. 'I never drink.'

'Then, by god, I'm a-coming down to git you started!'

He came down and Zack decided this was just as good a time as any to get started. He tilted the jug and choked on one swallow of the red-hot poison. It was worse whiskey than the bootleggers sold the agency Indians.

The mountain man cackled and slapped Zack on the back. 'Pe-yore lightnin', ain't hit?' he said.

While Zack got his breath, the mountain man turned up the jug and the raw mountain moonshine rattled down his gullet like water running over rocks.

'Now,' said the man, wiping his mouth on his shirt-sleeve, 'if you want them there buzzards down off that waggin, jest say the word. I'll shoot 'em off. I'm the best damned squirrel shot in Brefitt County!'

Zack said he guessed there was no use in doing that. He said he had a show to put on right away and no time to be dragging off dead bodies. He stepped back inside the big top before the best damned squirrel shot in 'Brefitt' County decided to take a crack at him.

Inside the big tent, the clowns were entertaining the crowds with their little dogs. The show was ready to open with the Grand Entry. A tall, gangling mountaineer came suddenly to his feet and stepped over the arena net. He waved a hand toward the opposite side.

'Why, thar's the son-of-a-bitch now!' he shouted.

He tore open his shirt-front and jerked out a six-shooter he had lying against the bare skin of his belly.

A man on the other side of the arena rose to his feet and dived under the net. He came up in a half crouch, thumbing back the hammer of a big old hog-leg six-shooter he'd dragged from his ragged clothes.

In the dead silence that gripped the crowd inside the tent, they took about six steps toward each other. Then they opened up, shooting right across the heads of the clowns and other performers already inside the arena.

The first two shots came so close together that they sounded like one. Both men were hit and went down. Women came to their feet screaming. The clowns outran their dogs heading for the back of the tent.

One of the mountain men managed to get back up on his feet. But not for long. The other wasn't dead yet; he'd raised up on his elbows and was holding his six-shooter with both hands to steady it while he took aim. They fired again, their shots rolling together almost as closely as they had the first time. The man on the ground grunted and fell to one side. The other stood weaving on his feet for the length of a long breath. Then his six-shooter spilled out of fingers too limp to hold it and he pitched forward on his face.

They were dead before Zack could get to them. Both had fired two shots; each had two bullet holes in him.

Joe Miller came up and looked them over. 'It's a damned good thing they were both sure-shots,' he said, 'or somebody else would have got hurt. We better get out of this place.'

They hurried through the show, cutting the performance in half. Zack sent word to the cook-house to hurry up supper. They were scheduled for a night show, but they didn't want to stay now.

When it came time to knock down the tents, Joe found that the canvasmen had been sampling mountain moonshine during the show and now more than half of them were drunk and down. Joe prodded the rest, however, and things were moving fairly fast when a bunch of liquored-up hill-billies interfered.

'Hell, you can't take down them tents!' hollered one. 'We-uns aim to see the night show.'

Joe said nothing. He just called a halt on the work while Eddie Arlington sent a fixer downtown to bring the sheriff.

The sheriff was as tall and gangling as the mountain men. He had their same nasal drawl in speaking. It's pretty likely that he was one of them. He shook his head when Joe called on him to protect the canvasmen from the mountain drunks.

'Now, Mr. Miller,' he said, 'I'll do what I can in the name of the law. But them's good men out yonder. They're just a-pranking and mean no harm. And I ain't a-killing nobody over having a mite of fun.'

So Joe called off the canvasmen. The mountaineers stood around and kept watch. And the 101 outfit showed again that night.

After the performance, the show was about half-loaded when a big tall Kentucky girl came up to Joe.

'Mr. Miller,' she said, 'I want to leave town with this here show. I'm full tired of the feudin' and killin' a-goin' on in this here country. Pert' nigh all the menfolks of my family has been kilt off lately and I ain't hankerin' to see the death of the others. . . . I've rid horses all my life. I can ride as good as ary woman in that there show. But if you can't give me a job, I want you to let me ride this here train out a piece anyhow. I'm a-quittin' the mountings, for good!'

Joe told the manager of the girls to let the girl ride the coach that night. Next day he told the arena director to give her a tryout. He thought she might look pretty good on a horse.

And she did. She'd ridden mountain mules and horses all her life and she could handle them and handle herself on them. Joe kept her with the show, and that fall, when the outfit went into winter quarters back at the ranch, she married one of the ranch blacksmiths, Johnny Goodrich.

They raised a couple of good boys there on the ranch, Johnny Goodrich and his Kentucky mountain girl. One of the boys, the little one called Toughy, learned to ride on the 101 milk-calves and finally made a jockey out of himself. The other, Verne Goodrich, is now one of the crack rodeo hands of the United States.

Another tough town to show in was Gulfport, Mississippi. It was the Negroes there. Zack never did know what had them stirred up unless some other show outfit had paid off their leaders to cause the 101 trouble. They ganged up by the hundreds and tried to force their way into the after-noon show.

Zack called on the law for help. A Gulfport policeman showed up in time to take supper with Zack. He was a big, burly man who talked in a raspy voice.

'I'll handle 'em,' he told Zack. 'I've killed five of the black bastards since I've been on the force, and if one gives you trouble tonight, I'll make it six!'

They were still eating when a Mexican boy came in, all one side of his head bloody. He said he'd been hit with a rock. He said the Negroes were ganging up at the back end of the lot and chunking the tent men and performers with rocks.

The policeman got to his feet. 'I'll go get on one of them cars,' he told Zack. 'Let me catch one of them sons-of-bitches throwing a rock and I'll blow a hole in him he can shove his fist through.'

The show tents were pitched close to the railroad tracks on which the 101 show cars stood; there was just a narrow passage in between. The policeman stepped through the back door of the tent and turned right into this dark alley.

To the left, down the line a piece, Lon Sealy, the top-ranking white bulldogger of the show, was loading some steers into a cattle car. He saw a Negro throw a rock into the open door of a tent and he spurred toward him, run-ning the Negro down with his horse. Lon was packing a six-shooter, but he'd been warned not to use it.

A moment later, he dropped down off his horse at the door to the cook-tent and stuck his head inside.

'You better get the canvasmen out to help fight off these niggers,' he shouted to Zack. 'I've just run one down back here and now there's a swarm of the black devils coming in and talking up trouble!'

He stepped back into the dark alley. Out there, Zack could hear the coarse angry voices of the Negroes. He headed toward the tent door, following Lon.

He heard a wild yell, then the crashing report of a gun. The noise of the mob chopped off. Zack went out of the tent on the run.

Just outside, he ran into the little Mexican with the blood-smeared face.

'*Los negros*, Meester Zack!' he cried. 'They keel Lon Sealy!'

Scared and chattering like a magpie, the little Mexican led Zack down the dark alley to the right. He halted and pointed at the ground.

Zack could see nothing. He struck a match. In its wavering light, he found the body of Lon Sealy, lying flat of his back with a six-shooter still clutched in his hand. And lying flat of his back, with his feet almost touching the bulldogger's, was the big policeman.

Zack could have sworn he'd heard only one shot. But there lay the two men, each with a bullet hole through his hatband. Evidently, they'd run into each other there in the dark and both fired at the same instant.

A thousand stories spread through the town then, like fire in dry prairie grass. Downtown, rumor had it that a 101 Mexican had killed the policeman, who was a well-known and popular man. Ugly-tempered crowds, white men this time, began to gather and mill around the show lot. Zack hurried up the night performance, which he had already cut short. The canvasmen had the big tents ready to come down the moment the people cleared out. Zack told the performers to go to their cars, lock the doors and windows, and light no lights.

The sheriff came while the canvasmen were still loading. He gave orders for the train not to move. He told Zack none of the show outfit was to leave before the inquest was held.

Joe Miller went downtown with the sheriff to attend the inquest. Just before he left, he told Zack, privately, to get that train out of town if he possibly could.

'High-ball it for New Orleans,' he said. 'I'll handle things here.'

Zack got the train loaded and started working on the train crew, trying to get them to move out. They didn't want to; they'd had their orders from the sheriff.

Zack looked across the street. He saw one of the 101 Mexicans who'd disobeyed orders and left the train. The Mexican was sitting in a restaurant eating a lunch. Somebody in the mob that milled around the show cars recognized him as a member of the 101 outfit. He raised a howl, centering the attention of some three hundred trouble-hunters onto the Mexican. The growl of the mob got louder.

'Get that Mexican! Hang the son-of-a-bitch! Burn the goddamned show!' They jammed into the restaurant.

Zack headed in a run for the depot. The trainmaster of that division was there, raising hell about the Mexican, too.

'Goddamn him!' he said. 'Ain't he got sense enough to keep out of sight? He'll stir 'em up till they're apt to burn this train!'

That looked like the opening Zack had been waiting for.

'All right,' he said, 'let's get this train out of here. This is getting to where a lot of people are liable to get killed!'

'But the sheriff!' protested the division manager.

'To hell with the sheriff!' Zack bawled. 'You want to get this train burned up?'

The division manager didn't. He sent word for the engineer to pull out. Not a switch was to be lighted up, he said; and a switchman was to follow and close all switches behind the train.

Without a light on the train showing, the engineer backed up for slack, started easy to get drive, then opened the throttle wide. Here and there a gun cracked outside and broken glass clattered down inside the coaches. The show people lay down on the coach floors; nobody was hit.

Zack got a wire from Joe next day. Both he and the Mexican were safe. He was staying over another day, Joe said, to bury Lon Sealy there at Gulfport.

A man would think a bunch of cowhands performing in an arena every day could get enough roping and riding to satisfy them. But that wasn't the case with the 101 rodeo outfit on the show. They were always on the lookout for something new to rope or a tougher animal to ride.

The 101 outfit was Sundaying in Poughkeepsie once about 1910 when a bull elk and two cows escaped from the city zoo and swam over to an island out in the Hudson River. The head keeper of the zoo came around to the 101 show lots, calling on some of the hands to help him get the animals back.

'I can get a flat and a tugboat big enough to take six men and their horses over and bring the elk back,' he said, 'if you've got six men who aren't afraid to rope an elk.'

Talking that way was like waving a red flag in a bull's face. The 101 rodeo hands set out to put that keeper straight on one thing right then and there — they didn't back off from roping anything that walked, crawled, flew, floated, or ran on a track. They'd rope it and then ride it if it needed riding. They told him if it was a few little old elk he wanted captured, they were his huckleberries.

They got their best horses, the keeper got his boats, and the whole outfit moved out to the island in the middle of the river. The island was about four city blocks long and about one wide, with a little thicket of brush humping its middle. In the brush was where the bull elk and his two cows were hiding out.

The boat ran up solid on the shore and the cowhands walked their horses off onto the land and took out after the elk.

There wasn't anywhere for the elk to go except into the water, so that's where they went. But the elk cows didn't make their get-away fast enough and a couple of long-looping riders reached out into the river after them and tied on.

It was no job to pull the elk cows out of the water, but once out, they turned into cyclones, jumping, pitching, kicking, and fighting everything in sight. A couple of good heelers soon picked up their hind feet, however, and stretched them out. With their feet tied, it wasn't too much trouble to drag them aboard.

That left the big bull elk. He'd swam out a little way, then headed back for the island, taking up his stand at one end. There he stood with his hair standing on end like the bristles of a mad hog. He was stamping his forefeet, blatting like a goat, and shaking his big horns. He was on the prod aplenty and daring them to come after him.

They went; and the old bull came to meet them. One of the boys just barely got his horse to one side in time. The bull charged on past and the cowhand reached back over his shoulder with a backhand cast and latched onto one of the bull's big horns.

The bull never even hit the end of the rope before he'd wheeled and was charging back.

'Head for the boat!' yelled one of the others.

It sounded like a good piece of advice and the cowhand hooked spurs to his horse and headed for the boat, the roped elk charging him from behind.

'Pick up his heels before he goes onto the boat!' yelled the roper.

That was a good piece of advice, too, but the cowhand who tried spilled his loop on the sand.

That big elk was gaining on the horse every step he took. He went onto the boat right with him and drove his horns into the horse's rump. The drive of his charge jammed the horse against the two-by-four railing, splintering it; and horse, rider, and bull elk, all piled off into swimming water.

They sank, and when they came up, all three were tangled in the rope till it looked like nobody could get loose. The cowhand made it, however, the only trouble being that he couldn't swim. He grabbed his horse's tail and started hollering.

That's about all anybody else was doing by then, just hollering.

The current caught the horse and elk, sweeping them

down-river, with the cowhand still hanging to the horse's tail. The men in the boat took out after them. They pulled up beside the elk, who'd kicked loose and was swimming some ten feet to one side of the horse and man. One of the cowhands in the boat reached out and grabbed the bull elk by the horns.

'Turn that goddamn elk loose and come get me!' squalled the cowhand hanging to his horse's tail and just barely keeping his head above water. 'That elk can swim; I can't.'

The boatman cut the rope holding the elk and horse together. He held on to the elk end of the rope and shoved his boat toward the cowhand. Hands reached out and pulled the man aboard.

Now the problem was to get the elk to the far side of the river. One of the men pulled him up beside the boat and tied his head up alongside. But they couldn't land that way; they'd either kill the elk or he'd get up on the boat and kill somebody.

'Tie on another rope and let him have more slack,' a cowhand suggested.

So they did. They tied on another catch-rope, giving the big bull some sixty feet of slack and let him swim ashore. That was fine until the boat landed and the bull got his feet on the ground again. Then he made a run against the rope. And the cowhand handling the other end got his tie in a tangle around a post and couldn't get loose in time. The charging bull hit the end of the rope and turned a wildcat, unjointing his neck in the fall.

He was dead in about a minute.

On the road, especially back East where some folks looked to see horns sprouting out from under a cowhand's hat, Cactus Kurt Reynolds could get a lot of satisfaction out of playing it tough, making a big show of being a dangerous character.

Just the sight of the rodeo hands stamping into some of those eating places, rattling their spurs and talking like they owned a controlling interest in Oklahoma, was enough to make the waitresses and kitchen help duck and cut for cover. And if the waitress who came to serve Cactus Kurt's table happened to be young and skittish-looking, Cactus would always wait till the others had put in their orders, then hang a bold, hard eye on the poor girl and say: 'Listen, baby! Don't bring me meat. I eat prickly-pear. Just toast it over the fire a little. But be damned sure you don't scorch the thorns!'

What with that mean look and tough way of talking, Cactus would just about scare the pants off some of those little girl waitresses. And it never failed to get a big laugh out of the cowhands. It got to where they'd gang up and go into a restaurant, just to hear Kurt order his prickly-pear meal.

That's how they got to calling him Cactus Kurt. It wasn't till one night in Kingman, Kansas, that he finally earned his name, however.

The bunch entered an eating place there and Cactus Kurt put in his usual order.

The waitress didn't turn a hair. She just went back to the kitchen where the cook had already fixed up a prickly-pear pad that Zack had brought in ahead of time. She served old Cactus Kurt's prickly-pear broiled, with a little dab of fried beef gravy for an appetizer. Then she stood back, sober as a judge, to watch him eat it.

Cactus Kurt's eyes stood out on stems, but he was game. With the rodeo hands whooping and yelling all around him, he backed his ears and waded in. He did his best, but he couldn't cut the mustard. Before he'd downed half the pad, he knew he was whipped. He shoved back his plate, got to his feet, and handed the waitress a dollar tip.

'All right, sister,' he told her. 'You win!'

The waitress nodded and went on back to serving other customers. She never cracked a smile. It was plain to see that she'd been satisfied from the start that nobody could eat a mess like that.

Muchacho, the little Mexican kid who adopted Zack in Mexico City, was about ten years old when Zack smuggled him into the States.

The show was headed for the 101 Ranch on the Salt Fork, going into winter quarters, when they left Mexico. The boy stayed there on the ranch all winter, waiting on tables about the house and tending Zack's horses for him. Zack's wife Mabel helped him to learn English, and the next year he went with the show again. For some curious reason, he'd have nothing to do with the other Mexicans with the outfit; he threw in with the Indians, taking on their dress and manners, learning their language. He called himself Sky Eagle.

He was a shrewd one, this little Sky Eagle. He watched everything that went on around the show, and by the time he was eleven or twelve years old, he'd learned more about human nature than many a man learns in a lifetime. At fifteen, he was using this knowledge to his own advantage.

Up in Cincinnati, Sky Eagle bought some little yellow flowers, put them in a glass gallon jug of whiskey where they could be seen, and started selling 'Chief Sky Eagle's Wonder Remedy for Old Men!' He'd worked himself up a stunt of sticking a trick knife through one arm to attract a crowd and then starting his ballyhoo.

'Gentlemen!' he'd say, 'if there are any ladies present, I think maybe you more better walk away. I talk to men — important business. I have a story for old men.

'When I little boy, my father, he die. I live with uncle. One time my cousin, he come to my uncle. My uncle, he have many cattles, and this cousin, he come to help my uncle take care of these cattles. Until cow three year old, my cousin, he not let bull come around. Every year, we have old worn-out bull. We put him in good grass with heifers. He no bother them.

'One year, new kind of weed grow in that pasture. My cousin, he find old bulls hunting weed, eat up. Next year, all heifers in pasture with old bulls, they have calf. My uncle ask cousin how come. Cousin show uncle weeds the bulls eat up. Uncle watch bulls. He tell my cousin pick flowers, put them in whiskey. Uncle, he want to see will this weed work on old man like old bulls.

'Old man, he live there close by my uncle. Old man worn out. No good for woman. All time drink whiskey. Uncle, he give old man drink of this whiskey with flower in it. Pretty soon, uncle catch this old worn-out man in bed with pretty girl. Girl, she say this good man now. More better than young man.

'Come spring, my uncle, he hire many boys gather that

weed. Flowers like this flowers in this jug. Flowers hard to get. Old men come to my uncle. Buy this medicine. All have young pretty girls.

'My uncle, he dead now. I the only man know about this little flower. But I have it for sale. One dollar a bottle. You take my medicine five days, tablespoon three times a day. Then you be just like when you have twenty years ... You think I lie? You try one bottle. No good, I pay you one dollar. I pay more than one dollar; I pay dollar and a half.'

In the years he was with the show, Sky Eagle sold thousands of bottles of his young hope for old men. If the Mexican ever had a dissatisfied customer, Zack never knew it. But he did know of hundreds of orders Sky Eagle got in from previous customers, proving time and again the Bible quotation: 'As he thinketh in his heart, so is he.'

Sky Eagle's Rattlesnake Oil Liniment sold well, too. It was a mixture of gasoline, oil of mustard, and a few drops of rattlesnake oil, the last put in to get by the government drug inspectors. According to Sky Eagle, this liniment would cure anything except old age, and he had the remedy for that in his first bottle.

For his liniment spiel, Sky Eagle carried in his pocket a sponge soaked with the oil. He'd invite a man from the crowd to come up on the stand. With oil on his thumb, Sky Eagle would shake hands with the stranger, rubbing off the oil onto the back of the man's hand. Then he'd take out his bottle, pour a little of the oil into the palm of his victim's hand. He'd pause and wait dramatically for a moment, then invite the man to smell of the back of his hand. And the oil Sky Eagle had previously put there was strong enough to make the man sneeze.

'You see,' the supersalesman would exclaim. 'It prove what I say. Any liniment what soak through the human hand in one minute, she got to take out all pain.'

With this build-up, Sky Eagle could sell almost as much rattlesnake oil liniment as he could his wonder remedy for old men.

Zack sometimes thought maybe Sky Eagle had sold himself on his wonder remedy, judging from the number of women he had from the time he was old enough to use them. At a glance, the youngster could strip a woman with those roving eyes of his and make her wish he'd done it with his hands. He had as many as two wives a year, but they never seemed to be able to keep him from prowling wherever the range looked greener.

They were showing in Boston. Joe Miller came running into the ammunition wagon where Zack was having his trick shooting guns loaded with blanks.

'My god, Zack!' he said. 'There's three of our Indians got the smallpox!'

Zack got high behind in a hurry. It was bad enough for the Indians to have it, but if the word got out that there was smallpox with the show, the Miller Brothers would be ruined.

'Round the whole bunch up, Joe,' he said. 'We'll put them in a box car and ship them home.'

There were thirty-three Indians with the show. Zack and Joe had them all to paint their faces to keep anybody from seeing what was wrong, then loaded them into a box car and locked them up. The car was billed for White Eagle Station on the Salt Fork.

Zack, who'd been vaccinated against smallpox, rode the same train. Whenever the train stopped, Zack would get food and hand it to the Indians inside the pest car. He wouldn't let anybody else open that car or fool around it.

'I've got a mad Indian inside that car,' he said. 'He's lost his mind and he's dangerous. Better keep away.'

The car was sidetracked at White Eagle Station and left there till he could go get wagons to haul the sick Indians in. Six of them had the plague by now.

He hauled the Indians out to a little old abandoned shack that sat in the sand hills a few miles east of the 101 Ranch headquarters. He left them there and headed for Ponca City to get food and a doctor.

But the doctor could do little. Among the Indians, it is the custom to keep a dwelling shut tight around a sick one. This is to keep out the evil spirits. Zack and the doctor would enter the shack and wait on the Indians. They'd open all doors and windows to air the place out when they left. But before they were out of sight, the red men would shut every window and door down tight again.

Every Indian in the group took the disease. They lay there on the floor, day after day, with every door and window shut. Eleven died.

When the rest recovered, Zack and the doctor stripped them and bathed them in Lysol. Then they threw the discarded clothes in the shack and burned it to the ground.

There's one thing about a show on the road, Zack says. Time never hangs heavy on a man's hands.

19

THE ARMY THAT ZACK BOUGHT

WHEN WORLD WAR I first broke out in Europe, the price of good mules took a jump, and Zack went on the prowl again. If there was anything the 101 bushwhacker liked, it was dealing in mules. In the coming months he covered half a dozen states, buying hardtails where he found them and selling wherever he found a profit.

He teamed up with a friend, O. E. Kirtley, and the two started buying a lot of their mules out of the Mexico State of Coahuila. Kirtley knew some places in that wild country along the Rio Grande where, when the moon was right, a man bold enough to take his chances could cross livestock to the Texas side of the river without having to pay the Mexican export duty. It didn't hurt a man's profit any when he could do that.

This was during the time that Pancho Villa, the Mexican rebel leader, was making a strong bid for fame and glory in northern Mexico. That made it a little difficult for Zack and Kirtley. Lots of times a Mexican mule man wanted to know where a buyer stood on the *revolución* before he talked trade. Was he a Villa man, or was he *simpático* with the Huerta federals? And every time Zack and Kirtley met up with an army official, whether he was a Huertista or Villista, he demanded to see their permits.

Zack had managed for a permit signed by a Huerta leader and Kirtley had one bearing the signature of a Villa general. That way, they could get into country controlled by either army. If Zack ran into a Huertista, he showed his permit and passed Kirtley off as low-grade hired help. If they ran into a bunch of Villistas, it was the other way around. Where the hitch came was in always knowing which permit to show.

They finally worked that out smooth as silk, however. When they'd meet a strange army official, one of them would call out in greeting: '*Viva Mexico!*' If the official replied '*Viva Villa*,' Kirtley showed his permit. If they got a '*Viva Huerta*' answer, Zack took over.

In January of 1914, the two headed south from Marfa, Texas, bound for Presidio on the Rio Grande. Just across the river from Presidio was the Mexican town of Ojinaga, where Kirtley was due to receive seventy-five head of mules he'd bought out of Villa-held territory deeper in the State of Chihuahua. When they landed in Presidio after dark, Kirtley found they were too late. He came rushing back to the hotel where Zack was ordering supper.

'We're in a hell of a fix!' he told Zack. 'The Huertistas are in possession of Ojinaga and there's a big army moving in from the south, due here tomorrow. What'll we do about them mules? Every head's liable to be stolen if I can't get them out.'

Zack didn't have the answer to that one. Two mule-buyers couldn't make much of a showing against a couple of Mexican armies. Zack guessed about the best thing they could do was go to bed.

At sunup the next morning, all signs pointed to big doings on the Mexican side of the Rio Grande. Moving up through La Mula Pass was a dust cloud that nothing short of a big cow drive or an advancing army could stir up. And judging from the way the Huertistas were scampering about like red ants before a thundershower, it wasn't a cow drive lifting that dust.

The Huertistas were entrenched in a broad sand and gravel *vega* just under the high bluff on which sprawled the old adobe-walled town of Ojinaga. There were about three thousand of them under command of General Mercardo. Zack and Kirtley were half a mile away, but they could hear the Mexican officers barking orders right and left and see the men wheeling the cannon into position and the cavalry ranks shaping up outside the trenches.

There was plenty of activity on the Texas side of the river, too. The American general in charge of the United States garrison had his troops on the alert, his cannon loaded and trained across the river. He sent messengers across the Rio Grande to contact leaders of both Mexican armies with warnings to keep their war on the south side of the river. He told them that if one bullet kicked up dust on the north bank of the Rio Grande, he'd shell the hell out of both sides of the fight. Then he got his spyglass, Zack and Kirtley got theirs, and they all rode to a high point above the river to watch the show.

It was a good one while it lasted. The Villistas moved in over a slight ground rise and swarmed down upon the Huertista entrenchment, about four thousand strong. There wasn't much order to their attack; the cavalry came charging in, spread out like a big fan. But there was plenty of shooting and yelling.

The Huertistas were all set for them. Their cannon fire shook the hills and the shells knocked holes in the Villista ranks that a man could have driven a wagon and team through. But that didn't stop Pancho Villa's rebels. They filled the gaps and charged right up into the mouths of those cannon, throwing everything but their straw hats into the Huertista trenches.

It cost them heavy, but the Villista bunch poured on into the first of the three lines of Huertista trenches and cleaned it out with slashing sabers before they pulled back to get their breath and reorganize.

This gave all the Texas folks north of the river who hadn't witnessed the first clash a chance to join their neighbors on top of their houses where they had grandstand seats for watching the next Villista assault.

It wasn't long in coming. And it was just as fast and vicious as the first, with louder yelling and more shooting. Horses raced here and men there and both went down on either side, mortally hit and screaming through the last agony they'd know in this world. The foot-trampled dust rose in clouds, mixing with the smoke of roaring cannon and bursting shells, till finally the whole mad scramble was smothered in a hazy fog that drifted out over the valley of the Rio Grande.

Right in the big middle of the slaughter, one little Huertista found he needed a drink of water. Zack's eye fell on him the moment he spurred out of the boiling dust and headed for the Rio Grande. A hail of shot kicked up river sand all around the thirsty one, but none hit him, and he kept coming. At the water's edge he fell off his horse and bellied down for a drink. His horse was boogered, shying and snorting and stomping the ground. The Villista sharpshooters, bent on pegging his hide down while they had him out in the broad open, knocked sand and water all over him. But the Huertista held to his horse's reins and took his time about drinking all he wanted. When his thirst was satisfied, he swung back up into his saddle, waved his *sombrero*, and made a grand bow to the spectators across the river. Then he spurred back for the trenches, ready to kill more Villistas.

They knocked his horse from under him just as he reached the lines. He went down with the horse, but rolled clear of the saddle and came to his feet. He lifted his hat in one final wave, then dived into the trenches.

From the chances he took, that little Huertista soldier sure must have been thirsty. Zack and Kirtley hoped his luck held and he lasted the battle out.

This second assault of Villa's army drove the Huertistas back into the third and last line of trenches before the rebel leader withdrew his forces for a breather. Then out of the desert skyline came another dust cloud boiling up. It was fresh rebel forces, moving in to clinch Pancho's victory.

Mercardo had made a strong stand-off fight, but his goose was cooked now. He had his back to the river and all escape routes cut off. His was a groundhog case; it was take to the water or the dogs'll get you. Pancho Villa wasn't in the habit of taking prisoners.

Mercardo took to the water.

Leaving a suicide force in the last line of trenches to fight a rear-guard action, the Huertista general plunged into the river with the rest of his army and equipment, moving it into Texas.

That crossing was a tangled, bloody slaughter. The Villistas poured shot and shell into the retreating federals, knocking wagons clear out of the water, killing men, killing horses, dogs, women, jackasses. The screams of the wounded and dying were sharp and shrill against the rattle and thunder of the Villista gun-fire. There were long bloody streaks in the muddy waters of the Rio Grande that day; the catfish and turtles would feed well for a week.

But Pancho's men kept their aim low; not one bullet kicked up dust on the Texas side of the Rio Grande.

Mercardo made the crossing, bringing across alive some two thousand men, women, and children, and about thirty-six hundred horses, mules, jackasses, and burros. It was a noisy, motley band, with lost, naked children running about and screaming for their parents, and wives and camp-followers wailing for their dead. Then there were the wounded men, the pet dogs, monkeys, parrots, fighting cocks, and house-cats. They were strung out on the north bank of the river for half a mile, along with their plunder and salvaged equipment of war. Their cries of pain and distress filled the valley with sound.

Mercardo, a big, elegant Mexican of about fifty, with black mustaches framing a full-lipped mouth, rode up to the American general and offered his sword in surrender. The American general took the sword, but didn't know what to do with it or Mercardo or the army he'd brought with him. The general went down to the telegraph office and wired El Paso for instructions. El Paso wired Washington, D.C. That put the big bugs in Washington to running in circles. They didn't know what to do, either. The United States wasn't at war with Mexico and had been holding a neutral stand on the matter of the revolution. Therefore, Mercardo's horses, arms, and accouterments couldn't be considered as spoils of war. All they knew to do was to arrest the entire army and hold the equipment, subject to the customs duty imposed on imports. But just who was to pay this duty, and what was to become of the equipment, nobody seemed to know.

The American general did the best he could under the circumstances. He disarmed the army, placed men, animals, and equipment under guard, and waited for further instructions.

In the meantime, the authorities at Mexico City had got word of Mercardo's plight; they wired the office of the Mexican consul at San Antonio, giving that office full authority to sell the army equipment if a buyer could be found.

There was too much of G. W. Miller's trading blood in Zack for him not to be keeping up with everything going on and watching his chances to make a cleanup. He'd already sized up Mercardo's horses, mules, and equipment; and when he learned that the Mexican Government was ready to throw the stuff on the market, he was right there with an offer. He'd never bought an army before; he'd never heard of another American citizen who had. But in his time, he'd bought and sold just about everything else ever put on the market, and he guessed there was a first time for anything.

He wired the Mexican consular office in San Antonio. Would they lump the whole outfit off to him for forty-five thousand dollars?

Then he wired his brother Joe at the 101 Ranch:

COME AT ONCE   HAVE BANK GIVE ME FORTY-FIVE
THOUSAND DOLLARS CREDIT OR BRING THAT MUCH IN
GOLD   GOT A HELL OF A BIG DEAL ON

Joe didn't stall around calling for more information. He went down to Ponca City and had a bank wire Zack that they'd pay a draft for forty-five thousand, then caught a train south.

Mexico City held off on Zack's offer. Maybe it was a good one and maybe not; the authorities wanted to find out before making the trade. The consul general at San Antonio had recently been killed; so they wired his secretary to get in touch with a certain Salazar at Marfa and consult him in regard to selling at that price.

Zack knew this Salazar. He'd had some dealings with him one time when the Mexican worked on the railroad that was constructed through the 101 pastures up in Oklahoma. And all the affection there was between Zack and the Mexican wouldn't make a great long love-story. Zack knew if Salazar got a finger in this pie, he'd demand a great big cut — and get it, or throw a wrench into the deal.

Zack hit a run of luck when he started searching for Salazar. He found him locked up in the Marfa jail. That's where Milt Chastain, the Presidio County sheriff, had thrown the Mexican after catching him heading into the Chisos Mountains with four packs of silver stolen from the mines at Terlingua, Texas, and loaded on mules wearing the United States Government iron.

Zack had managed to get a line on a few of Salazar's other recent activities and was loaded for bear when he went up to the jail. He talked with the Mexican through the jail bars.

'Salazar,' he said, 'I can get you out of this jail and I'll do it — if you want out. But I don't think you do. You're a Huertista man here in a country that's strong for Pancho

Villa. Last year you caught the son of an American banker on a hunt down in Chihuahua and beat hell out of him, just to be showing off. People around here haven't forgotten that. If I take you out of here, you may be all right, and then again, you may wind up decorating one of the telegraph poles between here and the railroad station.'

Salazar sat on the jail cot, running nervous fingers through his coal-black hair and considering. The longer he weighed his chances, the less appetite he had for freedom. He finally told Zack he guessed he'd better just stay in jail.

That's what Zack had been after from the first. With Salazar held under lock and key by his own request, Zack was left to trade directly with the consul's secretary in San Antonio. By the time Joe arrived from Oklahoma, Mexico City was ready to sell out for Zack's first offer: forty-five thousand dollars. Joe looked the outfit over and gave the go-ahead sign. They closed the deal.

According to the agreement worked out finally between the Governments of the United States and Mexico, the army was to be moved under guard to Marfa. There, the soldiers were to be sent by train to Fort Bliss at El Paso for internment for the duration of the Mexican Revolution, while the refugees and their personal belongings were to be sent to Brownsville at the expense of the Mexican Government. There, they could be safely crossed back into Mexico at Matamoros, which was Huerta-held territory. The big problem now was getting the stuff moved over the rough mountain road to Marfa, seventy-five miles to the north.

Another problem presented itself, however, before Zack and Joe could get started on the first. A United States customs inspector seized all the horses Zack had bought, holding them for duty. The inspector evaluated the horses at thirty-five dollars a head and demanded three dollars and fifty cents on every one.

Zack got frothy about that. He claimed that much duty would ruin him; he said he didn't think he'd have to pay any duty, anyhow.

The inspector gave him the big laugh. 'You'll pay,' he declared, 'or you'll never move them.'

That started Zack to boiling. He went to see Joe. He said it looked like they were going to have to fist-whip some sense into that inspector's head or take a big loss on the horses they'd bought.

Joe told Zack to simmer down, that he couldn't fight the whole United States Government with his bare fists. 'Let me see what I can do by sending a wire or so,' Joe told him.

The next morning Zack looked out of his hotel window and saw the inspector and some of the border guards riding the pick of the Mexican cavalry horses. He knew they were his horses; he recognized an especially fine bobtailed gray horse that had stood out in the bunch the first time he'd looked them over. He roused Joe and they went down to jump the inspector out about riding horses that didn't belong to him.

The inspector sat his saddle and looked down upon the Miller brothers. 'These'll be your horses when you pay the duty on them,' he said bluntly. 'Until then, they belong to the Government, and government men will ride them if I say so.'

'All right,' said Joe. 'You're holding the whip hand now. Go on and ride them. But you'll be turning them over to us by four o'clock tomorrow afternoon.'

'I will — if you've paid that duty!' the inspector said.

'A hundred dollars,' said Joe, 'says you'll turn them over to us by four o'clock. And we don't pay the duty.'

The inspector called the bet. They let a hotel clerk hold stakes.

At four o'clock the following afternoon, the inspector came hunting Joe. The big official was wearing an ugly look on his face and carrying a telegram in one hand. 'Go pick up your hundred dollars,' he said. 'You get the horses.'

Joe didn't have to read that telegram to know who sent it and what it said. Joe and William Jennings Bryan were thick as three in a bed and right now Bryan was Secretary of State.

By night the Millers had everything in shape for moving, and at daylight the next morning threw the army, horses, and refugees on the long trail to Marfa. Joe handled the drive, just as he'd helped his father handle cow drives out of Texas into Kansas in his earlier years. He strung the outfit out in three separate sections, under troop guard, and they moved at the same speed that a longhorn herd moves — at the pace of the drags.

And there were plenty of drags. There were horses with their feet worn off to the quick and leaving blood in their tracks every step. Some were nothing but bone-racks held together by their hides, so starved and weak that they'd fall under the weight of a single rider.

When a horse of this kind fell, the rider would call on

others to help get the animal back on its feet; then he'd mount and ride on again.

Some had huge saddle sores on their backs, over which the Mexicans tied goat hides before mounting. There were mules and jackasses with collar and pack sores from which huge chunks of flesh had rotted out.

There was plenty of human misery, too. There were men and women who had to walk that rough, flinty road barefooted. A lot of the wounded soldiers were afoot. One by one, they began to fall out and had to be loaded on the wagons hauling guns and ammunition. On the wagons, they were bounced and jostled about, too weak and pain-racked to do more than groan now and then.

The drive stretched out along miles of twisting mountain road. Mile-high dust clouds stood over each section of the drive, and the sounds of the wagons, the livestock, and the people echoed among the sun-parched hills.

The norther hit them just before sundown. It came howling down across the ridges, driving ahead of it a roll of dust that hid the sun. It was icy cold and kicking up flinty gravels that stung and cut at a man's face. Joe threw the outfit into dry camp on top of the high, bald *mesa* where the storm hit them. That's all he could do. There was no timber for firewood. There was no water for the men or animals. But Joe knew he'd never be able to keep this outfit on the move in the dark and against a cold norther. The weak livestock would never face it, and the thinly clad Mexicans would freeze to death.

If the norther had been a wet one, they'd have frozen to death, anyhow. Half of the children were naked, and the few clothes the older ones wore were little more than rags.

The supply wagons carried blankets and wood to help keep them warm, but there wasn't enough to go around. The wounded and the food for the outfit had used up too much wagon space.

With the cold wind putting an ache in their bones, the shivery Mexicans lined up to receive army rations. The women cooked the food over what little wood they could get and the greasewood brush the children could gather. By the time supper was over, all the wood hauled into camp was gone, and the entire outfit was combing the *mesa*, fumbling about in the dark for greasewood, dry yucca stalks, anything that would burn.

It was poor firewood they got, however. Both the greasewood and the yucca flamed high and hot for a few minutes, then died out; a moment later the high-crying wind had whipped it away, even to the ashes.

Some of the Mexicans crawled in between sacks of oats, trying to keep warm. Some dug holes in the ground and covered themselves with dirt and any sack or tattered piece of blanket they could steal from the next one. Children cried out with cold and the wind chopped off the sound.

Finally, in desperation, the Mexicans started burning saddles. The saddles were slow burning and kept a good heat for a long time.

Zack and Joe Miller had driven into Marfa in an automobile to spend the night, leaving Kirtley with the refugees. And when Kirtley caught the Mexicans burning up perfectly good saddles, he got up out of his bed and tried to put a stop to it. But he didn't have much luck. Some of the bolder or more desperate Mexicans let him know in no uncertain terms that they'd just as soon scrap him for the chance to burn a saddle as they had to freeze to death. And what did he expect to do about it?

That wasn't hard for Kirtley to answer. Using a six-shooter, he might whip some of them. But he couldn't hope to whip them all. And who wanted to get his guts carved out on a cold night like this?

Kirtley went on back to bed.

By daylight, the refugees had burned over four hundred saddles.

When Zack and Joe came driving in a little after sunup, Kirtley told them what had happened and showed them the heaps of cinch rings and metal stirrups the wind had left after blowing away the ashes. Kirtley seemed mighty put out about losing those saddles.

Joe Miller grinned at him. 'Hell, Kirtley,' he said, 'what'd you try to stop the poor devils for? Cold as it was last night, I'd have burnt my own saddle if I'd been caught out without a wind-break or firewood.'

That day was cold, and the next night. But the norther had really blown itself out that first night; so the Millers didn't lose any more saddles.

Three days later, the drive pulled into Marfa. Three graves back along the mountain trail marked the loss in human lives on that drive. But since three babies were born on the same trip, Zack figured they were about even on that score.

He also got a colt or two. But not nearly enough to re-place the fifty head of horses that had died. Some starved to death because they'd never eaten oats before and wouldn't touch those Zack tried to feed them. Others ate too many oats and foundered themselves. Some died from simple exhaustion and the pain of infected wounds.

But there were plenty of horses left when the outfit went into camp just outside of Marfa — good horses, too. One of them was the war horse of General Mercardo. He was a heavily built, thoroughbred-looking horse, a creamy *grulla* dun with a black stripe down his back and a coal-black mane and tail. Seven bullet scars marked his body, three of them showing in the flesh just above the neck bone where wild horses are sometimes creased for capture.

At the stockyards where the horses were corralled, the big Mexican general put his arms around the *grulla's* neck and held him a long time, crying like a baby.

'Seven times you have been wounded in battle,' he said to the horse, 'and seven times you have saved my life. And now comes the final parting.' He turned to Zack.

'Promise me, *Señor*,' he said, 'that he will not know hunger.'

Zack promised, and the general seemed satisfied; but when he left, he had the walk of a man who had just lost a son.

Word of the big army buy had made the rounds by the time the Millers had pulled into Marfa with the outfit. And waiting for them when they got there were a couple of men vitally interested in horses. One was a brand inspector, in the employ of the Texas Cattlemen's Association. He demanded to be allowed to cut the horse herd for animals wearing the irons of Texas ranch outfits he represented and for Mexican members of the Association. He said there'd been many a good horse stolen out of Texas in the last few years that had wound up south of the Rio Grande and he was satisfied he'd find some of them in this bunch.

This inspector's claim was valid enough. The Millers had no desire to hold stolen stuff; they turned the inspector loose on the herd. He rode through the horses and every time he located a brand that was registered in the little brand book he packed, he cut out the animal wearing it and the Millers had it thrown into a separate corral. By the time the inspector was done, the Millers were short close to a hundred horses, most of them good ones.

This was bad. But what was worse was the claim of the second man, a Mexican official from El Paso. He also claimed a hundred head. He claimed them on the ground that the Mexican Government had been swindled on the deal, that the Millers had taken advantage of the ignorance of the consul general's secretary at San Antonio and hadn't paid half what the stuff was worth. He said his pick of a hundred head of horses might make him see his way clear to letting the deal go on through. Otherwise, he'd be forced to stir up a big stink on both sides of the Rio Grande about why the trade wasn't transacted through his office instead of the one at San Antonio. Which, naturally, would keep the Millers from selling off any livestock or equipment until the matter had been cleared up.

Any way Zack and Joe looked at it, this was just a plain, bald-faced case of high-handed graft, with the trimmings left off. All the Mexican official needed to make it an old-style hold-up was a loaded six-shooter and a bandana with slits cut for eyes. But all they could do about it was swear at the Mexican. Which they did, to his face. But the Mexican didn't let it get under his skin; he just handed them a smug grin and went to inspecting the horses. He knew he had them over the big barrel where they couldn't get away. And they knew it, too. Let him stir up a big international row over this deal, as he could do, and they'd be twenty years getting the red tape cut away to where they could sell a horse or mule.

Joe and Zack moved over to the corner of the horse corral to talk it over. They worried it around in their minds for an hour, but they couldn't find an out.

'Maybe,' said Zack, 'we can pay the son-of-a-bitch off and get him out of the way.'

'Hell!' said Joe. 'It's horses he wants and we've got more horses than money.'

'Well, I'll be damned if I aim to let him top out the herd,' Zack said.

He went back to wrangle with the Mexican. They argued back and forth for the better part of an hour before the Mexican finally agreed to cut the horses with Zack, the Mexican choosing a horse, then Zack choosing one. That way, the Mexican couldn't get the pick of the bunch.

In the herd of livestock Zack had bought off the Mexican Government were six hundred head of burros. As far as Zack knew, the little animals were absolutely worthless and he told Joe that the only thing he knew to do was just turn them out on the range.

A bystander heard that remark and spread the information around, and in a little bit, three disturbed ranchers had Zack cornered and were telling him what he could do and what he couldn't. They said he'd play hell turning those burros loose on the range. They said those burros would crawl through any fence ever built, that grass was too scarce to carry that extra load, and that they'd be goddamned if they'd put up with it.

That horse-stealing Mexican official already had Zack fighting mad and he was just drawing in a long breath to tell these Presidio County cowmen where to head in when a short fat man resembling a dry-land farmer slid down off a corral fence and put in a word.

'What'll you take for them burros?' he wanted to know. 'I got grass out in the Chisos yonder that ain't never been et!'

Zack nearly jumped down his throat. 'What'll you give?'

'Well,' said the fat one, 'considering the setup here, I'd give maybe a dollar for the whole six hundred.'

'You've bought you some burros,' Zack said. 'Pay me!'

The fat man handed Zack a dollar. The cowmen backed off, looking a little sheepish. Zack saddled to go cut horses with the Mexican official.

Zack was whipping the Mexican bad on that cut, picking horses for their build instead of the fat they carried, as the Mexican was doing, when two Jews entered the corral. They wanted to buy the army wagons, offering so much per wagon.

'Hell!' flared Zack, 'I got no time to go back to Presidio to count wagons. I'm too busy getting robbed. Tell you what, there's five or six acres of them wagons down there. Go measure off the ground they cover and I'll sell the whole kit and boodle for five hundred dollars an acre. And that's my trading price. Don't come back here trying to jew me down!'

The Jews left in an automobile to go measure the number of acres the wagons covered. Before they were out of sight, the fat man who'd bought the burros came wading through the corral dust.

'My boys,' he told Zack, 'they don't want me to buy them burros. They say we've got no use for them. I reckon I better let you have them back.'

'And I reckon you won't,' said Zack. 'You bought them burros just the same as if you'd paid fifteen hundred for them. Now they're yours and I want you to get the damn' things out of that corral yonder. We're needing it, bad.'

The fat man tried to argue, but Zack went right on back to cutting horses and wouldn't listen.

About sundown, the fat man and his boys turned the burros out of the corral and headed toward the Chisos with them.

The Jews came back from a fast trip to Presidio with the information that there were five acres of wagons down there, but that they'd decided they couldn't pay over two thousand for the whole lot.

'I told you,' Zack said, 'that my price was five hundred an acre.' And he went on cutting horses.

The Jews looked at one another, did some fast talking for a minute, then started following Zack out into the swirling clouds of hoof-trampled dust.

'We pay you twenty-five hundred now,' the big one said.

Zack looked at him. 'Like hell,' he said. 'You wouldn't take me up when I offered to sell for that. Now my price is twenty-seven-fifty. And if I'm stopped again, it'll be three thousand dollars!'

Blood rushed into the face of the big Jew and his features took on a pained expression. But his smaller partner was tugging at his sleeve.

'Trade with the man, Ike!' he crowded. 'Trade quick. He means what he says!'

Zack stopped cutting horses long enough to receive a check for twenty-seven hundred and fifty dollars. Before he could get away, the big Jew was trying to bargain for the harness.

'I'll take eighteen hundred for the harness!' Zack told him.

'Eighteen hundred!' From the look on the big Jew's face, Zack might as well have cut him between the eyes with his quirt.

But the little Jew was excited and twitching the big one's coat-sleeve again. 'Trade with him, Ike!' he begged. 'Trade quick. The man means what he says!'

It took exactly one minute for Zack to sell the amount of harness necessary to pull off five acres of wagons.

Early the next morning, Zack went down to see the freight agent about cars to ship his horses to Oklahoma.

'We'll need eighty cars,' he said. 'What'll the rates be?'

The agent started thumbing through his book to find the freight rates on horses.

'From here to Bliss, Oklahoma,' he said, 'it'll cost you a hundred and eighty-five dollars a car.'

Zack studied on that a moment. At that price the railroad company was going to cut a bigger slice out of this pie than he liked to see slip through his hands. There'd already been two big slices cut out — that hundred head of stolen horses the brand inspector had claimed, and the other hundred head that the Mexican official had stolen. Zack was getting mighty fed up on that sort of thing.

'Let me see that book,' he said.

The agent lifted an eyebrow, but shoved the book toward Zack. Zack thumbed through it till he came to the pages giving the freight rates on horses. Down at the bottom of one page, he saw a starred footnote referring to a certain page in Speiden's tariff book. Zack looked that up. In effect, the passage stated that horses and mules used for herding purposes, dispatched from the same place to the same owner, went for the same rate as cattle, plus ten dollars per car — a saving of over a hundred dollars a car, or eight thousand dollars in all. The only rub was that Zack wasn't shipping cattle.

But the trading son of the trading G. W. Miller wasn't called the '101 Bushwhacker' for nothing. He'd lived too long under his father's schooling. Without saying a word to the freight agent, he picked up a telephone and put in a call for W. D. Measdy, a cowman at Alpine.

When connections were made, Zack said: 'Measdy, what would you take for three carloads of calves, delivered here at Marfa by tomorrow night?'

Measdy hedged. 'How bad do you want them?'

'Not too bad,' Zack lied.

'Like hell you don't!' Measdy pounced. 'They'll cost you twenty dollars a head.'

'That's a hold-up price!' Zack shouted.

'Sure it is!' agreed Measdy. 'You want them?'

'I'll give you eighteen dollars,' Zack said. 'And not a damned cent more.'

'You've bought some calves,' Measdy said, then goaded Zack a little. 'You must want them bad. I'd have taken fifteen.'

'That's all right about how bad I want them,' Zack said. 'You just have them here in time to load on that night train to San Antonio tomorrow night. Or it's no deal.'

Measdy said he'd have them there and Zack hung up.

He turned to the freight agent. 'I'm shipping a car of cattle with each of the three trains going out of here to-morrow night. The horses on the other cars are just for herding the stock — so I'm claiming that eighty-dollars-a-car rate.'

The freight agent was staggered. 'My god!' he said, 'you can't make that stick. Whoever heard of needing two thousand horses to herd a hundred and twenty calves?'

Zack got up to leave. 'You don't,' he said, 'know how wild them goddamned Measdy calves are!'

He grinned and walked out, ready to go help Joe super-vise the storing of guns and ammunition into warehouses that Joe had rented.

And the rate stuck.

The wagonloads of knives and firearms with which General Mercardo's army had been equipped would have made a fine study in the evolution of man's weapons. There were fist-sized *puñales* for stabbing, single-action Colt six-shooters, long bladed *machetes* for slashing, sabers, muskets, buffalo guns, muzzle-loading shotguns, saddle rifles, .30–.30 Winchesters, and seventeen hundred and twenty machine guns with thousands of rounds of ammunition. The ma-chine guns had never had the covers off; nobody knew how to operate them.

All this, the Millers stored, eventually shipping it to Brownsville where it was sold back across the border to the Huertistas. Along with it, they sold a full carload of saddles.

That same afternoon, under government supervision, a livestock dipping-vat was primed with a fresh solution and the Mexican soldiers and refugees, down to the last baby and hairless dog, were herded through it. Rid of their fleas and lice, they were loaded on a train bound for Brownsville, where they were eventually crossed back into Mexico, some five hundred miles down the Rio Grande.

The afternoon train on the following day brought the three carloads of calves Zack had bought from Measdy, and the horse-loading began. The Millers had hired every hand they could get, but the work still ran on into the night. One bunch of mules balked on them. When one of the workmen walked into their pen and cracked a whip, the mules, instead of rushing toward the loading chute, all ran to the far side of the pen and lined up, shoulder to shoulder, standing expectantly with their heads held high. No amount of crowding or whipping could budge them from their stand.

Nobody could figure them out. Zack had the loading crew let the mules alone awhile, then try them again. Dark came, and still every time a man walked into the pen and shouted at the mules or cracked a whip at them, they rushed to the far side of the pen and lined up. And there they stood, plainly waiting for something. But nobody knew what.

Finally, a little old Mexican who'd been watching the proceedings from his perch on top of the corral fence, climbed down and sidled up to Zack.

'*Señor*,' he said timidly, 'theesa mulas, she train good for seelver mine. You pop the wheep, she line up for packs to be put on. Maybeso, more better usa the bell-mare.'

Zack recollected now an old swaybacked bell-mare they'd loaded earlier in the evening. Somebody who wasn't wise to the nature of mules had cut her away from her charges.

Zack ordered her found and unloaded. Then he turned
her over to the little Mexican who'd tipped him off.
Proudly, the old one led the mare past the pack mules, with
her deep-toned bell bonging and clanging. The mules fell
in behind her. They followed her right on into the car, so
fast that the little Mexican just barely escaped their
trampling hoofs.

An hour later, this same little Mexican opened his bag
of tricks and pulled out an even neater one. He was the
one who suggested that Zack load the horses claimed by the
brand inspector and the Mexican official. Who could
blame them, he pointed out, if they happened to ship the
inspector's horses to the Mexican official in El Paso and the
ones the official claimed to Oklahoma. 'Just a leetle
meestake in the dark, no?'

That 'leetle meestake' was made in the dark, yes, and
the brand inspector notified of the slip — after the train
had pulled out. The Mexican official was left in the dark,
however, and didn't learn what had happened till the
Millers were unloading at Bliss, Oklahoma. He sent them
a hot wire then. He was forced to refuse the horses they'd
shipped him, he said; they were stolen horses and a brand
inspector was there to claim them. He demanded, in the
name of his office, that he be shipped the horses he'd spent
all day cutting out of the pens at Marfa.

Zack was very much disturbed and sent him a quick
wire back, inviting him to come get his horses — if he
thought he could.

Evidently, the Mexican official didn't think he could.
The Millers never did hear any more out of him.

Turned out on the 101 range, the Mexican army horses
healed up and put on good flesh. Most of them sold to a

New York buyer at sixty dollars a head. Two hundred and thirty went into the Miller Brothers 101 Wild West Show. Of these, some ninety head finally wound up as courier ponies on the battlefields of Flanders. Back in the thick of another war.

About a year later, Zack got an order from the Greek Government offering fifteen dollars a head for burros if he could fill an order for five hundred. Zack thought he could. He caught a train for Marfa and hunted up the Chisos Mountain rancher who'd paid him a dollar for six hundred. Zack offered the man twelve-fifty a head for the burros, but the rancher was cagey.

'I'll not take a cent less than fifteen,' he said. 'You're getting thirty or thirty-five and I want some of that fat profit.'

Zack denied this and spent a couple of days trying to buy those burros, but he never could shake that fat rancher from his starting price of fifteen dollars. He finally gave it up as a bad job and pulled out home.

The next time he heard from that Chisos Mountain rancher, the man and his sons were shooting the burros and selling their hides at six-bits apiece.

This Mexican army was the only army Zack ever bought, but he's still in the market if the price is right. He cleaned up around sixty-five thousand dollars on that one.

His mule-buying friend, Kirtley, though, didn't do so well. Kirtley never did learn what happened to that seventy-five head of mules he'd bought down in Chihuahua. His guess was that Pancho Villa got off with them. And Kirtley had paid out good hard cash for those mules, too!

20

THE SHOW IN ENGLAND

In 1914, when the Anglo-American Exposition was held in London to celebrate a hundred years of peace between English-speaking peoples, the Miller Brothers split their show in New York, loaded half of it on a boat, and crossed the Atlantic to take part in the big doings. They showed in the Shepherd's Bush Stadium where the Olympic Sports events used to be held, and started making some good money. The take was so good, in fact, that Zack, in charge of this show, was considering making a big prowl all over Europe with the outfit. But a war bobbed up in his face and knocked the props from under his plans.

The boat docked on April 29 and before Zack could get the show unloaded, Sir Thomas Lipton, the big tea mogul, sent around his automobile and chauffeur with an invitation for Zack to come spend the night on his private yacht. Back in 1911, when the Millers had the show outfit making moving pictures in Santa Monica Canyon at Venus, California, Sir Thomas Lipton had visited the lot and Joe had taken time off to show him around. Now the big tea man wanted to return the hospitality.

Zack couldn't get away till the show was unloaded, but the next night he went. Sir Thomas had a party arranged for him by then and it was the swankiest blow-out Zack ever mixed in. Sir Thomas was a big portly man who saw the silver lining in every cloud; and when he entertained, he didn't stop to count the cost. There was champagne enough on that yacht to have floated it and the amount of food put before the guests would have fed a big trail crew all the way from Texas to Montana. And to top it off, there were sixteen of the prettiest actresses in London at the time — two to a man. Which gave even Zack, who claimed he always ran second in any woman chase, a fair-to-middling chance. Zack guessed that, for just an old Oklahoma prairie cowhand, he was sure traveling in high cotton at that party.

That night he met the Earl of Lonsdale, the biggest sport in England. Everybody addressed the earl as 'your lordship,' but that didn't set well with Zack. He just called him plain 'Lonsdale,' shocking the hell out of everybody except the earl — he liked it.

Lonsdale told Zack that he was managing a horse show at the time and had just received a big disappointment; he'd engaged five of the most wonderful Cossacks to perform during the exhibition, but had been advised that same day that they'd be unable to fill the engagement.

The champagne had Zack's world looking rosy and level; he offered to help out. 'I've got five Cossacks on my show that you can borrow,' he said. 'And if they're not able to do anything the ones you had engaged can do, then yours are supermen.'

Lonsdale was happy to accept the offer. So on the night of his horse show, Zack pulled the Cossacks out of the 101 outfit and sent them over.

Those Cossacks were good. They could ride fast horses, standing on their backs and balancing with poles. Sometimes they'd hang by their feet to the saddle, or maybe two of them would ride standing in the saddle on horses running as a team while a third stood with a foot on each of their shoulders. They went over big in Lonsdale's horse show and their loan helped to make Zack a friend among the British royalty.

The 101 show made good beer talk in the pubs all over England. The British especially liked the Indians. But, as usual, the humane societies started kicking up a row. They thought the way Bill Pickett twisted a steer's neck to throw him was horrible and wrote pieces in the paper about it. And human nature being what it is, these newspaper stories made good publicity; people read them and shuddered and then hurried down to buy a ticket to witness this savage event and shudder some more. Zack guessed if Bill Pickett had still been bulldogging steers with his teeth, the outfit couldn't have seated the crowds. But Bill had had to give that up; the humane societies in America had romped on him too hard.

With the aid of these British humane societies, the 101 Wild West Show enjoyed a good business. Finally, somebody brought pressure to bear and had Bill Pickett arrested, charged with cruelty to dumb animals. Zack paid Bill out, and when he learned that the fine amounted to only twenty-five dollars, American, he made an agreement with the proper authorities to pay that amount once a week and let Bill go right on with his 'horrible steer torture.'

Zack didn't want to lose the good publicity the humane societies were giving the show.

For his stay in England, Zack rented a house at 68 Holland Road, from the wife of an English doctor who'd just died. With it came an excellent cook, a butler, and a governess for his little seven-year-old daughter Virginia. The butler, George, a long tall drink of water who'd been with the house since a boy, probably had more pride in the household and its honorable traditions than its owners, and every Sunday morning he'd come up to Zack's room, shocked to death.

'Sir,' he would say, 'downstairs there is a warrant for you, sir.'

And Zack, knowing that it was a couple of bobby cop representatives of the humane societies, would send down Bill Pickett's twenty-five-dollar fine, and George could rest easy for another week.

If the butler ever slept, Zack never caught him in the act. Zack could come in off a big party at four o'clock in the morning and head for the front door with his key; but he'd never get to use it. George would be on hand, ready to open the door and take Zack's hat and coat the minute his bootheels popped the steps.

That got on Zack's nerves a little. 'Look, George,' he said one night, 'there's no need for you to stay up this late to open a door for me. I've got a key.'

'Sir,' said George haughtily, 'I've been with this house for thirty years and never yet has the master unlocked this door!'

That let Zack know he'd been whipped in this argument before it got started. You couldn't any more explain George's loyalty to this old English house than you could explain the loyalty of the catch-dog Friday that had saved Zack from a steer-goring on the 101 range, back in the nineties. There wasn't any reason to it. So Zack just let it ride and quit bothering to pack a house key.

Zack couldn't see much reason, either, back of the British Government's demand that he install one toilet, consisting of a commode and a shower bath, for every eight people on the lot.

There were some forty Indians with the show and Zack tried to explain that you couldn't blindfold and back an Indian under one of those showers. But the authorities were firm; Zack had the toilets installed and the Indians kept right on going behind a high wall to relieve themselves and doing what little washing they found necessary — mostly just removing their war-paint — in a standard number three washtub. Some of them did rake up the nerve to reach in and flush a commode or two, dodging back to safety like maybe they'd just sprung a bear trap. And they got a devil of a big kick out of listening to the roar of the water pouring through the basins. But not many of them were bold enough to try that.

In their second week of showing at Shepherd's Bush, Lord Lonsdale came to Zack and asked him to prepare a show for the royalty of England. He said King George V, Queen Mary, his mother Queen Alexandra, and Empress Marie of Russia would attend the show as his guests. He explained that special feature acts would be required, since it wasn't considered ethical for royalty to see a whole show from beginning to end.

Zack fixed them up the best feature acts he knew. Besides some of the regular performances, he staged a push-ball game between the cowboys and Indians, with all players on both sides mounted on horses. Then there was the best of the trick riding, trick roping, Cossack riding, bronc-busting, and Bill Pickett's bulldogging act.

Evidently, it proved a thriller for the royal group. They sat there and patted each other's hands back and forth — regular hand-clapping being only for common people — until the special feature acts were over and Zack called a halt to give them a chance to leave. But they didn't take it. They just kept sitting there, still patting each other's hands, till finally Zack went on with the show.

Zack's daughter Virginia got the shock of her young life at that show. She was all prettied up to present flowers to the King and Queen; and while she was making the presentation, King George got so excited watching old Chain Foot try to unload a bronc peeler that he forgot and started clapping his royal hands like a commoner. And the Queen caught him at it and slapped his hands to stop him. And Virginia came away from the royal tribune with her mouth open and her eyes round as saucers.

'I didn't think,' she said in an awed voice, 'that *anybody* could slap a king!'

His Majesty and party sat in their royal boxes till the last stunt was pulled. In the meantime, the Earl of Lonsdale sent word to Zack to line up the entire troupe at the gate when the show was over; that the royal party wanted to shake hands with each performer. Which they did, bowing and smiling and saying over and over: 'Most wonderful exhibition! Most wonderful exhibition!'

Lonsdale told Zack later that that was the first time he'd ever seen the King and his party sit through a whole show. Empress Marie couldn't get through talking about the daring rides made by the Russian Cossacks.

One day Bill Pickett came to Zack, wanting to know if

it'd be all right if he took supper with an English earl who had invited him out to his estate.

'The gentlemun,' the bulldogger explained, 'wants that his younguns git to see a black man what can throw a bull.'

'Sure,' said Zack. 'Go ahead, Bill, if you want to.'

Bill guessed he wanted to. He said it'd been a long time since he'd been out of town now and he'd like to see what kind of crops these English people had on their land. Bill always had been a great hand to want to see crops growing.

The Negro left — and was back by a little after sundown with his eyes bulging out of his head.

'Fo' gawd's sake, Mistah Zack,' he said, 'if I eveh comes to you askin' to go someplace agin, you tell me no!'

'What happened, Bill?' Zack wanted to know.

The big bulldogger took a deep breath. 'That white man,' he began, 'he takes me out to the biggest house I ever see, Mistah Zack. The eatin' room, it's half as big as the barn back on the ranch. He takes me in there and sots me down right beside the white folks at the table and there was lots of ladies and chilluns, too!

'They sots me down at that table, and I sweah, Mistah Zack, we had a dozen knives on one side of the place and a dozen forks on the other. And spoons all around. And there was a white man waiting on that table, just like niggahs back home, and one waited on me. He stood right behind where I eats and ever time he brung me some vittles, he'd catch his breath like he'd dropped something or other. But he hadn't — I looked.

'Right first off, they brings me wine. And I don't swallah quick enough and bubbles went running up into mah nose. But after that I swallahed quick and they don't.

'This man waiting on mah plate, he'd come set me down something I doan know how to eat. So I'd watch the gentlemun across the table and see how he et it. But befo' I'd catch on and try mah hand, here come this waitah and takes it away from me. Purty soon I gits 'way behind, Mistah Zack, and I'm a shamed niggah. Finally, I quits trying to eat and just sets there and looks down at mah plate and wants for to be back on the Salt Fork with a bait of spareribs and dutch-oven bread. Them was scrumptuous vittles, suh, but this niggah doan git none.'

Bill finished and stood looking down at his feet.

Zack said: 'Bill, why don't you go into the mess tent and see if you can get the cook to rustle you some left-overs.'

The face of the big Negro lighted up. 'Yassah, Mistah Zack,' he grinned. 'Ise a hongry niggah, all right, suh. I sure is!'

George Hooker, the big breed trick rider, made out a lot better in English society than Bill Pickett. George was a good showman, but he had a bad reputation around women. Let him get one cornered and she could be willing or not, it didn't matter much to George. He had the strength to take her anyhow.

Back in the States, Zack had nearly beaten the big Negro-Mexican to death once with the butt-end of a shot-loaded quirt for hemming up a fifteen-year-old girl and trying to rape her. That hadn't stopped George, though; it'd just taught him caution. He kept right on at his woman-hunting. And in London, he hit the jackpot.

Just how he managed it, nobody ever knew. But they hadn't been showing at Shepherd's Bush more than a week when every night some grand English lady, as pretty as a New Year's calendar, came driving up to the show lot in a long shiny automobile and sent her chauffeur out to get George. She'd take George off somewhere and rig him out in garments like the British noblemen wore, then they'd hit the town's swank night spots. And George wouldn't show up on the lot again till time to put on his riding act the next day.

None of the race-conscious cowhands from Texas and Oklahoma would have admitted that they envied the big yellow-skinned breed, but they made it up to fix George for slow traveling if they ever caught him bragging about bedding up with a white woman. George either got wind of it or had the sense to know it wouldn't set well with the hands to talk. He just went right along with his affair and never opened his head about it, one way or another. And when he left England, he was wearing a finger ring with a diamond that gathered light like a sun glass. Evidently, this English lady appreciated all George Hooker had to offer.

They had been showing in London six months when one morning Zack's butler came to his room with the usual shocking report: 'There's a warrant for you, sir!'

Zack thought it was the same bobby cops coming to collect Bill Pickett's fine; he sent George back downstairs with the usual twenty-five dollars.

In a minute, George was back in the room, shaking all over. 'They're coming up, sir,' he reported. 'There are soldiers with them. Excuse me, sir, but I would make haste, sir! They seem to be in somewhat of a hurry.'

Zack dressed and went down to be met by a couple of bobby cops and five soldiers. They greeted him with official dignity and one of the officers served him with a warrant that no mere twenty-five dollars could handle. It was a royal impressment warrant which read:

National Emergency. *Impressment Order under Section 115 of the Army Act.*

To Zack T. Miller, 68 Holland Rd. W.

His Majesty, having declared that a national emergency has arisen, the horses and vehicles of the 101 Ranch Show are to be impressed for the public service, if found fit (in accordance with Section 115 of the Army Act), and will be paid for on the spot at the market value to be settled by the purchasing officer. Should you not accept the price paid as fair value, you have the right to appeal to the County Court (in Scotland the Sheriff's Court), but you must not hinder the delivery of the horses and vehicles, etc. The purchasing officer may claim to purchase such harness and stable gear as he may require with the horse or vehicle.

Charles Carpenter, Sergt.
Place *Shepherd's Bush Exhibition*
Date *7th August, 1914*

When the British Government finished with the confiscation of the 101 Wild West Show animals and equipment for its war with Germany, Zack had six horses left, a wagon or two, and some harness — and a bale of ten-shilling bank-notes. These bank-notes, printed in red and only on one side, amounted to seventeen thousand pounds (about eighty thousand dollars) and somehow reminded Zack of the Duke-of-Durham cigarette coupons he used to save as a kid to get prizes.

And the show was ruined!

Zack collected from the British Government for his horses and equipment on Tuesday following the Sunday confiscation. That same day, every bank in England was closed by governmental order for a period of two weeks. A war panic was on and the people had been going to the sock with what money they had. All silver money faded from circulation overnight; there was no change anywhere.

Zack had a little English secretary with a money-making bent at that time. The two men caught a cab after leaving the government offices where Zack had collected his money.

In the cab, the secretary said: 'You know, Mr. Miller, I've been thinking. I believe I can get you six dollars American money in checks or express orders for every English pound you've got there.'

Zack doubted that. The rate of exchange was then four dollars and eighty cents to the pound. 'That's a whole lot of profit,' he said.

'I can get it if you'll let me have the money,' the secretary insisted.

Zack never had been in the habit of looking the other way when the chance for profit came along. 'Well,' he said, 'I'll let you make a try. If you can swing it, I'll give you five per cent of all the clear profit you can make.'

Zack handed his secretary a hundred pounds for a starter and dropped him off at the Savoy Hotel, then went on to the house on Holland Road to put the rest away and try to figure out how to get his show troupe back to America. That was apt to prove a problem. With Great Britain at war, nobody would want to ride one of her ships; they were too likely to get torpedoed out of the water. Everybody would be trying to get passage on American ships and maybe there wouldn't be enough to go around.

There was another problem, too. Two or three weeks back, Zack had leased a bunch of his Sioux Indians to a circus man named Sarraisani who was showing in Germany. With all communications cut off now between England and Germany, how was he to get those Indians back home?

Zack was eating lunch and still wallowing these problems around in his mind when his secretary called him by telephone.

'I have six hundred dollars for you,' the man said jubilantly. 'And I'm sure that I can put out two hundred pounds more this afternoon.'

Zack did some quick calculating. Already, the secretary had made a hundred and twenty dollars. And if he could put out twice that much money between now and night, that would be two hundred and forty more. 'Bring me what American checks you've cashed,' he said, 'and I'll let you have two hundred pounds more.'

That evening Zack wired Joe at the 101 Ranch to try to get in touch with Sarraisani in Germany and tell him to get those Indians back to England or America. He figured Joe could maybe reach Sarraisani; America wasn't yet at war with Germany. Then Zack started making the rounds of the steamship offices, trying to book passage on American ships for his troupers. It was a pretty hopeless job. The steamship offices were jammed with Americans, all scared sick of the war and howling for quick passage home. Zack found that it was useless trying to get all his show bunch on the same boat. All he could do was book passage for a few here and a few there and some of these would have to wait for weeks.

The next morning, his secretary was out to the house early, after more English money. From the looks of things, the money exchange he'd set up down at the Savoy was a going concern.

In the days that followed, the little secretary kept swapping off those ten-shilling bank-notes at a good profit till Zack stopped him.

'We'll need some of this cash to pay off the performers,' he said.

But the secretary had that one figured out, too. 'You cable your brother, telling him how much you owe. We'll pay off the performers in checks they can cash back in America and we'll keep speculating with what we've got here.'

That sounded all right to Zack; he cabled Joe and let the little secretary keep right on cleaning up.

One morning early the butler, George, came to Zack's room and woke him up. 'There is a gentleman downstairs to see you, sir,' George said. 'He wishes to get two hundred pounds from you.'

Zack put on a smoking-jacket, went to his safe and got out the money, then told George to send the man up.

The visitor was a kettle-bellied banker from Ohio who had a smooth way of talking past a long cigar. Zack's secretary had sent him; that little money-changer didn't have enough cash on hand to let the banker have two hundred pounds.

Zack counted out the two hundred pounds and laid them on the table. The banker endorsed a thousand dollars' worth of American bank checks to Zack and reached for the ten-shilling notes.

Zack beat him to them. 'No,' he said, 'the price is twelve hundred dollars.'

The banker's blood pressure took a turn for the worse; he nearly collapsed. 'Twelve hundred!' he cried. 'Why, that's robbery! I'm willing to pay you twenty cents on the pound over the regular exchange. But the very audacity, asking for that kind of profit. It's —— It's —— Why, it's robbery.'

'That's what you said the first time,' said Zack, and slipped the English money into the pocket of his smoking-jacket. 'If you don't want it, that's all right. You haven't been hurt. And there's plenty of others who do.'

He turned to George, who had come to the door at the sound of the banker's shouting. 'George,' he said, 'show this gentleman to his cab.'

'Now, wait, wait!' said the banker, biting savagely at his cigar. 'I've got my two daughters over here. We've tried for two days to get these checks cashed. We've got to have the money!'

'Sorry,' Zack said. 'I can't let you have it — yet. I'm getting too much satisfaction out of this. You're the first banker in my life who's ever begged me for money, and I've begged a thousand bankers! Why, I've gone to one to borrow money when he knew he was going to let me have it. But he had to make me tell him all about my business, just the same. He wanted to see me beg and crawl a little first. I never had a chance before to turn a banker down. I like it!'

By the time Zack finished, the banker had his cigar chewed down to a flat stub and was about to swallow that. He looked sick.

'Well, all right!' he said. 'I'll take it at your price. But I feel like I'm being gypped.'

Zack laughed. 'Do you think,' he asked, 'that I'd ever get any money from a banker if I told him I thought I was getting gypped?'

The banker got down to serious begging then. Zack held on to his British money and listened to it till he got tired, then let the banker have the two hundred pounds.

The days stretched out into weeks, with the little secretary still making them money and with Zack loading his show troupe in little dribbles onto whatever ship he could get them.

Finally, the day came for the Russian Cossacks to leave. They were all packed, and Zack was in their quarters talking to them when in walked some British officers with orders to put the Cossacks on a boat going into Belgium. From there, they would go into Russia and eventually into the war.

Lucca, the head Cossack, broke down and cried like a kid.

Zack tried to console him. 'When this is over,' he said, 'I'll still have a place for you boys.'

But Lucca shook his head. 'For us, sir,' he said, 'it is all over now. We shall never see the 101 again.'

And they never did. Zack guessed they died on some Russian battle front; he never did learn.

At the end of seven weeks from the time war was declared, Zack had all his show people home or on the way. All, that is, except the Sioux Indians that Sarraisani had in Berlin. Zack could get no word to or from Sarraisani. Joe had cabled him that he'd ordered Sarraisani to send the Indians back to Zack in England any way he could. But the redskins hadn't shown up. And the *St. Paul*, the mail boat on which Zack had booked passage to America for himself, was scheduled to leave within the next few days.

Zack was bothered. It was time he was getting out of England; he had no business there now and a country at war had no time nor use for him. Yet, he'd brought these Sioux from off their reservation and it was up to him to see that they got back. He knew he could never face their people back in the Dakotas and confess that he'd left these red men in a far-off land of strange tongues where they were helpless to manage for themselves.

But just what he could do, he didn't know, either. He was in a hell of a spot.

Then two days before his boat sailed, a man came to him at his Holland Road house to report that a bunch of his Indians were running away.

'They must be yours,' the man said. 'I just saw them down at Tillbury Station, trying to get on a train.'

Zack couldn't understand that. The last of his Indians were supposed to have left London a week ago.

He went down to Tillbury Station to investigate.

The wild whoops and screeches that greeted him when he turned in at the station came close to starting a panic in that part of London.

It was his lost Sioux, yelping with joy at the sight of him.

'My friend,' grunted their leader in his native tongue, rushing up with outstretched hands, 'we greet you with glad hearts!'

Zack was willing to bet no truer words were ever said, especially after he'd heard the tale of their wanderings.

Sarraisani, they said, had put them aboard a ship five weeks ago. The ship went to a place called Denmark. Then to another place. Then out into some big waters called the North Sea. Then to some other places.

No, they didn't know the names of those places. They couldn't understand the strange tongues spoken by the people. And nobody could understand the Sioux tongue. So nobody knew where they were going and there hadn't been enough food and they were tired of sailing around in a big ship that didn't know where they wanted to go and it was best now that they all go eat with their white friend Zack and be happy together once more.

Zack took them and fed them, then managed to squeeze out passage for them aboard a freighter bound for America.

On the day that Zack himself left, he gave George, the butler, twenty dollars.

George was worse shocked by that gift than he'd been the day the officers had come with the impressment order. But it was a pleasant sort of shock that put the only human look on his long sad face that Zack ever saw.

'I say, sir,' George said. 'It 'as been a pleasure to serve a man such as you, sir. I 'ave tried to do my best, and I believe I 'ave because not one word of censure 'ave you used on me. Few servants in England can say that of their masters. Few h'indeed, sir!'

Then he got control of himself and became a dignified and sober-faced butler who hurried about in the last-minute efforts to get his master ready to leave.

The *St. Paul* had been built to carry two hundred and

fifty first-class passengers and the mail. This trip, she carried seven hundred, filling to the last square inch of space makeshift berths below the water-line.

Zack went to the purser's office and got the number of his cabin and went down to investigate his quarters. It was like going down into an old and smelly cellar. There wasn't a breath of fresh air.

Zack was the third man in his cabin and consequently got the top berth. He left his luggage and went back up on deck. He was headed for the smoking-room when he met his pot-gutted banker friend from Ohio. The banker was walking in circles, mad enough to eat another cigar.

'Can you imagine it!' he ranted at Zack, likely because he was the only man handy. 'A first-class passenger, and they put me on a cot in the smoking-room.'

Zack agreed that was terrible, all the time wishing he had a cot in the smoking-room. At least, a man could breathe in there.

'Tell you what,' he said, 'I'll be playing poker all the way across. I guess I could swap quarters with you if you like.'

The banker was tickled silly. 'That'll be wonderful,' he said, and packed his big belly off in a fast run to get the purser to make the change.

Zack stayed in the smoker while the banker went down to take a look at his new quarters. In a minute, he was back, with his blood pressure up again.

'I can't take that!' he shouted. 'I'll have to have my cot back. I'd rather have it than that dark hole of Calcutta. You can't put a thing like that off on me. I won't stand for it!'

'Now, look,' said Zack. 'If we start pestering that purser again, he's liable to put us both off this damned boat before it leaves the docks. People are mobbing him for quarters, some offering as much as five hundred dollars!'

The banker left in a fine rage; but he didn't go bothering the purser about getting back his cot in the smoking-room.

He did cut Zack's acquaintance cold, however. He didn't speak to him one time on the whole crossing. Sometimes they'd meet and Zack would say 'Howdy,' but all the answer he'd get would be a banker's stare and a cold silence.

Zack was mighty put out about it!

21

THE BREAK-UP

ZACK HAD TAKEN the best part of the Miller Brothers 101
Wild West Show to England with him. Now the prize
horses and mules were gone. Every trick car and vehicle
that could be of any possible use to the British war machine
had been taken over. The Cossacks were fighting in
Russia. The whole outfit was badly disrupted and dis-
organized.

The three Miller brothers patched up the show the best
they could and kept it on the road; but they weren't fooling
anybody, least of all themselves. It wasn't the same show.
The fire and the color were gone; the heart had been torn
out of it. It crippled along till 1916, then Jess Willard
made them an offer on it and they took him up. They had
a feeling that the United States would be in this war before
it was over and Zack had learned in England what happened to a show outfit in wartime. They sold out, with
the agreement that Willard wasn't to use the Miller Brothers' name in connection with advertising the show, or
mention the 101 Ranch.

With the show gone, Zack went back to his old game of
bushwhacking, buying and selling. A lot of his business
was buying mules for the United States Army. His younger
brother George got to dabbling in oil, made a small killing
or two, then started to biting off bigger and bigger chunks
of the Oklahoma oil business. Joe went back to supervising

the farm and ranch work and to looking after the Indians.

Mother Miller died; but aside from that, the 101 continued to operate about like it always had.

But Joe wasn't satisfied. 'Way back yonder when they'd started building up the wild west show, Joe had had a dream. He'd thought about how the Old West was fast going out and how there were kids growing up who'd never had a taste of the old wild, raw, care-free way of frontier life, and he'd set out to do something about it. And he still couldn't turn that dream loose. Some of those kids were grown now, but he knew they were still kids at heart — they'd still enjoy the sight of men matching strength and skill against brute animal force. And there were old-timers, too, shunted into the backwash of progress, with little to live on except recollections. A chance to relive a little of their old lives through the scenes of a good show would do more to warm the blood of these boys than a big shot of bootleg whiskey. And, as much as anything, Zack's brother Joe had been a daddy to that show and the show people, the same as he'd been to his Indian friends; he couldn't bear the idea of letting anything die that he'd put that much of himself into. Joe kept saying all along that when he and his brothers got together enough money again, he aimed to put the 101 show back on the road.

George piled up a fortune in the oil business. Zack made another in livestock. The ranch did well. By 1923, it looked like the brothers could pool their money now and have enough to put a real show on the road.

Then the flood came.

That was late in June of 1923. On the evening of the twenty-first, a big black cloud stacked up in the east and moved in from across the Arkansas River. Another came in from the south, over the Salt Fork and Bird's Nest Creek. A third one made up across Chicaski and Bois d'Arc and hung there. Lightning ripped long jagged holes in these clouds and the rain poured through.

It had already been raining for a week. The Arkansas River was bank-full. So was the Salt Fork and every creek and wash that ran into it. There was nowhere for this new water to go.

By morning, the brown flood-waters of the Salt Fork were spreading all over creation and rising at the rate of five feet an hour. The Millers knew they were in for trouble and started moving their hogs and other livestock out of low places to higher ground. But they weren't half fast enough about it — and there wasn't enough high ground. The water came on up to the store building and poured into the basement. It came on up and started filling the basement of the White House.

It made an awful sound, that water did, pouring into the White House basement. The displaced air had the water bubbling and gurgling like it does when you pour water into a jug — only this sound was so much bigger and louder.

Old man George Van Hook, the chicken man, got panicky when the water started getting up around his poultry. He took ten hands and started wading out and wagging his chickens back in coops. He had the hands stacking the coops on an upstairs gallery of the White House.

He kept going till the water was up around his neck. Joe hollered at him. 'Come back here, George!' he said. 'To hell with them chickens! You'll get drowned!'

But Van Hook kept going. 'I've got to get them out, Joe,' he said. 'These are the finest chickens in the world; we couldn't get more like them.'

But by the time he made it to the chicken run this time, the rest of his chickens were gone.

The flood kept rising, picking up horses, cows, buffaloes, chickens. It carried them along, with the wild things it had picked up here and there — snakes, rabbits, skunks, 'possums, deer, prairie chickens. The 101 cowhands and visitors at the ranch kept wading out and rescuing these animals till the front gallery of the White House was over-run with everything from buffalo to hound dogs, all of them bawling, cackling, barking, and crying out against the flood. 'By God, old Noah didn't have much on us,' Joe Miller said, looking the outfit over. 'We've damned near got a pair of everything on earth.'

Counting hired help, visitors, Indians, and strangers whose automobiles had been trapped between the Salt Fork and Cow Skin Creek, the White House sheltered over two hundred people during that flood. The people helped take the furnishings of the lower floor of the White House up to the second, where they could stand out on the gallery and watch a three-mile-wide river get wider and deeper, washing off fences and floating away buildings and finally taking away the automobiles they'd arrived in.

The Millers kept four Negro cooks at work day and night feeding the crowd. Fried ham and biscuits was the main bill of fare. The water had risen in the store building now till everything was submerged except flour barrels and cured hams which floated to the top and were rescued by men moving about in two rickety motor boats. The visitors slept on the floor, those who slept. A lot of them just sat around in little scared groups, afraid to sleep. Some joined the Miller brothers and Jess Willard in a poker game. Jess and his manager Tom Jones had been visiting at the 101 when the flood caught them.

The Millers could play poker, all right. They'd learned long ago to make the best of whatever came, that howling about a thing like a flood was like a dog barking at an empty knot-hole — nothing could come of it.

But they were worried. Especially Joe. Joe knew that the 101 was taking a bad loss on this flood, and if it kept up, would take a worse one. Maybe a loss so big that it would knock the props out from under their plans to put the 101 Wild West Show back on the road.

And the flood did keep up. It took out the highway bridge across the Salt Fork on the twenty-second of June and was still going strong by sundown of the twenty-third.

That was when Jess Willard finally got tired of watching that horse hanging by his neck in a telephone wire about seventy-five yards from the house. The horse had been there for a couple of hours already, fighting to free himself from that wire; but he couldn't make it.

'I'm going after that horse,' Jess declared suddenly. 'I can't stand to just sit here and watch a game animal like that drown.'

Joe tried to stop him. Zack did, too.

'Don't be a damned fool, Jess,' Zack said. 'You go out there after that horse and you're liable to drown.'

'Yes,' said the prize-fighter. 'And if I don't go, it's a damned cinch that horse'll drown.'

With everybody begging him not to go, Jess stripped,

got him a pair of pliers, and swam out to the horse. He cut away the entangling wires. The tugging current caught the freed animal and swept him away, but the horse could keep his head up now and move about. He might make it to high ground. Jess swam back to the house.

That rescue encouraged a boy who worked on the 101 to try getting a swimming hog out of the water. He went out in a rotten old skiff, paddled up beside the hog, and tried to drag the animal aboard. All he did was swamp the boat. He and the hog both went out of sight.

Zack yelled: 'Get a boat!'

But somebody was out in the motor boats already and there were no others. The boy came up, went down and came up again, his frightened face white against the brown waters.

Joe stood helpless on the porch. 'When he goes this time,' he predicted, 'that'll be the last. We'll never see that boy again.'

But a miracle saved the boy. When he started down the third time, he landed square on the top of a tall post, the only post within three hundred yards of there. The boy clung there till Jess Willard swam out and got him.

'Which proves,' Zack told the boy, 'that if you're born to hang, you'll never drown.'

But if that was a good joke, the boy was too scared to appreciate it.

The flood lasted four days before anybody could get out. The cars that had been out in front of the store and White House were all gone. The roads were gone. There was no bridge now over the Salt Fork, which was still bank-full and would be for a week.

That's when Joe got the idea for the ferry. He called Bliss, around by Ponca City. He called the lumber-yard and told the manager to start hauling him some heavy timber to the highway crossing. He said to bring all their carpenters and start building a ferryboat, that he'd come across and show them how.

The second day after the carpenters started work on the ferry, they had it ready. Joe and Zack got oil-well cable and had it stretched across the river and then put mule teams on each end of the ferry to pull the boat across. Already there was a mile-long line of cars backed up on each side of the river, waiting to do business.

Joe had no authority to run a ferry, no government permit or insurance to take care of possible accidents. He just started in business and went at it, turning a stroke of bad luck into something that paid off. He charged a dollar to cross all automobiles except Fords. Ford drivers paid six-bits. And doctors rode free.

Joe was lucky and had only one accident. Benny Burnett from Billings came down in an old Mitchell car, got on the ferry, and stepped on the gas instead of the brake. The old Mitchell jumped ahead like something scared, crashed through the end cables, and took a nose-dive into the Salt Fork.

A long string of bubbles came up, then Benny. He was white as a sheet and scared stiff.

One of the ferryboat men grabbed him by the hair, then caught one of his waving hands. But Benny kept pulling back, shouting: 'My hat's gone! Where's my hat?'

One of the boat men saw his hat floating down the river, but Benny never got it. He did get back his old Mitchell automobile, however. One of the boys dived down with a cable and hooked it to the automobile. Six mules, by hard scrabbling, managed to pull the car out of the river.

The Government sent men down to build temporary low-water bridges across the Salt Fork. But the rains kept up and they built seven of these bridges before the floods ever let them use one.

Joe ran his ferry for eighteen months and cleaned up about twenty-five thousand dollars. Just about what the 101 had lost to the flood in the first place, Joe said. He said he guessed they could still go ahead and put the show back on the road again.

When Joe started putting together the second Miller Brothers 101 Wild West Show, he went at it whole-hog, thumbing his nose at the cost. He hired Tom S. Tucker, known everywhere big shows are known, to shape up the equipment and put it on wheels. Joe told Tom that they wanted the best of everything and told him to spend the money necessary to get it. Tucker took him at his word and at Marland began to assemble the equipment. Everything was new with the exception of the sides of the band-wagon, which were made up of two life-sized wood engravings, the work of a German wood-carving artist, done years before. These pieces of art represented the *Aztec Sacrifice* and the *Landing of Ponce de Leon*, and could be equaled nowhere in the world at any price.

It took thirty new steel cars to haul the show, with cook-wagons built so that forty minutes after the wagons got on the lot, the crew of five hundred performers could be fed. The private car of the Miller brothers was a palace on wheels and even included a library.

While Tucker was busy getting the equipment shaped up, the brothers laid out their performance programs and started scouring the world for performers and for livestock. They hired such famous trick riders, ropers, and bulldoggers as California Frank, Hank Durnall, Mamie Frances, Reine Haefley, Tad Lucas, Buck Lucas, Mildred Douglas, Buff Brady, Milt Kinkle, Fred Carter, Jose Darera, Cotton Ashley, and plenty of others. They had old Ezra Meeker, the first man ever to take a wagon over the Oregon Trail, along with a prairie schooner and an ox team like the one Ezra had driven. They imported an entire troupe of Cossack riders, the best Joe Miller could find in Russia. Zack went to Mexico City and hired dancing girls from famous theaters there, to go with the Ziegfeld Follies girls Joe picked up in New York. Their agent hired more dancers from Buenos Aires, New Orleans, Cuba, and the Orient. Slayman's famous troupe of Arabs was dragged in to perform. Elephants, outlaw horses, bad Brahma bulls, trained camels, buffalo, elk — the Millers bought anything and everything that could be fitted into the show. Money disappeared like water poured into a rat-hole; but they put together the biggest and most elaborate show that was ever assembled in the history of man.

The super-show opened in Oklahoma City, April 21, 1925. It dragged down good money and continued to do so. But operations costs ate it up as fast as it came in. When they went into winter quarters at the ranch at the end of the season, the Miller brothers hadn't cleared a dime. Joe wasn't bothered, however. Joe recollected how it had been when they first started out with the show back in 1908. They had a show now like no show on earth; next year they'd get rolling and coin a mint of money.

But they didn't the next year, either. They couldn't stand the cost of the high-paid performers Joe went on hiring to keep the show top-rate. And competition from the other big shows, Ringling Brothers, Sells-Floto, Hagen-beck-Wallace, and others, was a steady drain. Those shows fought the Millers tooth and toenail, sending out hired crews to trail the advance agents from town to town, tearing down the 101 handbills the same day they were put up. Sometimes they sent out hired thugs to start gang fights with the 101 canvasmen or stir up scare riots among the 101 audiences.

The Millers fought them back, the way they'd fought back in the old days when the Witherspoon outfit had tried to grab off a part of the Salt Fork range. One year, Ringling was scheduled to come out of California, through Texas, and on into Virginia. The 101 was in Virginia and had a billing that would put them a day ahead of Ringling some days and a day behind in other towns.

'I think,' said Joe, 'that I'll put a little heat on those boys this time. I'm getting a bellyful of the trouble they're giving us.'

He put some men out to get up a petition not to let the Ringling show into Virginia. His men pointed out how dangerous it would be for the cattle industry of Virginia for Ringling to come through out of Texas with their show stock probably infected with the dread Texas hoof and mouth disease. The way they told it, half the cattle of Virginia would likely die before the year was over. They built the scare up to where Virginians were even afraid for their children.

They got over forty thousand signatures to their petition,

and the governor of the state banned Ringling as if it were some horrible plague. The 101 took up the Ringling dates, and where signboards said Ringling was going to show, the 101 put on streamers showing that it was to be there. In many places, the people thought both shows would be there on the same date. The 101 did a turn-away business.

But this was just one winning bout among the many that the 101 lost. And with the overhead the 101 show carried, just a few losses could hurt. The 101 went into winter quarters at the end of 1926, more than a hundred thousand dollars in the hole.

Joe was worried now. But he wasn't quitting. It wasn't in Joe Miller to quit as long as he was able to fight. He still had money, and he still believed in the show. So in the spring of 1927, he plunged still deeper. He aimed to put the show on its feet if it took every dollar he and his two brothers could rake and scrape together. Zack and George plunged with him.

They made a little money that year, but a mighty little. And that fall at the ranch, October 21, 1927, W. A. Brooks stepped into the closed garage where he heard the motor of Joe's automobile running and found the eldest of the Miller brother trio dead, a victim of monoxide gas poisoning.

They held the funeral at the White House, where some five thousand Indians, cowboys, ranch folk, show people, statesmen, and tramps came to see a good man put away. The Reverend G. Frank Sanders, pastor of the Christian Church at Ponca City, delivered the funeral oration for the whites. The Ponca chiefs, headed by Crazy Bear and Horse Chief Eagle, stood in their mourning blankets and chanted a death song for the man who'd helped to find a new home for the lost Ponca tribe back in the early eighties.

When the weird dirge was done, Horse Chief Eagle, son of old White Eagle, stepped forward, pulled his blanket tighter around him, and said solemnly in his native tongue:

'Our brother Joe, he is one of us. He is gone. When he went away, it meant more than anything to the Indian. The Indian weeps. Because our brother Joe will not be good to us any more. He has reared us from boys, some of us. He gave us encouragement. God is a right God, so the Indian says. He gives each man a time. We all have a time. You see the paint upon our faces. We paint our faces because our brother Joe who lived with us all these years is dead. That is all. We are sad!'

They buried Joe in the 101 funeral lot in the Ponca City Cemetery and that night the prairie winds carried the wails of the Indian mourners.

Will Rogers didn't get to attend Joe's funeral, but he came down to the 101 a little later. He had a lecture engagement in Ponca City and he always made the 101 his hangout whenever he showed up in that part of the country. He and May Lily, Pawnee Bill Lily's wife, would usually wind up at the piano before the night was over, May playing and Will singing. Like you'd expect of an old-time cowhand, Will's singing wasn't much for music, but it was hell for stout and gave him and Zack and all the others listening a lot of satisfaction.

This trip, he didn't sing, though. He and Zack sat around the house, drinking and talking about the old days till the conversation got around to camp cooking.

'You know what I'd like?' Will said. 'It's a mess of hog jowl and black-eyed peas. I haven't eaten any for years — and always did like it better than anything else.'

A little later, he told Zack that it'd do him a lot of good just to ride down to that South Nigger Pasture and watch some cows eat grass. Zack told him that, by god they'd just go right then. But before they left Zack put through a private telephone call. He talked to Jimmy Scott, a Negro cook in a Ponca City restaurant.

'Jimmy,' he said, 'you got any black-eyed peas?'

'Yassah, Mistah Zack,' Jimmy said. 'Ise just got in half a bushel of black-eyed peas. Got some collard greens, too. How's about them and some co'n bread?'

Zack told him that'd be fine, and to be sure and cook those peas with hog jowl. Then he went and got Will and they drove down to the South Nigger Pasture and spent the whole evening standing around and watching big steers eat grass. On the way back to town, Will remarked that if there was any more satisfying sight than watching good steer cattle grazing and packing on the tallow, then he'd never run across it.

Will's grin spread from ear to ear when they entered the restaurant that evening and were served a big helping of Jimmy Scott's peas and hog jowl. He went right to work on them.

'This,' he told Zack, 'will sure put me in the prime for them lecture doings tonight.'

Will loaded up with a big bait of his favorite grub, went back into the kitchen to praise Jimmy Scott for the way he'd cooked them, then shook hands with Zack and went to make his talk. And that was the last time Zack ever saw Will alive.

Joe's death, besides being a personal loss to Zack and George, was a crippling blow to the powerful trio of showman-farmer, trader, and financier. Zack and George tried to gather up the loose ends and go on as usual, but things weren't the same. Joe had plunged heavily on the show, trying to make it pay off, and neglected the 101 ranch and farm till it was in debt. The show had been losing steadily.

Zack went back on the road with the show.

George reached deeper into the oil business, buying up leases in Texas, Oklahoma, and Kansas in a desperate attempt to make a big pile of money and pull the outfit out of the hole. The 101 had weathered financial storms before, gambling for big stakes and coming out on top. George was counting strong on his gambler's luck and natural financial genius to boost them over the hump this time.

Zack didn't like the squeeze they were in. He was having to spend all his time with a show that kept losing money, feeling all the time that if he were out from under that load, he could make a cleanup in the trading business or maybe make the farm and ranch pay off. He kept on the lookout for a chance to unload the show; and the spring following Joe's death, he located an interested party. He brought the buyer to the ranch, primed him with good whiskey, fed him well, got the contract drawn up and the buyer's signature on the dotted line. Zack signed, then called George in for his signature.

George took his time and read the contract over carefully. One clause he reread, then looked up, shaking his head.

'I can't sign that,' he said. 'This contract gives the holder the right to use the Miller name in advertising the show. We'll never sell the Miller name to anybody.'

George put the paper down and walked out. Zack tried to talk the buyer into redrawing the contract, leaving out the clause George had objected to, but it was no soap. The buyer wanted the Miller name backing the show or he didn't want the show.

Zack went back on the road again, stuck with a losing show, but making a game try to put it back on its feet.

It was rough going. Times were changing. Where once a man could spend big money and get it back with profit, now he spent it and it was gone. And where once a man could show for weeks without having to bother with a damage suit, now they were cropping up by the hundreds. The country was overrun with two-bit shyster lawyers hungry for any sort of a case that would net them a fee. Let a show horse kick a speck of dust in a woman's eye, and before morning some lawyer would have her primed to sue the 101 outfit for all the law allowed. Women tore their silk stockings and filed for damages. Old Babe, one of the elephants, reached her snout toward a passing child, hoping to get a peanut. The father sued for damages on the ground that the elephant had come so close to striking the baby that he himself had had palpitations of the heart from which he failed to recover. One lawyer had a boy suing the outfit because of the fright he'd suffered when a bad horse went over the arena net, scattering the band and audience. The lawyer had the boy claiming he should have something for having his life placed in jeopardy. Another suit grew out of the same incident. A woman swore that, because of her fright, she had borne her child a month prematurely.

The 101 lawyer hit the ceiling at that. 'My god!' he yelped. 'Instead of our owing you, you should be paying us. A doctor would have charged you two hundred and fifty dollars and not done as good a job!'

The suit cost the show two hundred and fifty dollars, just the same.

Down in Alabama, one of the big steers on the show got his foot hung in a railroad switch and pulled the hoof off one of his toes. Out on the grounds, he lay down to ease his crippled foot. Along came a drunk who stopped in front of the steer and started prodding him with his foot.

'Better let him alone,' warned one of the Mexican stock handlers. 'He's just crippled himself and he might fight.'

'Dammit!' the drunk roared, 'I've paid to get in this show and I've got a right to make this damned steer get up so I can look him over.'

He walked up, put a hand on each of the steer's horns, shook the animal's head, and kicked him in the nose.

The steer got up on his hind feet, balanced a moment on his crippled foot, then went down under his own weight, lunging forward as he did so. The forward lunge drove a sharp horn up under the stooping drunk's jaw, drove on up and shoved out one of the man's eyeballs. The man died and the Millers show was sued for twenty-five thousand dollars.

Two drummers happened to be passing at the time of the accident. They saw the whole thing and backed up the word of the Mexican handler with corroborating testimony. That was all that saved the show from damages on that charge. Still the case had to be fought to the Supreme Court, and cost plenty in lawyer fees.

One boy working with the show cost the outfit over thirty-one thousand dollars. That happened in Eugene, Oregon. In letting the show wagons down off the cars, a rope broke, crashing a wagon down and hitting the boy on the head.

Zack thought the boy was dead. They rushed him to the hospital, where he stayed about six weeks under the care of one of the best brain specialists in the United States. The boy recovered and came back to the show and finished the season. The show paid his hospital bills which ran to about eighteen hundred dollars.

The show had been in winter quarters on the Salt Fork about a month when a lawyer got to the boy and found out he was a minor, in spite of the fact that he'd signed a contract with the 101 when he'd hired on, claiming he was twenty-one. Immediately a suit was filed against the outfit for thirty thousand dollars.

The case was tried first in Tulsa. The court decided against the show, ruling that a minor could not be held responsible. The Millers took it to the Supreme Court. There, the ruling of the smaller court was upheld and the show was forced to pay off.

It would have cost the 101 outfit only five hundred dollars to have let the boy die in the first place.

Some of the claims were legitimate, of course. There'll always be accidents around a show. But the 101 Wild West Show seemed to be considered legitimate prey for anybody who could figure out some way to hang the hook on them. Zack figures that in those last few years before the show went completely on the rocks, they were taken for over a hundred thousand dollars on shakedowns alone — suits with nothing behind them but predatory lawyers.

There were other aggravations in those years, too, that the show had never had before. There was trouble for men who bought concessions to sell balloons, pop, hamburgers, and trinkets along with the show. There were always trailers who had paid no concession, but who attached themselves to the show and competed with the concession men. These had to be fought off.

There were the pickpockets, the ticket-sellers who held out on the gate receipts, chiselers of all sorts. Their take didn't amount to too much, yet was a constant drain on the profits.

Sometimes it was just freak hard luck that went against the show. There was a time in Boston when a dead priest cost the show at least twenty thousand dollars. And the priest had been dead for thirty years, at that.

The show had gone in right behind a horse show. The press agents had gone to the bottoms of their bags to pull out the best stunts to get good publicity. The show moved in, expecting to depend principally on the press for publicity instead of having to use billboards; they had spent plenty of good money on newspaper advertising. Yet in the news columns they got only three show pictures during the time they were there. All the publicity was going to 'The Grave of Crutches,' and apparently all the people were going there, too.

It seems that some cripple had gone and prayed at Father Joe's grave and had regained the use of his legs. That started the ball to rolling. Cripple after cripple went to the priest's grave, prayed, threw his crutches in the ever-mounting pile beside the grave, and walked away on his own two feet. The miracles put the town to humming with excitement. The newspapers carried pictures and stories by the ream. There was no room for circus pictures or anything else. There was no time to bother with circuses and wild west shows when miracles were being performed right before the very eyes of the Bostonians. Crutches piled up at the grave by the thousands; there weren't enough people attending the 101 show to pay for the lighting.

You can't fight a dead miracle-man who's been buried for thirty years. There's nothing to fight. The show was whipped from the start, and Zack knew it. He moved on as quickly as possible, hoping for better luck at the next stand.

But he didn't get it. He never did. The losses continued, growing heavier each year.

Then one night in February, 1929, George Miller skidded his car on an icy pavement between Ponca City and the ranch. The careening vehicle quit the road, crashed into an embankment, and overturned.

When Oscar Clemmer came upon the wreck about four o'clock in the morning, he found George crushed and pinned beneath a front wheel. Before Clemmer could get George out and to a hospital, Zack's younger brother was dead.

22

THE CRASH

WALL STREET toppled in '29, and coming as it did right after the death of Zack's two brothers, the market crash caught Zack out on a limb.

It's a toss-up whether the 101 could have kept its head above water if all the brothers had been alive. George had already mortgaged too much of the ranch holdings in oil leases; and the bottom had dropped out of oil. Joe had put everything he could take off the farm and ranch for the last few years into the show, leaving the place badly in need of repairs and restocking. Now, after the crash, the ranch couldn't even support itself on the ridiculous prices that livestock brought, nor the almost worthless agricultural products.

Zack did the best he knew; he jumped here and jumped yonder, trying to hold the sinking enterprises together.

But Zack was a trader. He wasn't the farmer and showman that Joe had been, and he wasn't the wizard in finances that George had proved himself time and again. He was a trader and depended entirely on turnover. And now, with the markets shot all to hell and people clutching desperately at their last dollars, the 101 bushwhacker could find nothing worth buying and nothing that would sell. He ran himself ragged from show to ranch to bankers to creditors and back to the show again, feeling his feet sinking deeper and deeper all the time into the financial bog that was ready to suck him under at the first false step.

He talked it over with his nephews, sons of his brother Joe. They agreed and saddled the ranch holdings with more and heavier mortgages, borrowing half a million to see them through 1930. Zack was convinced that 1930 would be a better year. The 101 had pulled out of the panic of 1893 in something like a year's time, hadn't it? This depression couldn't be much different.

But Zack was wrong. Nineteen-thirty was a worse year than he had imagined. And at the end of it, nothing had been paid toward the debts, and the 101 was over three hundred thousand dollars deeper in the hole.

Early in 1931, Charles Bulware made Zack a proposition to take the show off his hands. Bulware agreed to lease the show for two hundred dollars a day if Zack would finance him till the backers Bulware claimed he had came through with their money.

Zack was thinking the proposition over when Fred Armstead, a man who had worked with George in the oil business, called on him to come to Longview, Texas. The first East Texas oil fields were just coming in. Zack caught a train and went down, getting there in time to see the first core brought in. It was oil sand, just as Fred Armstead had expected.

'Jesus Christ!' Armstead said. 'Here's our chance to clean up! Leases are selling for five dollars an acre around here yet. Let me have fifteen thousand dollars and if this thing is half as good as it looks, I'll pay out every dime the 101 owes — in less than a year's time.'

The thing looked good, but Zack was cautious. He figured it was oil more than anything else that had got the 101 into the jackpot it was in. Anyhow, oil had been George's line; Zack didn't know much about it.

'No,' he told Armstead, 'I'd better stick to something I know. I figure the show's still my best bet.'

And that was Zack's second wrong guess. If he'd let Armstead have that money, he'd have got well again. East Texas oil made millions for those who took a chance.

Back at the ranch, Zack signed with Bulware and advanced him twelve thousand five hundred dollars. Bulware promised that his backers would meet Zack in St. Louis at the time they'd appointed and pay him back every cent.

Zack met Bulware in St. Louis when the time came, but Bulware's creditors didn't show up. They'd sent word, Bulware said, that they'd meet with him in Erie, Pennsylvania. In the meantime, could he have a little more money to run on?

Zack let him have the money.

When Bulware's creditors didn't show up in Erie, Zack knew he was stuck with another bad proposition. But his only out, it looked like, was to keep the show on the road. He let Bulware have five thousand dollars more and re-routed the show into New England where he felt it would make the most money.

Maybe Bulware didn't like to be told where to take the show or maybe he was just a poor manager. All the signs pointed to even worse: it looked as if somebody, wanting to grab off the 101, got to Bulware with enough long green to make him try to bleed Zack white and kill off the show. Anyhow, Bulware was routing the show in such a manner that it couldn't possibly make money. He'd show in this town today, jump two hundred and fifty miles at a freight cost of about a thousand dollars, show there, then come back within thirty miles of his first showing for the third show. No show could stand that sort of thing for long.

Zack learned what was going on, but he couldn't stay with the show. Things were in too bad a shape back at the ranch. Every time he turned around, he was slapped in the face with a lawsuit for collection of back debts.

He called a conference of his creditors at the ranch. 'Give me six months without a lawsuit,' he asked them. 'Give me six months without a creditor filing for the 101 to go into the hands of a receiver, and I'll beg, borrow, or steal enough money to settle my debts and put the outfit back on its feet.'

The creditors were listening and seemed in favor of Zack's proposal. They were talking it over when Zack got a telegram from Bulware. Bulware had the show in Washington, D.C. He'd ignored Zack's orders and had routed the show through Virginia two months too early for that fall territory. Now they were in Washington, three months behind time, and, as Zack learned later, without any advance publicity in the newspapers or a billboard advertising of their coming. Bulware wired that the show was out of money and that the performers hadn't been paid in three weeks.

Zack answered that there was no more money coming. He told Bulware to fold the show and bring it home to the 101. Any of the performers who wanted to come with it would be welcome at the ranch, he said.

That's when the show performers went off the deep end. They staged a riot and maliciously destroyed every piece of show property they could lay hands on. They took axes to the cars that the Millers had so elaborately designed for their comfort and convenience. They hacked the harness and saddles to pieces. There wasn't a mirror, a window, or a piece of plumbing left intact. The wood masterpieces, *Aztec Sacrifice* and *Landing of Ponce de Leon*, were hacked so as to be unrecognizable. The performers wouldn't let the canvasmen knock down the big tent to load the equipment on the cars. The elephant man walked off the lot, leaving the elephants to get along the best they could.

When Bulware wired what had happened, Zack sent sixty men to Washington to move what was left of the Miller Brothers 101 Wild West Show back to the ranch. He called Sidney Rink, a Negro elephant trainer at Wichita, Kansas, and asked him to go take over the elephants.

Sidney was a tough Negro and plenty mad when he learned what had happened. 'I know them elephants,' he told Zack. 'I worked with them on another show. I can take any two of them big critters and run everybody off the lot.'

Sidney didn't have this to do, however. He and Fred Armstead went up to take over the show and met with no opposition. The performers, sullen and disgruntled, stood around and watched the newcomers salvage the wrecked show, but made no more moves to interfere. Fred Armstead and the big Negro elephant man brought the wreckage of the once magnificent show to the 101 for the last time.

The day the show pulled in to the ranch, Zack found in his mail a circular from a big-game hunting outfit in Africa, advertising a safari that was making up for a hunt in a couple of months. Down in one corner of the folder were penciled the initials: 'I. R.'

It seemed to Zack those letters just jumped right out of the page at him, shouting, 'Ida Red!'

Quick as a man could draw a short breath, Zack's mind back-tracked thirty years. He was standing in the dark outside the back of Missouri John's saloon in Ponca City. Beside him was Frank Potts, that hard-bitten, half-outlaw cowhand. At their feet lay a blow-hard, four-flushing constable with what looked like all of his throat shot out, wallowing and pitching in his own blood. And out yonder in the dark, with the sounds of the hoofbeats fading fast, rode the bronc-fanning, banjo-picking Ida Red — quitting the Salt Fork one jump ahead of the John Laws, and riding out of their lives forever.

It was just a hunch, of course. That might not be the laughing, song-making, quick-tempered cowhand who'd got such a big kick out of helping the 101 whip the Wither-spoon cow outfit off the Salt Fork range. But the hunch was too strong for Zack to let it slide. He sat right down and wrote the man who'd sent him the game-hunting folder.

'If there's a red-headed, banjo-playing American with you,' he wrote, 'tell him the man he shot down in Ponca City didn't die. Tell him that no warrant was ever issued for the arrest of Ida Red. Tell him it's safe to write me.'

Zack folded and sealed the letter, a deep nostalgia making an ache come to his throat. Back in the days when Ida Red had been with the 101, a man's enemies had been flesh-and-blood creatures, something you could fight with fists and guns. Now that was all changed Today, those enemies were signatures on a bank note, parties of the first and second parts in a contract, vague pen-and-ink names on legal documents that a gun or fist couldn't dent.

Zack mailed his letter and went to bed that night, feeling like an old man for the first time in his life.

On August 27, 1931, Joe's son, George W. Miller, along with the Exchange Trust Company of Tulsa, representing the heirs of the late George Miller, filed in the district court of Kay County a petition for the 101 ranch to be placed in the hands of a receiver.

This was a surprise move to Zack. He hadn't expected it after that conference when the creditors had apparently agreed to give him six months to straighten out his business. But according to the inference of the petition, Zack was using poor management and allowing the estates of his brothers Joe and George to go to rack and ruin. On these grounds the executors of these estates asked for a receiver to be appointed.

The John Hancock Life Insurance Company and the Passumptic Savings Bank of Maryland jumped in with the same complaint, calling for a receivership. Representatives of all these outfits met at the ranch, wrangled it over, and finally agreed upon Fred C. Clarke, a ranchman near Winfield, as general operating receiver. Judge John S. Burger, of Kay County district court, confirmed the appointment. On September 16, 1931, for the first time since it was established back in the seventies, control of the 101 Ranch went out of Miller hands.

This news spread about was like a blood call to the wolf pack. Lawsuits burst upon Zack like popcorn in a hot skillet. Creditors, big and little, closed in, howling for the kill.

Shakedowns and legitimate cases left from the collapsed show were brought to trial. Court controversies sprang up over land the Millers had bought from the Indians back as far as 1892, accusing the Millers of buying from noncompetent Indians for inadequate consideration.

Zack's divorce from Marguerite Blevins Miller, filed in a Louisiana court in March of that year, had been granted, but Zack's former wife had appealed the case to the Supreme Court of Louisiana. And while that case was being harangued, Zack's creditors even tried to attach Joe Miller's eight-thousand-dollar saddle which had passed into Zack's hands. But here, the law played on Zack's side. The Oklahoma bankrupt law frees a man's saddle, horse, and milk cow; no mention is made of how high the value of these articles may be.

But Zack's hands were tied on everything else. He was helpless to do anything at all about his debts; loss of the 101 had taken away his only source of income. Yet the suits of his creditors kept piling on. The little ones had a big one crippled and cornered and they were hell-bent to drag him down.

If Fred Clarke, in charge of the 101, turned a hand toward restocking or trying to re-establish the ranch and put it on a paying basis, nobody caught him at it. He started leasing out 101 grassland and farm property to individual farmers. He fired all the 101 hands that were left, replacing them with what Zack called 'Kaffir-corn cowhands.' He started selling off every loose piece of ranch equipment and farm implements he could find a buyer for. He sold the 101 corn crop to his son-in-law and his son-in-law's father, delivered at Ponca, for twelve cents a bushel less than a neighboring outfit received for corn hauled half the distance. He turned livestock in on the orchard of some four hundred trees that Luther Burbank had selected and presented to Joe as a gift. In a week's time, of course, the horses and cattle had those fruit trees torn down and ruined.

The nagging, worrying lawsuits, the loss and ruination of the ranch that had been the empire of the Millers for half a century — they were all too big a strain on Zack. He cracked. His nerves went to pieces and he collapsed.

Bill Pickett, the only one of the old 101 bunch still with him, took Zack to his bedroom in the White House and went for a doctor. Bill and Selma Zimmerman, a showgirl who had stayed on at the ranch, took care of Zack the best they could. But they didn't expect him to pull through. Nobody did.

In March of '32, Clarke advertised a sale of the personal properties of the ranch — hogs, horses, cattle, buffalo, saddles, harness, farm machinery, everything that wasn't tied down to the land. Sick and wretched, Zack appealed to the court through his lawyer for twenty-four hours in which to separate his own personal horses — which were in no way connected with the 101 property — from the ones to be sold. The judge granted that appeal, but along with it slapped Zack in the face with an order confining him to the White House for that same period of time. For the twenty-four hours, Zack wasn't to go near the barns, the stables — in fact, he wasn't to leave the house under any circumstances. Even the courts were trying to get a knife into Zack now. He wondered who'd bought off the judge.

Along with this bitter news, Zack's attorney brought the afternoon mail. One letter had come all the way from Africa — it was from Ida Red!

There were ten pages of that letter, written in Ida Red's chicken-track scrawl. Ten pages of cheer and hope of the brand that Ida Red could always dish out. Ida Red was in British East Africa. The way he told it, he'd done what hundreds of saddle hands all over the West were always promising themselves to do. When he'd left Ponca City that night on the fast-stepping gray horse belonging to Frank Potts, he'd made up his mind that if he got clear of the law, he wasn't stopping till he'd located him a new country where opportunity was wide open for the man with the guts to hang and rattle. And he'd kept on the move, just like he'd made up his mind to, till he'd landed in British East Africa. Which was just what he was looking for.

'She's the kind of country for grass and water that the Cherokee Strip was in the days your daddy tied into it,' he wrote. 'The antelope are just as thick, and the lions thicker than the coyotes ever was in Oklahoma. But a man can raise cattle here — lions or no lions.'

The way Ida Red said he'd done it in the beginning was to hire Negro families for about five dollars a month and three or four bushels of corn to herd the cattle by day and put them in a thorn-bush corral at night, where they beat drums to keep the big cats scared off. He claimed he'd killed more lions than any man in Africa, but there was no hope of killing them all off. He said they were like the flies in Oklahoma — you kill one, and ten come to take its place.

But Ida Red wasn't bothered with lion trouble any more. He said he'd located him a big sink that he reckoned must be the crater of an old filled-up volcano. There was one gap broken in the rim-rock, just wide enough for a man to ride through on horseback. He had him about twenty thousand acres of land down in that sink where grass grew high enough to brush a man's saddle stirrups. And in the middle was a fresh-water lake that never went dry. He'd killed the lions out of that sink. He'd partly stocked it with zebra mares he'd roped wild off the open range and was breeding to Percheron studs, selling the colts as three-year-olds to a sugar company down in the tsetse-fly country where common horses would die. By accident, he'd learned that his zebroid mare colts would breed back to a horse stud; so now he was making a clean-up on that zebra stuff.

Ida Red sure made that Africa country sound good. He was raising a fuss for Zack to sell off his Oklahoma holdings and come throw in with him.

'Get out from under, there in Oklahoma,' he urged. 'Bring forty thousand dollars down here and build you a packing plant. I'll guarantee you'll be in the clover from here on out!'

That letter of Ida Red's warmed Zack's heart, put new life and hope into his sick body. He didn't have forty thousand dollars, but he did still have a bunch of horses. Sell them, and they'd pay passage to Africa for him and Bill Pickett. There, with old Ida Red giving them a little boost now and then, they could wipe the slate clean and make a new start. It'd be like old times again. Zack wasn't old — only fifty-four. Given a little hope, and he'd soon be a damned sight younger.

He sat up in bed. Let him get free of this mess here and, by god, he'd roll his pack and hit for Africa.

'Bill!' he shouted to Bill Pickett. 'Come in here, Bill!'

Bill came. He was shaking all over and there were tears of anger streaming down over his black cheeks. He'd heard about the order restraining Zack from leaving the White House, and he was opening and shutting his big bull-dogger hands, wanting bad to come to grips with something.

He didn't wait for Zack to give orders; he started talking first.

'Mistah Zack,' he said, 'my old woman Maggie, she's dead and gone now. All my chilluns is married off and scattered out. I ain't got me nobody but Bill Pickett to look out after. Ise been here thirty years, and when this ranch is gone, Ise got me no place else to go.'

He swallowed and his Adam's apple jumped and settled back into place. He went on. 'You know, suh, they'd have this here niggah to ketch befo' they can do something about it.'

As usual, when Bill Pickett was uneasy about anything, he was circling all around the subject, but not getting to the point.

Zack interrupted to pin him down. 'What the hell you driving at, Bill?' he demanded.

The old bulldogger looked down at his hands, then back up at Zack again.

'Well, suh,' said Bill, 'it's that there receiver, Clarke, suh. If you wants him removed at nine o'clock in the mo'ning when he comes, I'll remove him where there can't no judge put him back. I'd neveh be sorry fo' nothing I done to that man, suh, the way he's a-carrying on and destructioning this ranch.'

In the black face of Bill Pickett was an expression of loyalty and courage that reminded Zack of the day the Negro had come to him in Mexico City, asking to be taken back to the ranch for burial in case the Mexican bull happened to kill him. Then, as now, he'd tried to belittle his own risk — a risk of his life for the 101 and its owners.

Zack didn't have the words to rightfully thank Bill

Pickett for what he was offering. He shook his head. 'Hell, Bill,' he said, 'we've got troubles enough. We'll find a better way out of this mess. Maybe I already have.' And he read Ida Red's letter to the black bulldogger.

'We just might get enough out of those horses of mine to pay our passage to Africa,' he said. 'We'd hit there broke, but Ida Red would put us on our feet again. I'll be out of this bed in no time. What do you say?'

Bill's lips parted in an uncertain grin. 'Sure, boss,' he said quietly. 'Sure, we could do that, maybe.'

Whether or not he believed in Zack's plan of heading for a new country, Bill Pickett went down to get Zack's horses separated from the ones that were to go under the auction block the next day.

The hair was long on the horses this time of year, but Bill could read the brands. He knew most of Zack's horses, anyhow. He went into the corrals and, disregarding the stares of the new hands Clarke had all over the place, started cutting out the horses he wanted.

There was one big four-year-old sorrel in the bunch that kept cutting back and running to the far side of the pen. Bill remembered that sorrel. The horse had been about half-broken, then left to run loose again. Now he was boogery and skittish — he had the makings of a bad outlaw if he weren't tamed down soon.

Bill got him a rope and pitched it around the sorrel's neck. The animal fell back, rearing and plunging. Bill started up the rope, hand over hand, to put a halter on the animal. The sorrel snorted and reared again, chopping at Bill's hatbrim with his forefeet.

The years stack up on a man; the Negro bulldogger

wasn't as fast-moving as he'd once been. He dodged back, but he wasn't quick enough. One of those hoofs grazed the side of his head, knocking him to the ground.

Even then, Bill wasn't hurt. Not bad. He was just stunned a little. Any quick-thinking man of the old 101 cowhands could have stepped in, fought the horse off and saved the greatest bulldogger the world has ever known. But not that bunch Fred Clarke had signed on after he'd fired all the old hands. They just stood there with their mouths hanging open like flytraps and watched that sorrel horse stomp Bill Pickett's brains into the corral dust.

Even with his skull cracked and his brains oozing out of his head, Bill Pickett wasn't dead. They packed him out of the corral and put him on his bunk, where he lay wallowing and groaning in delirium. A doctor came, cleaned up his head; but there was little else he could do. The bulldogger was slated for death; all he needed was time to die.

With Bill knocked out, Zack had no one left to get his own horses out of the 101 stock going on sale the next day. He sent his lawyer, Henry Johnson, to ask the judge for more time. Johnson explained the full circumstances; but Judge Claude Duval wouldn't grant the request.

When Johnson came back with this word, Zack sent for Clarke. He was already fit to be tied over Bill Pickett's accident.

'Them goddamned Kaffir-corn cowhands!' he raged to Johnson. 'Anybody with an ounce of sense could have saved Bill from that horse. But nothing that idiot Clarke ever hired had the guts or gumption to fry an egg!'

Clarke wouldn't come to see Zack. He played it cautious

and sent his son-in-law, Neal Sullivan, and his lawyer, Wilson, up to talk to the angry ranchman. They came up to Zack's room, each wearing a leather jacket buttoned up tight to show the bulge of six-shooters underneath.

'Neal,' Zack stormed, 'what do you aim to do with my horses?'

Neal was well-heeled and wasn't going to be bluffed out. 'We're going to sell them horses,' he said. 'We're going to sell every goddamned one of them, and if they don't bring but a dollar apiece, you don't get the dollar! What are you going to do about that?'

The long pent-up rage in Zack flared to white heat. He grabbed at a ten-gauge shotgun leaning in the corner of the room beside his bed. 'You son-of-a-bitch!' he roared. 'I'll show you what I'll do about it!'

Sullivan wheeled and leaped toward the door in panic, butting Wilson in the jaw. The two men fell through the door in their wild scramble to get out. Zack aimed the shotgun at the floor behind them and pulled off. The concussion, within the close confines of the room, sounded like the roar of a cannon.

Sullivan squalled in terror, came to his feet, and stampeded down the stairs and out the front door, losing his six-shooter in his wild run across the White House lawn toward the safety of the 101 store building.

Wilson, in his scare, missed the stairs going down, sighted those going up to the third floor of the house, and charged up them.

Zack jacked another shell into the firing chamber of the pump shotgun, eased toward the door where he could look out and command the staircase up which Wilson had fled.

He called to Wilson. 'Drop that pistol, Wilson, you yellow-bellied bastard, and come on down here.'

Wilson started begging. 'Don't kill me, Zack!' he cried. 'My god, man, think of my wife and children!'

'You ought to have been thinking of them yourself,' Zack told him. 'Drop that pistol and come on down. Then I'll make up my mind!'

Wilson waited for a long minute, hesitating to risk it. Finally, he called down the stairs. 'All right,' he said, 'I'm dropping my gun. But for god's sake, don't kill me, Zack.'

'I haven't heard that gun drop yet,' Zack said. 'God-dammit, you better let me hear it before you show yourself on that staircase!'

Wilson tossed his gun down the stairs. It clattered to the floor. Slowly, he followed it, his knees shaky, his face the color of ashes.

Zack kept the shotgun trained on him till he reached the landing of the second floor. Then he said: 'Now run, you stinking bastard!'

Wilson ran. Wild-eyed, he tore out of the house and into the store-building office where he found several deputy sheriffs holed up. Clarke or somebody had evidently been looking for trouble and had them sent out.

Down in that office, Sullivan had already been telling it scary. 'My god,' he'd said when he came charging into the store, 'Zack shot at us.'

Zack's sister Alma was there when he came in. She wasn't too perturbed about the shooting. 'No,' she contradicted Sullivan. 'Zack didn't shoot at you. If he had, you wouldn't be here to tell about it.'

But that didn't stop Sullivan and Wilson from swearing

out a warrant for Zack's arrest, charging that he'd shot at them with intent to kill. So the sheriff came out to the 101 then to serve papers on Zack again, bringing along plenty of extra deputies to reinforce the ones already there and to help make an arrest.

Harley, Zack's houseboy, came up to Zack's room and told him the law was coming to get him. Zack set his shot-gun down, picked up a .30–.30 Winchester. He went to the window and flung up the sash. At the edge of the lawn he saw an automobile drawn up, with armed men piling out of it.

Zack bawled at them: 'Now who in the hell do you men think you're coming after?'

'You!' one of them shouted.

Zack laid the barrel of his Winchester across the window-sill. 'I'm counting three,' he called down, 'and when I finish, any son-of-a-bitch in range is going to get shot!'

There wasn't anybody within range when he finished counting. There were mighty few in sight.

Selma Zimmerman came into the room carrying a loaded rifle. 'I'll guard the back door,' she told Zack calmly, then went down to take up her watch in the kitchen.

Harley was white-faced and trembling, but he wasn't to be outdone by a woman. 'I can't shoot,' he said. 'But I can load guns.'

So the three of them barricaded themselves in the White House, ready to make a stand-off fight against all comers. A sick man, a woman, and a frightened boy.

Just before dark, Harry Cragin, a lumberman, came cautiously to the edge of the lawn, called to Zack and identified himself. Zack let him come on into the house, but wouldn't let him come up the stairs.

'Officers are coming from Newkirk,' Cragin called up to Zack. 'They're coming with high-powered rifles and tear-guns to take you. You'd better do something.'

Zack let Cragin come on up to his room then and had him to call Bruce Potter, the county attorney. Zack told Cragin what to tell Potter.

'Tell him,' he said, 'that when the Newkirk officers come, they're going to get shot. Tell him I aim to stay right here and keep gunning till the last dog is dead!'

That relayed statement stopped the Newkirk officers.

Long after dark, Bruce Potter came out to the White House and called from the edge of the lawn, claiming he'd managed to make bond for Zack. Zack let him in. Cragin put his name on the bond and Zack was a free man till his trial came up on this shooting case.

But he still wasn't able to cut his privately owned horses from the rest of the 101 stuff sold at auction. There were a hundred and forty head of those horses, good breeding stock. They should have brought some good money. But Zack never got a cent of it.

Bill Pickett lived eleven days after the accident. When he died, funeral rites were held for him on the front gallery of the White House, same as they had been when Joe Miller died. A Negro preacher from Ponca City conducted the services and Bill's kinsfolk from down in Texas came to the burying.

These kinsfolk came with the idea of putting Bill away in a fancy store-bought casket like white folks were buried in. Bill had been a big man among his kind and they wanted to do right by him. They held out for a satin-lined casket, even after Zack told them how Bill had always wanted to be buried in a coffin built of heavy walnut timber that grew there on the ranch. So they finally compromised by putting Bill's body inside the box with the fancy fixings, then putting that one inside the walnut coffin Zack had hired some carpenters to build.

Weak as he was, Zack came down to pay his respects to the dead bulldogger. When the Negro preacher had finished, Zack had a few words to say.

'We're telling Bill good-bye,' he said to the congregation. 'He's dead now, and this is one time when a Negro and a white man are all the same. If there ever was a white Negro, it was Bill. His hide was black, but his heart was white. If all white men had been as honest and loyal as this Negro, the world wouldn't be in the shape it's in today!'

They planted Bill in the hard ground, as he'd requested of Zack down there in Mexico City in 1908. They buried him in the soapstone on a high knoll near old White Eagle's monument and covered him deep, where the coyotes couldn't scratch him out. And Zack stood there beside the fresh raw mound of the bulldogger's grave and knew the infinite aloneness of a man with his back to the wall and not a fighting friend left to side him.

He went to bed that night with a raging fever.

23

THE KILL

For ten days, Zack lay in bed, unable to take a bite of food or hold it on his stomach when it was forced upon him. Half the time he was in delirium. Doctors Nieman, Northcutt, and Gordon pronounced his illness a nervous breakdown and did what they could to pull him through. Selma Zimmerman acted as day nurse to wait upon him, and Harley stayed up nights to give him medicine. But in spite of the care he got, it looked as if Zack Miller was booked for the Long Trail.

On the afternoon of the tenth day, Doctor Nieman gave him up. Down in Ponca City, he remarked to Corb Sarchet, an Associated Press man, that Zack likely wouldn't last till daylight. Corb, who'd been looking for this, gathered his notes on the last of the 101 Millers and started writing Zack's obituary.

News of Zack's coming death swept through town and out onto the prairies; the Indians got hold of it. And just a little before sundown that afternoon, several Poncas in ceremonial paint and blankets appeared at the front door of the White House. Four of them entered without invitation, leaving the rest behind. These four climbed the stairs to Zack's room. They brushed the startled houseboy aside and stalked into the room where Zack lay.

One of the Indians was Jim Williams, now head medicine man for the Ponca tribe. Another was Horse Chief Eagle, who had pronounced the eulogy at Joe Miller's death. All were members of that religious sect known as peyote eaters. They regularly performed strange rituals under the influence of the potent narcotic derived from a cactus plant that grows in southwestern Texas and northern Mexico. And all were friends of Zack.

Zack recognized the ceremonial bag in Jim Williams's hands; it held the sacred peyote. Horse Chief Eagle carried a small bundle of cedar branches. Another of the Indians carried a sack of sand. All had their ceremonial eagle-feather fans.

Jim Williams started giving Selma Zimmerman orders in tones of authority that left no room for argument. She was to take out of the room all of the white man's medicines. She wasn't to leave a tray, bottle, syringe, or thermometer. Everything must go and she must go with them.

The Indians stood proud and haughty in their robes, waiting for her to obey orders. Selma hesitated, at loss as to what she should do. She glanced at Zack. He nodded weakly. The girl cleared the room and left.

When she was gone, the Ponca medicine man squatted in the center of the room and emptied the sack of sand upon the floor, smoothing out the pile and carefully shaping it into a design that resembled a horseshoe. Or maybe it was a heart; Zack couldn't tell. In front of the sand, one of his helpers spread a grass-woven mat where the Indians placed their eagle feathers and the bundle of cedar branches. Moving the cedar to the sand, Jim Williams started a tiny fire. And as the smoke rose, he rose to his feet with it, lifting his hands.

Downstairs, a rawhide drum started talking in measured

beats. The dry rattle of another joined it. Then came the steady tapping of a third drum. And in a moment the whole house was filled with a pulsating beat of sound that Zack could feel more than he could hear. The sound gripped him and he felt again that queer thrill he'd known as a boy when he'd lain in that old Salt Fork dugout of a dark night and listened to the talk of the Ponca drums rolling across the prairies.

Jim Williams spoke in the Ponca tongue. 'Zack Miller,' he said, 'you are sick and white man's medicine cannot save you. You are our friend; so now we bring you the faith cure.'

The Indians started chanting, weaving the chant into the measure of the drumbeats.

First, Jim Williams brought Zack a tin can that held about half a pint of the peyote brew. Zack drank it down. It had a taste that was four times as bitter as quinine, but Zack held it. A little later, the medicine man fed him another dose. The taste wasn't nearly so bad. Two more canfuls Zack drank while the drums kept going. Then the medicine man brought him a peyote 'button.' It looked something like the shriveled half of a dried peach and was bitter as gall. But Zack chewed and swallowed it.

There was a roaring in his head now, and it grew louder and louder — louder than the drumbeats, it seemed to Zack. Or was it the drumbeats? He wasn't sure.

The fire burned down. Jim Williams said: 'Watch now, my friend, how the ashes scatter and a flower grows in their place and a bird flies in from the window to light upon it.'

Zack watched the dying fire. He saw a tiny plant rise out of the ashes, grow, and burst into flower. The flower had the pink bloom of a prairie primrose.

Jim Williams stood with his head thrown back, chanting to the beat of the drums. He spread his hands above Zack and lifted them. Zack felt himself rise from the bed and hang suspended in space. Gently, the medicine man lowered his hands and Zack settled back into a bed that was cool and restful.

'An old friend, gone a long time,' said the medicine man, 'comes to visit once more.'

A little stoop-shouldered man appeared out of the fog that seemed to hang about the walls of the room. The man came to the fire and sat down upon a log that had come from nowhere. The man was Jimmy Moore, dead these forty years.

Zack watched the little Irishman sit upon the log beside the fire and start whittling his cut of Climax tobacco, filling his stubby clay pipe with the shavings. Jimmy tamped in the tobacco with the forefinger of his right hand. That finger had once become calloused from tamping hot tobacco into that pipe. And Zack could see the callus now.

Jimmy Moore reached into the fire. He caught up a hot coal. He juggled it in his hand till he could drop it into the bowl of his pipe. He sucked hard and the Climax shavings began to pop and fry. Then he leaned back, contented-looking, and blew a lungful of smoke in Zack's direction. The smoke billowed out, filling the room, hiding Jimmy Moore from Zack, hiding the Indians, too . . .

It was three o'clock the next afternoon when Zack awoke, weak still, but very much alive and with a gnawing appetite.

'Selma!' he called, with a new strength in his voice.

'Selma, bring me something to eat. I'm hungry as hell!'

Selma Zimmerman got so excited that she cried. She called the doctor and told him what had happened. The doctor said to feed Zack orange juice and lemon, crackers soaked in milk, and a poached egg. That was the first food Zack had had in ten days, but he could have eaten five times as much. Next morning he ate two eggs and a slice of ham. That afternoon, he was able to put on his clothes.

Two days later, he went into Ponca City and read the obituary Corb Sarchet had written for him. He made a correction or two and told the newspaperman to put it away and hold it; it might still come in handy — twenty or thirty years from then.

Zack was alive, but that was about all that was in his favor. The minute he got out of bed, his creditors were on him again, cutting and slashing like a pack of hungry wolves trying to drag down a crippled steer. For months, he was kept in the courtroom, harangued and harassed for immediate payment of debts by the very men who'd finally made it impossible for him to pay. About all that kept the gray-headed bushwhacker going during those months were the letters that he and Ida Red exchanged, the dream of turning the clock back and starting all over again in a new frontier.

In September, Zack filed a petition to have Clarke dismissed as operating receiver of the 101, on the grounds that he was incompetent. He knew he had a case against Clarke; but he also knew that no case he brought into this bought-off court, with a judge trying to throw the book at him, would ever amount to a damn. His petition would be docketed and then pigeonholed till long after he'd been brought to trial on the most serious of all the charges against him: shooting with intent to kill. Still, he filed it; in a stand-off fight like this, a man had to bring into play every weapon he could get his hands on.

In that same month, his former wife, Marguerite Blevins Miller, filed suit in Oklahoma for back alimony, in spite of the fact that the appeal she had made to the Louisiana Supreme Court on the divorce had not yet been settled.

According to law, until that case had been settled by the Louisiana courts, the courts of Oklahoma were without jurisdiction in the matter. But that didn't bother Judge Duval; he allowed the case to be brought to trial. The decision was against Zack, as it had been on all the previous charges. He was to pay the back alimony, the courts said, when the very food he ate was paid for by a friend.

When in November, Zack still had not come through with the alimony, he was arrested and jailed for contempt of court.

That's when William H. Murray, Governor of Oklahoma, stepped in with his big feet. Alfalfa Bill never had been a hand to let law get in the way of justice, and he didn't now. The minute he learned that Zack Miller had been jailed for inability to pay back alimony, the rawboned governor reared up on his hind legs and started calling out his dogs. In one broad swipe he wiped the red tape from his battered-top desk and wrote out an order for Zack's release from false imprisonment, at the same time pardoning him of all offenses for which he stood convicted 'and all orders and decrees of the judge, Judge Claude Duval, or any other court in Kay County, Oklahoma.'

'Goddamn them!' Alfalfa Bill roared. 'Maybe I can't do anything with them for stealing Zack's property; but when they start fooling with his liberty, they're violating the Constitution of the United States, and I've got the state militia of Oklahoma to enforce its provisions.'

And he gave orders for Adjutant-General Charles F. Barrett to use the militia, if necessary. Alfalfa Bill leaned to the opinion that the liberty of a citizen was a thing of vital concern, and the Governor was on the prod.

Zack had been thrown in jail Saturday afternoon at three o'clock. Monday at noon, the Adjutant-General and a couple of his men arrived at the jail, demanding Zack's release. The sheriff was back at the jail now and in charge of the jail keys after a week-end of visiting his father-in-law and leaving Zack in charge. The sheriff hadn't liked the way Zack was being treated, and he was glad to see help coming for the cowman. But he couldn't let Zack out without the consent of Judge Duval.

'All right,' said Barrett, 'then call the judge and have him come on over.'

When the judge appeared, Barrett presented him with Alfalfa Bill's order. It was a long paper, and in it, Alfalfa Bill hadn't been bashful about calling names and stating opinions. He'd written in the beginning that under the Bill of Rights of the State Constitution, no man can be imprisoned for debt, where the obligation is agreed to and acknowledged. '... hence,' the order continued, 'how much less authority has a court to imprison a citizen for something over which he has no control and for acts placing him in a position whereby conspiracies, corrupt combination and design on the part of creditors, aided and abetted by the Court of Justice ...'

Duval was getting hot under the collar by the time he'd read this far, but he was to get hotter. Alfalfa Bill had listed everything he considered an injustice done Zack in the last several months, then summarized:

'These acts, together with others, as detailed to the Chief Executive from time to time since the fall of 1930, would make it clearly appear that there is a collusion and conspiracy between the said creditors, L. K. Meek, L. H. Wentz, and certain loan companies, aided and abetted by the said Duval, acting as Judge, using Miller's divorced wife further to harass him with the apparent purpose of wrecking Miller and taking from him the world-known estate, the 101 Ranch, by denying him access to his own property, or the sale of any part thereof; and then executing an order compelling him to pay alimony and attorneys' fees, which was impossible for him to do; and then imprisoning him as a culmination of the design of wrecking Miller and his estate . . .'

Alfalfa Bill was throwing his rocks straight and hard.

Judge Duval quit reading and handed the paper back to the Adjutant-General. 'This,' he said, with great dignity, 'is an illegal order. I'll pay no attention to it.'

Barrett said gently: 'I'll be a little more courteous to you than you've been to me. I'll let you read my instructions of authority to back up this order before I serve it on you.' And he handed the judge a second paper.

Duval read it and his jaw dropped. 'You mean,' he exclaimed, 'that you would resort to bloodshed?'

'I'll resort,' Barrett said firmly, 'to whatever is necessary to enforce this order for Miller's release. Battery B at Perry is standing by its trucks and can be here within an hour. The Chillocco Company can be here within thirty minutes.'

Duval's feathers fell. 'I'll telephone to Blackwell and have an associate judge come over for consultation.'

'How long will it take him to get here?' Barrett wanted to know.

'About an hour.'

'All right,' said Barrett, 'but when he comes, you will have been in jail forty minutes.'

Without waiting for the judge to ask, the county sheriff handed the jail keys to him. By the way Duval tossed them to Barrett, a man would have thought those keys were red-hot.

Barrett unlocked Zack's cell door. 'Let's go,' he said.

Zack's trial on charges of shooting with intent to kill came up in March. Before court proceedings started, Zack and his lawyer, Henry Johnson, met in private with Judge Heitzel and the county attorney, Bruce Potter.

'There's one thing about it,' Judge Heitzel remarked. 'We'll have to impanel another jury. This is the one that tried you on the last case.'

'Forget the jury,' Zack told him. 'We don't need one. I'm willing to have the case tried before you, Judge. All the witnesses I'll need will be ten men, and you'll only need to ask them one question. Ask them this: if I had intended to kill those two men, and had had them together in a room eighteen feet square, with a ten-gauge shotgun in my hands, would those rascals be alive today?

'You know, Judge, about that old Cherokee law which holds that if you hit a man over the head with a loaded gun, it is assault, but not assault with intent to kill. But if you hit him over the head with an empty gun with the same kind of blow, it's assault with intent to kill. I think that old law just about fits my case.'

Judge Heitzel thought maybe Zack had something there. He turned to the county attorney. 'Potter,' he said, 'I believe Zack's made a good point. And considering the stand Bill Murray's taken on this matter, I'm willing to dismiss this case if you'll make the motion. I don't want that old bear on my back!'

Bruce Potter made a motion to dismiss the case and the motion carried. Zack was a free man once more.

But being a free man didn't mean he was out from under the staggering load of debts that had piled up against him. Those debts had to be paid off somehow.

Zack called another creditors' meeting and made a proposition to the bunch. He wanted managership of a two-year operating lease on all the 101 ranch land, with an option to rebuy the outfit at the end of that time. The creditors agreed, appointing a couple of trustees to advise him. The Kay County District Court approved the reorganization plan and Fred Clarke was dismissed. On March 25, 1933, Zack took over, with at least the authority to pull the badly wrecked 101 together again if it was within his power. Carl Kennedy and Lee Russell were the trustees now.

The ranch was completely run down, fences wrecked, livestock all gone, tools and equipment sold off or plundered — and with a debt of $700,000 still against it.

Biting off a chunk of trouble like that wouldn't have appealed to most men. But, to Zack, it was everything in the world. Given a chance, he was convinced he could lick the thing yet! He still had influential friends. Look how Alfalfa Bill had bowed up to back him.

Zack thought back over the friends the Millers had had in the past. Take Willie Otis, now. If Willie were alive today, he'd be more than willing to put up the money Zack needed for livestock and equipment necessary to put the ranch back on a paying basis. Willie had been ready to gamble on the Millers back in '93; Willie knew the kind of men the Millers were.

There was Jim McGraw. Jim would be glad to come through with the hard cash. George Miller had made Jim McGraw a fortune in oil and Jim had used it to buy out the Farmers and Merchants Bank of Ponca City.

Zack's mind ran back down through the years and he smiled to himself, recollecting how Jim McGraw had always wanted to be a banker, instead of running 'McGraw's One-Horse Grocery,' where his wife did the clerking and Jim delivered in a one-horse rig. Jim had won a thousand dollars in a poker game and turned it over to George Miller, who'd used it to buy oil property and clean up a pot of money for his friend. And the day Jim McGraw got that first big oil check, he'd gone down to the Farmers and Merchants Bank, demanding that the president tell him how to go about buying a bank.

'Why,' the president had said, 'you'd have to buy my stock in this bank; then you'd be president.'

'Well, by god,' McGraw had exclaimed, 'get up out of that chair. I'm ready to set down!'

And sit down he did, buying the bank right then and immediately making it a bank for oil men who needed money to develop their property. And later, when the president of the Exchange National Bank at Tulsa died, McGraw took charge of it and within a few months had made a more powerful bank out of it than it had been when he took over.

Yes, Zack knew that Jim McGraw would be glad to give him a boost. Only Jim McGraw couldn't, of course; Jim McGraw had taken sick back in 1927 and gone to Hot Springs, Arkansas, for a rest cure and died while he was there.

There was Lew Wentz. The 101 had given Lew a shove up, back there when Lew was first trying to get a toe-hold in the oil business. Wentz was plenty able to help now; but Wentz was in the other camp, helping to drag the 101 down.

There was Ed Pulliam. Ed was a Ponca City grocery-man now. Ed would go with him to the end of the line. Ed never had forgotten the day Zack had pulled him out of a tight.

That was back in 1925, when the 101 was putting on a Labor Day rodeo at Ponca City. Ed was fresh married and his business capital that day consisted of exactly thirteen dollars, which he'd invested in bananas to sell at the show. Ed hadn't bothered about getting a license to sell bananas on the lot; he didn't even know he needed one. So when Zack Mulhall jumped him about it, ordering him to buy a license or get the hell off the lot with his bananas, Ed was sure up a tree. He didn't have the money to buy a license. Also, his bananas were a little overripe, and if he didn't sell out today, his thirteen dollars would go up in smoke and he'd have nothing to start a business on.

It was a tight spot for a fresh-married man to be caught in.

Zack rode up just in time. 'What the hell's the trouble?' he demanded.

Mulhall explained. Zack looked Ed over. He didn't know him from Adam's off ox, had no idea that Ed's last thirteen dollars were at stake. But he'd liked the man's looks and told Mulhall to let him go, that there was no other banana salesman on the lot and somebody might want a banana to eat.

Ed cleaned up fifty dollars out of those bananas that day. And that fifty was the shoestring start Ed needed to put him in the grocery business for life.

He'd come a long way on that fifty-dollar start, Ed had. And he wasn't a man to forget. More than once he'd told Zack that half of what he had was Zack Miller's, any time he wanted it.

There was Bert Colby, too, one of Zack's goat-herders 'way back yonder when Zack's father had bought him that bunch of Spanish goats from off the Colorado River, down in Texas. Bert had ridden for the 101 for years. Now he lived out east of Ponca City a piece, raising fine-blooded Hereford cattle.

Bert had already been to see Zack. He'd said: 'Let the thieving sons-of-bitches have the old 101, Zack. They've done ruint it. I've got enough for both of us and ours for the rest of our days. Let 'em have it and go to hell with it!'

But Zack couldn't do that, although he did later take his two younger children and go live with Bert.

It gave Zack a good feeling to know he had friends like Bert Colby and Ed Pulliam. But neither of those men had the kind of big money it would take to pull Zack and the 101 out of the hole.

Nor did Zack's friends, the Poncas. The Poncas were owing the 101 right now for loans made to various members of the tribe in times past. These were mostly small loans, but altogether amounted to a little more than a hundred thousand dollars, according to the ranch books. The Indians would pay that money back when times weren't so hard. But the way Zack looked at it, a man couldn't go dunning them for it now. They wouldn't understand. They'd think he'd quit trusting them.

Zack went farther down the line of friends the Millers had known. There were plenty. He and Joe and George had known some big men; some of them they'd helped to make big. But as the bushwhacker checked off the list, he learned an appalling truth. Too many of the really big men had died off. A lot of them had committed suicide with the crash of 1929. And the others had been sucked under in the following depression. The 101 bushwhacker shook his head in disbelief. There was not one man he knew who had both the money and the guts to gamble on as big a proposition as the 101.

What Zack hadn't known until he was released from jail by Governor Murray's order was that his present creditors had blocked every effort Zack had made to get a new loan. Nobody with the money would take a chance on him. Alfalfa Bill realized it and made a statement to that effect in his order, but Zack hadn't waked up to that fact till now. And now, he was cornered for good, and he knew it.

It was a bitter pill for a man like Zack Miller to swallow, having to stand and watch the 101 crumble in his hands. Piece by piece, the ranch holdings went under the auction block. The harder Zack fought to hold things together, the faster they seemed to go. More and more, he came to look for those letters from Ida Red and to lean upon the slim hope of salvaging enough here to start over in British East Africa.

In spite of all he could do, the ranch fell apart; and at the end of Zack's two-year lease, all he had left was the White House itself. And the John Hancock Mutual Life Insurance Company, along with Lew Wentz, was contesting his right to hold that. Through auction buying and mortgage foreclosures, they had already gained possession of all the land around the White House with the exception of the ten-acre tract upon which the building sat. And, hell-bent to make a clean job of it, they had filed injunction proceedings in the federal court at Guthrie, demanding that Zack vacate the White House.

Before this time Zack's lawyer had filed a petition that the ten-acre tract be considered as a homestead; but when Wentz and his partners contested the petition, Duval had ruled against Zack. According to Duval, the White House and the store building were both used for business purposes; therefore they could not be considered as homestead property.

On June 3, 1936, Edgar S. Vaught, federal district judge, issued the injunction which deprived Zack of the right to live in the 101 White House. No definite date was set, Judge Vaught indicating that the matter was to be settled between attorneys before a formal order was signed.

Zack refused to leave, and in a last-ditch effort to save the White House, advertised an auction sale of the entire contents of the house, leaving only a bed and two chairs in the room where he meant to stay.

But in spite of the best efforts of auctioneer G. R. Cowen, a long-standing friend of Zack's, the stuff went for a song. A famous buffalo painting by Landers sold for eighty-five dollars; once Joe Miller had refused an offer of twelve hundred for it. Buffalo robes, some of them made long before the Civil War, old buffalo guns, dishes, rugs, furniture, mounted steer heads, treasured personal belongings of every sort — they all went under the block at less than a tenth of their true value.

Gray-haired Alice Lee, whose sensational shooting and daring riding had once made the crown heads of Europe applaud, attended the sale. The sight sickened her. 'This is like a funeral to me,' she said. 'I've traveled all over the world with Zack and the show. I feel as if they ought to put me up there with the rest of the relics.'

Zack stood by, grim-faced and bitter, now and then calling on Cowen to pass up some article that was selling for nothing.

'If I've got to give it away,' he said, 'I'll give it to some of my old Indian friends.'

Once in a while, an old friend would walk up to Zack, shake hands in silence, then walk away.

The sale ended. The bargain-hunters drifted away. Zack stood alone at sundown on the front gallery of the gutted White House with nowhere near enough money to save it. About him lay the empty, ramshackle farm buildings that once had housed the state's finest cattle, horses, hogs — the deserted packing houses and power plants. Yonder was what was left of one of the finest orchards in the world, a block of ragged tree stumps. Farther out lay the wheat fields, weed-grown and ragged. And last of all

were the prairies, rolling out to the skyline, grassy prairies
that once had belonged to him and his. And now, one upstairs room held all his possessions, and those a gift of an
Indian friend — a bed and a couple of chairs.

The sun set. Without a word or a change of expression,
the fifty-nine-year-old rancher left the White House gallery.
The only place he had to go now was to the home of his
friend, Bert Colby.

Zack's red friends tried to come to his rescue. Horse
Chief Eagle called a meeting of the Ponca head men.

'Our friend,' he told them, 'is in trouble. He has been
here a long time. He has been a friend of the Poncas. His
brothers were friends of the Poncas, and their father before
them. Now his land is taken from him and he has no place
to go. It is time that we helped our friend.'

So between them, they voted to give Zack a half-section
tract of Ponca community land that lies between the Salt
Fork and Marland. But even this move was blocked.
Government officials in charge of Indian property refused
the grant, afraid of setting a precedent that would eventually lose to white men all lands belonging to the Indians.

And when the next letter came from British East Africa,
it was from Ida Red's wife. Ida Red was dead. That
laughing, fighting, banjo-picking Ida Red — he'd let a
big rhinoceros catch him out in the broad open and down
off his horse. And when the big brute was finished with
the red-headed cowhand, there was just barely enough of
him left to bury.

The last escape route for Zack Miller was gone now.
There'd be no new frontiers for him; there was nobody to

help him get a start in a new country. It was back off and start over, with nothing but his two bare hands, or tuck his tail and admit that he was done for good.

Many a man Zack's age would have thrown in the sponge and called it quits. And in the next few years to come, plenty of times Zack did ask himself what the hell he was still fighting for. The show was gone; the land was gone; and just recently the Government had stepped in and torn down the White House to basement level to supply material for one of its experimental housing projects. When a man's outlived his time, Zack would tell himself, all doors are closed to him. And a train-load of money wouldn't buy back the 101 and make it what it once was. The type of men who'd built it were gone, the horses, the longhorn cattle, the open range. That way of life was gone.

When those periods of black depression hit him, he'd get to thinking about that old split buffalo hide hanging in the Historical Society Museum in Oklahoma City. On that hide were branded the names of the four hundred original members of the Cherokee Strip Cowpunchers' Association, men who'd punched cattle with a bona-fide cow outfit on the Strip before 1893. Beside the name of each member who had crossed the Big Divide, a star had been burned. And now, that old hide was so star-studded that it looked like the sky on a clear night in the dark of the moon. Any time now, Zack would tell himself, they'd be burning a star beside his name — and he was ready.

But those bad spells didn't come often. In December, 1944, with the help of his Ponca friends, Zack bought back the old 101 Ranch store building and set up a curio shop. There, he couldn't make a thousand- or even a hundred-dollar profit on a deal. But he could still make five dollars, or one dollar, or a dime. Which was still profit.

And it's profit, big or little, that puts the spirit into a born bushwhacker.

THE END